response surface methodology

Response Surface Methodology

Raymond H. Myers

Professor of Biometry
Medical College of Virginia
Virginia Commonwealth University

formerly
Associate Professor of Statistics
Virginia Polytechnic Institute

Allyn and Bacon, Inc.
Boston

contents

preface   ix

1 | introduction   1

references   3

2 | review: matrix algebra   4

2.1 fundamental definitions   4 | 2.2 rules and operations in the multiplication of matrices   6 | 2.3 rank of a matrix   9 | 2.4 inverse of a matrix   9 | 2.5 orthogonal matrix   12 | 2.6 idempotent matrix   13 | 2.7 characteristic roots of a matrix   13 | 2.8 real quadratic forms   15 | 2.9 trace of a matrix   18 | 2.10 differentiation using matrices   19 | 2.11 use of matrix notation for means and variances of random vectors   21 | 2.12 further remarks   23 | exercises   24 | references .   25

3 | review: least squares and experimental design   26

3.1 method of least squares   27 | 3.2 hypothesis testing   30 | 3.3 estimator for σ^2 33 | 3.4 use of orthogonal polynomials in fitting regression model   35 | 3.5 factorial experiments   40 | exercises   59 | references   60

4 | fundamentals of response surface technology   61

4.1 basic concepts   61 | 4.2 goal of response surface methods   62 | 4.3 other considerations in the study of RSM   63

5 | determination of optimum operating conditions   67

5.1 analysis of a fitted surface   68 | 5.2 method of steepest ascent   88 | 5.3 method of ridge analysis   95 | exercises   105 | references   106

6 | designs for fitting first order models   107

6.1 the orthogonal design   107 | 6.2 addition of points in the center of the 2^k factorial design   114 | 6.3 simplex designs for fitting first order models   118 | 6.4 further remarks concerning adequacy of fitted response models   123 | exercises   124 | references   125

7 | designs for fitting second order models   126

7.1 central composite design   127 | 7.2 methods of comparing second order designs   134 | 7.3 rotatable second order experimental designs   139 | 7.4 summary remarks   165 | 7.5 coding of the independent variables   166 | exercises   174 | references 175

8 | response surface analysis and design for experiments in blocks   176

8.1 blocking in the case of the first order model   177 | 8.2 blocking in the case of the second order model   183 | exercises 193 | references   195

9 | other criteria for choosing response surface designs   196

9.1 design criteria of average mean squared error   196 | 9.2 the first order response model   198 | 9.3 the second order model 211 | references   218

appendix a   219

a.1 moment matrix of a rotatable design   219 | a.2 biases of model coefficients for rotatable second order designs   223 | a.3 moment matrix for equiradial second order designs in two variables   223

appendix b   226

b.1 average bias for first order model   226 | b.2 minimum value of average bias   228 | b.3 J value for optimum and all-bias first order designs in the presence of second order effects   229

appendix c   232

Table c.1 The Normal Probability Function   232 | Table c.2 Percentage Points of the Student's t-Distribution   235 | Table c.3 Percentage Points of the F-Distribution   236

index   245

preface

The primary objective of *Response Surface Methodology* is to aid the statistician and other users of statistics in applying response surface procedures to appropriate problems in many technical fields. Although methods are emphasized in the book, a certain amount of theory is presented so that a reader with sufficient background in mathematics, especially in the algebra of matrices, can obtain an exposure to the theoretical development. While response surface techniques are widely used, it seems that a need exists for an exposition which contains a considerable amount of the basic material under a single cover. At the same time it is felt that this book may create a continued awareness of the basic techniques among the potential users.

It is assumed that the reader has some background in matrix algebra, elementary experimental design, and the method of least squares, even though these topics are briefly reviewed in the early chapters. Chapter 2 presents some basic theorems and methods in matrix algebra which are pertinent to the response surface analysis and design material in the text. Chapter 3 is a review into the fundamental topics in regression analysis and factorial experimental design. The regression phase of this review is presented from the standpoint of the *general linear model*, from which least squares estimators are developed and discussed using the notation of matrices. In addition, 2^k factorial and fractional factorial design topics are reviewed, with emphasis placed on the use of designs to fit regression models. A clear understanding of these topics is essential for the reader to comprehend the material devoted to response surface designs.

The text material is given in two parts: analysis and design—in that order. The analysis involves the illustration of techniques which enable the experimenter to analyze the experimental information in a first or second order response model. In the design phase, experimental layouts are presented and illustrated for the fitting of first and second order models. A considerable number of practical examples are given which illustrate the use of the designs.

Many individuals contributed significantly toward the manuscript and to enumerate all of them would be an almost impossible task. In particular, I would like to thank Dr. William O. Thompson who proofread the manuscript and made helpful changes. I would also like to pass on sincere appreciation to Mrs. Boyd Loadholt for her efforts in the typing of the finished copy, and to Mrs. Sharon Crews who performed the computations in most of the examples. In addition, I would like to thank Mrs. Nancy Klapp for correcting the final manuscript.

Several of the examples are taken from actual industrial problems. I would very much like to thank those who gave permission to use their data to illustrate the techniques. In several instances tables are given which were taken from research articles with the kind permission of the editors and authors. I am indebted to Drs. George E. P. Box and Norman R. Draper for granting permission to reproduce certain tables in "The Choice of a Second Order Rotatable Design," University of Wisconsin, Department of Statistics, Technical Report No. 10, July 1962. Likewise, I would like to thank Drs. Box and J. Stuart Hunter for allowing the reproduction of certain material in "Multifactor Experimental Designs for Exploring Response Surfaces," *Annals of Mathematical Statistics*, Vol. 28, No. 1, 1957.

Finally, I would like to express my sincere appreciation to Dr. Boyd Harshbarger, whose constant encouragement was necessary in order that the book be completed.

RAYMOND H. MYERS

1 | introduction

Response Surface Methodology, sometimes referred to as RSM, is essentially a particular set of mathematical and statistical methods used by researchers to aid in the solution of certain types of problems which are pertinent to scientific or engineering processes. Its greatest application has been in industrial research, particularly in situations where a large number of variables in some system influence some feature of the system. This feature (e.g., reaction yield, cost of production, etc.) is termed the *response*; it is normally measured on a continuous scale and is a variable which likely represents the most important function of the systems, though this does not rule out the possibility of a study involving more than one response. Also contained in the system are input variables or *independent variables*, which have an effect on the response and are subject to the control of the scientist or experimenter. The response surface procedures are a collection involving experimental strategy, mathematical methods, and statistical inference which, when combined, enable the experimenter to make an efficient empirical exploration of the system in which he is interested.

A work which has generated initial interest in the use of this package of techniques is a paper by Box and Wilson. An important textbook, written by a team of chemists and statisticians and edited by O. L. Davies, contains a chapter entitled "The Determination of Optimum Conditions" which deals with the exploration of response surfaces. Many other papers have been published on this topic; among them are articles which contribute to the theory, and accounts which show the successful application of known RSM techniques in such areas as chemistry, engineering, biology, agronomy, textiles, the food industry, education, psychology, and others. Hill and

1

Hunter have given a brief review of some of the important features of RSM and a bibliography on the subject.

At the outset, early workers in the response surface area actually introduced little in the way of new statistical or mathematical techniques in the response surface analysis. Rather, the set of methods represented an ingenious common sense approach to problem solving, coupled with the use of reasonably well-known statistical and mathematical methods. It seems, on reflection, that since statistical techniques and the high-speed computer were just beginning to become a part of the researcher's tools, the research community was ripe for the "bag of tricks" that we now call RSM. The methods themselves are most often used to solve problems where one is attempting to optimize some system or process, although it should certainly be said that it would not be advisable to use response surface techniques in all optimization problems.

The impact of RSM initially has become apparent in the chemical industry, where nearly all process-oriented problems involve an optimization phase; that is, finding through experimentation conditions on the variables that give rise to desirable process yield. Generally, of course, this optimization activity involves arriving at a decision regarding what type of experimental plan should be used. This question becomes particularly critical in situations where a large number of factors are important. For example, in a biological study the experimenter may be concerned with a certain type of calf (the system) and how the gain in weight (the response) is influenced by the quantity of certain nutrients in the feed. These input variables might be the amount of phosphorus, the amount of calcium, the amount of a certain vitamin, and so forth. Once it is decided what is the proper range of experimentation, the task remains to decide what combinations of variable levels should be used in the experiment, each observation involving a certain amount of cost and effort. It is in this *experimental design* area of the methodology that original researchers have made their contribution.

Since the early publications presenting examples of the use of the analysis, the general techniques have been refined considerably through work which has led to better experimental plans. Imaginative criteria for choosing experimental runs have been established and the resulting plans have been used effectively by research workers. In some cases, these experimental designs, called *response surface designs*, merely involve an augmenting of the well-known factorial designs. In other cases, the designs presented are reasonably simple geometric configurations of *design points* or experimental runs in the space of the variables which are pertinent to the system.

A considerable amount of the text material is devoted to designs for response surface studies. In addition to the brief review of factorial designs given in Chapter 3, Chapters 6, 7, 8, and 9 are completely devoted to design.

references

Box, G. E. P. and K. B. Wilson: "On the Experimental Attainment of Optimum Conditions," *J. Roy. Statist. Soc., B* **13**, 1, 1951.

Davies, O. L.: *Design and Analysis of Industrial Experiments,* 2nd ed., Hafner Publishing Company, Inc., New York, 1956.

Hill, W. J. and W. G. Hunter: "Response Surface Methodology: A Review," *Tech. Rept. No. 62,* Dept. of Statistics, University of Wisconsin, 1966.

2 | review: matrix algebra

The use of matrices and matrix algebra is fundamental to the understanding of response surface techniques. In this chapter a review is given which displays several basic definitions and theorems used in the text. It is not meant to be an exhaustive review. Rather, only those concepts which are applicable to the main subject are considered, and even then, the development is brief.

2.1 | fundamental definitions

A *matrix* is simply a rectangular array of elements. For example, a matrix A with element a_{ij} in the ith row and jth column ($i = 1, 2,\ldots, r; j = 1, 2,\ldots, c$) is written as

$$A = \begin{bmatrix} a_{11} & a_{12} & a_{13} & \cdots & a_{1c} \\ a_{21} & a_{22} & a_{23} & \cdots & a_{2c} \\ a_{31} & a_{32} & a_{33} & \cdots & a_{3c} \\ \cdots & \cdots & \cdots & \cdots & \cdots \\ a_{r1} & a_{r2} & a_{r3} & \cdots & a_{rc} \end{bmatrix}. \qquad (2.1)$$

The *dimension* of the above matrix is $r \times c$, denoting the number of rows and columns, respectively.

A *square matrix* is a matrix in which the number of rows equals the number of columns. For example, the matrix

$$\begin{bmatrix} 2 & 2 & 3 \\ 1 & 4 & -1 \\ 2 & 7 & 4 \end{bmatrix}$$

is a 3-square matrix.

Notationally, a matrix is often referred to by a single lower case letter. For example, the matrix A given by Eq. 2.1 may be written (a_{ij}). Two matrices $A = (a_{ij})$ and $B = (b_{ij})$ are said to be equal if, and only if, they have the same dimensions and $a_{ij} = b_{ij}$; $i = 1, 2, \ldots, r$; and $j = 1, 2, \ldots, c$.

The *transpose* of a matrix A, denoted by A', is simply the matrix which is formed by interchanging rows of A with the columns of A. For example, the transpose of the matrix

$$A = \begin{bmatrix} 1 & 3 & 2 \\ -4 & 1 & 5 \end{bmatrix}$$

is given by

$$A' = \begin{bmatrix} 1 & -4 \\ 3 & 1 \\ 2 & 5 \end{bmatrix}.$$

If A is $r \times c$, then A' is a $c \times r$ matrix. A matrix A is said to be *symmetric* if $A = A'$; that is, the matrix is equal to its transpose. For example,

$$A = \begin{bmatrix} 2 & 3 & 1 & 4 \\ 3 & 1 & 5 & 3 \\ 1 & 5 & 2 & 1 \\ 4 & 3 & 1 & 4 \end{bmatrix}$$

is a symmetric matrix.

There are many special types of matrices which are often encountered in practice and are given particular consideration here. A *scalar* can be considered a 1×1 matrix; for instance, the number *4* is a scalar. A *row vector* is a matrix which contains a single row, whereas a *column vector* is a matrix which contains a single column. Vectors will be denoted in the text by lower case, boldface letters. For example,

$$\mathbf{a} = \begin{bmatrix} 1 \\ 4 \\ -2 \end{bmatrix}$$

is a column vector and $\mathbf{a}' = \begin{bmatrix} 1 & 4 & -2 \end{bmatrix}$ is a row vector.

A diagonal matrix is a square matrix that has all elements zero except those on the *main diagonal*. For example, the matrix

$$\begin{bmatrix} 2 & 0 & 0 \\ 0 & 1 & 0 \\ 0 & 0 & 4 \end{bmatrix}$$

is a diagonal matrix. If all of the diagonal elements are unity, the corresponding diagonal matrix is referred to as the *identity matrix*. The array

$$I_3 = \begin{bmatrix} 1 & 0 & 0 \\ 0 & 1 & 0 \\ 0 & 0 & 1 \end{bmatrix}$$

is an identity matrix, the subscript denoting the dimension of the matrix.

2.2 | rules and operations in the multiplication of matrices

In this section the rules for multiplication of matrices are reviewed. Unlike scalar multiplication, the *order* of the matrices in a product is quite important. Two matrices $A = (a_{ij})$ and $B = (b_{ij})$ are said to be *conformable* for multiplication in the order AB if the number of columns of A is equal to the number of rows of B. For example, the two matrices

$$A = \begin{bmatrix} a_{11} & a_{12} & a_{13} \\ a_{21} & a_{22} & a_{23} \end{bmatrix} \quad B = \begin{bmatrix} b_{11} & b_{12} & b_{13} \\ b_{21} & b_{22} & b_{23} \\ b_{31} & b_{32} & b_{33} \end{bmatrix} \tag{2.2}$$

are conformable for multiplication in the order AB. However, they are not conformable in the order BA. In other words, the latter matrix product is meaningless.

The rule for multiplication of matrices is very simple. Let the matrix $A = (a_{ij})$ be $m \times n$ and $B = (b_{ij})$ be $n \times q$. Then the product $C = AB$ will be the matrix (c_{ij}) such that

$$c_{ij} = a_{i1}b_{1j} + a_{i2}b_{2j} + \cdots + a_{in}b_{nj}$$

$$= \sum_{t=1}^{n} a_{it}b_{tj} \quad (i = 1, 2, \ldots, m; j = 1, 2, \ldots, q).$$

The dimensions of the matrix C will be $m \times q$. For example, in the case of the product AB with the matrices given by Eq. 2.2,

$$C = AB = \begin{bmatrix} \sum_{t=1}^{3} a_{1t}b_{t1} & \sum_{t=1}^{3} a_{1t}b_{t2} & \sum_{t=1}^{3} a_{1t}b_{t3} \\ \sum_{t=1}^{3} a_{2t}b_{t1} & \sum_{t=1}^{3} a_{2t}b_{t2} & \sum_{t=1}^{3} a_{2t}b_{t3} \end{bmatrix}.$$

As the reader should certainly have observed at this point, the commutative law of multiplication does not hold for matrices. In fact, even if

A and B are conformable in the order AB and BA, it does not necessarily follow that $AB = BA$. For example, let

$$A = \begin{bmatrix} 1 & 2 \\ 3 & 4 \end{bmatrix} \quad \text{and} \quad B = \begin{bmatrix} 2 & 1 \\ 0 & 0 \end{bmatrix},$$

then

$$AB = \begin{bmatrix} 2 & 1 \\ 6 & 3 \end{bmatrix} \quad \text{and} \quad BA = \begin{bmatrix} 5 & 8 \\ 0 & 0 \end{bmatrix}.$$

The associative law of multiplication holds for matrices just as it does in scalar multiplication. For example, consider the three matrices $A_{m \times n}$, $B_{n \times p}$, and $C_{p \times q}$. Then

$$ABC = (AB)C = A(BC).$$

A matrix is multiplied by a scalar by multiplying each of its elements by the scalar. For instance,

$$5 \begin{bmatrix} 2 & 4 \\ 3 & 6 \end{bmatrix} = \begin{bmatrix} 10 & 20 \\ 15 & 30 \end{bmatrix}.$$

Special consideration is given to a certain matrix multiplication which appears not only in response surface methodology but is encountered in all experimental design situations, namely, that of multiplication of a transpose of a matrix by the matrix itself. Consider

$$X = \begin{bmatrix} x_{11} & x_{12} & x_{13} & \cdots & x_{1k} \\ x_{21} & x_{22} & x_{23} & \cdots & x_{2k} \\ x_{31} & x_{32} & x_{33} & \cdots & x_{3k} \\ \cdots & \cdots & \cdots & \cdots & \cdots \\ x_{n1} & x_{n2} & x_{n3} & \cdots & x_{nk} \end{bmatrix}.$$

The elements of the symmetric matrix $X'X$ can be written

$$X'X = \begin{bmatrix} \sum_{p=1}^{n} x_{p1}^2 & \sum_{p=1}^{n} x_{p1}x_{p2} & \sum_{p=1}^{n} x_{p1}x_{p3} & \cdots & \sum_{p=1}^{n} x_{p1}x_{pk} \\ & \sum_{p=1}^{n} x_{p2}^2 & \sum_{p=1}^{n} x_{p2}x_{p3} & \cdots & \sum_{p=1}^{n} x_{p2}x_{pk} \\ \text{symmetric} & & \sum_{p=1}^{n} x_{p3}^2 & \cdots & \cdots \\ & & & & \sum_{p=1}^{n} x_{pk}^2 \end{bmatrix}.$$

That is, the result is a $k \times k$ symmetric matrix with the jth diagonal element being the sum of squares of the elements in the jth column of X, and the (i, j) element being the sum of products

$$\sum_{p=1}^{n} X_{pi} X_{pj}.$$

As an illustration, for the matrix

$$X = \begin{bmatrix} 1 & 2 & 4 \\ 1 & 1 & 1 \\ 1 & 3 & -2 \\ 1 & 1 & -1 \\ 1 & 2 & 0 \end{bmatrix},$$

the $X'X$ matrix can be written

$$X'X = \begin{bmatrix} 5 & 9 & 2 \\ 9 & 19 & 2 \\ 2 & 2 & 22 \end{bmatrix}.$$

The transpose of a product of two matrices is the product of the transposed matrices, with the order reversed. That is,

$$(AB)' = B'A'.$$

As an example, consider the matrices

$$A = \begin{bmatrix} a_{11} & a_{12} & a_{13} \\ a_{21} & a_{22} & a_{23} \end{bmatrix}, \quad B = \begin{bmatrix} b_{11} & b_{12} \\ b_{21} & b_{22} \\ b_{31} & b_{32} \end{bmatrix},$$

$$(AB)' = \begin{bmatrix} \sum_{p=1}^{3} a_{1p} b_{p1} & \sum_{p=1}^{3} a_{1p} b_{p2} \\ \sum_{p=1}^{3} a_{2p} b_{p1} & \sum_{p=1}^{3} a_{2p} b_{p2} \end{bmatrix}', \quad (2.3)$$

$$B'A' = \begin{bmatrix} \sum_{p=1}^{3} a_{1p} b_{p1} & \sum_{p=1}^{3} a_{2p} b_{p1} \\ \sum_{p=1}^{3} a_{1p} b_{p2} & \sum_{p=1}^{3} a_{2p} b_{p2} \end{bmatrix}. \quad (2.4)$$

It is easy to see that the two matrices given by Eqs. 2.3 and 2.4 are equivalent. This rule is easily extended to products involving more than two matrices. For example, if

$$B = A_1 A_2, \ldots, A_{k-1} A_k,$$

then

$$B' = A_k' A_{k-1}', \ldots, A_2' A_1'.$$

2.3 | rank of a matrix

Before reviewing the important definition of the rank of a matrix, it is
appropriate to define what is meant by a minor determinant. Suppose one
selects any $r < m$ rows and any $c < n$ columns of an $m \times n$ matrix A. The
resulting array of elements in the r rows and c columns is called a *minor
matrix* of A. If the minor matrix is square, the determinant of the minor
matrix is called a *minor determinant*.

If the matrix A contains at least one r-rowed minor determinant that is
nonzero but no $(r + 1)$-rowed minor determinant that is nonzero, A is said
to be of rank r. As an example consider the matrix

$$A = \begin{bmatrix} 1 & 2 & 4 \\ 3 & 2 & 2 \end{bmatrix}.$$

The matrix A is of rank 2, since all 2-rowed minor determinants are nonzero.
However, the matrix

$$B = \begin{bmatrix} 3 & 1 & 2 \\ 6 & 2 & 4 \end{bmatrix}$$

is of rank 1, since all 2-rowed minor determinants are zero. The determinant
of the matrix

$$C = \begin{bmatrix} 2 & 2 & 4 \\ 3 & 2 & 1 \\ 1 & 1 & 2 \end{bmatrix}$$

is zero and thus C has rank less than three. A close inspection reveals that
its rank is 2. An m-square matrix which is singular will have rank *less* than
m since the only m-rowed minor determinant, namely, the determinant of
the matrix, is zero.

2.4 | inverse of a matrix

Consider the m-square matrix $A = (a_{ij})$. The m-square matrix A^{-1} where

$$AA^{-1} = A^{-1}A = I_m \tag{2.5}$$

is called the *inverse* matrix of A. Any square matrix whose *determinant* is
nonzero will have a unique inverse. As an example consider the matrix

$$A = \begin{bmatrix} 1 & 3 \\ 2 & 8 \end{bmatrix}.$$

The inverse A^{-1} is written as

$$A^{-1} = \begin{bmatrix} 4 & -1.5 \\ -1.0 & 0.5 \end{bmatrix}.$$

It is easily seen that Eq. 2.5 holds for this example. Suppose one considers an m-square matrix $B = (b_{ij})$. The determinant of the $(m - 1)$ square matrix which results upon deleting the ith row and jth column of B is called the *minor* of the element b_{ij}, the minor being denoted by M_{ij}. The term $(-1)^{i+j} M_{ij}$ is called the *cofactor* of b_{ij}.

Suppose the matrix B is *nonsingular*, that is, $|B| \neq 0$. (If $|B| = 0$, the matrix is said to be singular, and the inverse does not exist.) Consider the matrix

$$B^{-1} = \begin{bmatrix} \alpha_{11}/|B| & \alpha_{21}/|B| & \cdots & \alpha_{m1}/|B| \\ \alpha_{12}/|B| & \alpha_{22}/|B| & \cdots & \alpha_{m2}/|B| \\ \cdots & \cdots & \cdots & \cdots \\ \alpha_{1m}/|B| & \alpha_{2m}/|B| & \cdots & \alpha_{mm}/|B| \end{bmatrix} \tag{2.6}$$

where α_{ij} represents the cofactor of b_{ij}. Through use of some elementary properties of determinants (see Browne), it can easily be shown that $BB^{-1} = I_m$. The uniqueness of B^{-1} is quite easy to prove. If there exists some m-square matrix B^* such that

$$BB^* = I_m,$$

then one can premultiply both sides by B^{-1},

$$B^{-1} BB^* = B^{-1},$$

and thus

$$B^* = B^{-1}.$$

As an example consider the matrix

$$B = \begin{bmatrix} 1 & 3 \\ 2 & 8 \end{bmatrix}.$$

The determinant $|B| = 2$ and thus

$$B^{-1} = \begin{bmatrix} 8/2 & -3/2 \\ -2/2 & 1/2 \end{bmatrix} = \begin{bmatrix} 4 & -1.5 \\ -1.0 & 0.5 \end{bmatrix}.$$

In the use of least squares as an estimation procedure, one is often called upon to invert matrices which are symmetric. A special procedure for this type of matrix is often used. One such method is called the *abbreviated Doolittle procedure*. This method, or one similar to it, is usually taught in elementary courses in experimental design and analysis. If the student is unfamiliar with this procedure, he should consult Li for a discussion of the method.

The rule for finding the inverse of a product of two square matrices in terms of the individual inverses is very simple. Consider two m-square matrices A and B. Assuming that both matrices are nonsingular,

$$(AB)^{-1} = B^{-1} A^{-1}.$$

This rule is identical to that for the *transpose* of a product. It is extended to the product of $k > 2$ square matrices in the same fashion.

Given an m-square nonsingular matrix A, the transpose and inversion operations can be permuted without changing the result, that is,

$$(A^{-1})' = (A')^{-1}.$$

The inverse matrix is important in applications as a means of solving sets of independent linear simultaneous equations. Suppose one is called upon to solve the set of equations

$$a_{11}b_1 + a_{12}b_2 + \cdots + a_{1k}b_k = g_1$$
$$a_{21}b_1 + a_{22}b_2 + \cdots + a_{2k}b_k = g_2$$
$$\cdots \qquad \cdots \qquad \cdots \qquad \cdots \qquad \cdots$$
$$a_{k1}b_1 + a_{k2}b_2 + \cdots + a_{kk}b_k = g_k.$$

These equations can be written in matrix form as

$$A\mathbf{b} = \mathbf{g} \qquad (2.7)$$

where A is the square matrix (a_{ij}); $\mathbf{b}$ and $\mathbf{g}$ are the column vectors;

$$\mathbf{b} = \begin{bmatrix} b_1 \\ b_2 \\ \cdots \\ b_k \end{bmatrix} \qquad \mathbf{g} = \begin{bmatrix} g_1 \\ g_2 \\ \cdots \\ g_k \end{bmatrix}.$$

Assuming A is nonsingular, we can premultiply both sides of Eq. 2.7 by A^{-1},

$$A^{-1} A\mathbf{b} = A^{-1} \mathbf{g},$$

and thus

$$I_k\mathbf{b} = \mathbf{b} = A^{-1} \mathbf{g}.$$

The system of equations, then, is solved through the use of the inverse matrix. If the set of equations is not independent there is, of course, no unique solution. In this case the matrix of coefficients is singular; that is, the value of the determinant is zero. For example, in the set of equations given by

$$\begin{bmatrix} 2 & 0 & 0 \\ 3 & 2 & 4 \\ 1 & 1 & 2 \end{bmatrix} \begin{bmatrix} b_1 \\ b_2 \\ b_3 \end{bmatrix} = \begin{bmatrix} 2 \\ 9 \\ 4 \end{bmatrix},$$

it is easily seen that the vector

$$\mathbf{b} = \begin{bmatrix} 1 \\ 1 \\ 1 \end{bmatrix}$$

is a solution. In addition, a second solution is given by

$$\mathbf{b} = \begin{bmatrix} 1 \\ 3 \\ 0 \end{bmatrix}.$$

A quick inspection of the matrix of coefficients reveals that it is singular and thus has no inverse matrix.

At this stage one should consider certain elementary rules concerning the inverse of certain special types of matrices. For example, consider the matrix

$$\text{diag} (a_1, a_2, \ldots, a_k),$$

the notation indicating a diagonal matrix with the elements $a_1, a_2, \ldots, a_k$ on the main diagonal. The inverse of this matrix is itself a diagonal matrix taking the form

$$\text{diag} (1/a_1, 1/a_2, \ldots, 1/a_k).$$

Consider now a nonsingular square symmetric matrix S. One can of course write

$$SS^{-1} = I. \tag{2.8}$$

Upon taking the transpose of both sides of Eq. 2.8, then *postmultiplying* by S^{-1},

$$(S^{-1})' S'S^{-1} = S^{-1}.$$

However, since $S' = S$, $S'S^{-1} = I$, and thus

$$(S^{-1})' = S^{-1},$$

which implies that *the inverse of a symmetric matrix is itself symmetric.*

2.5 | orthogonal matrix

An m-square matrix O is said to be *orthogonal* if

$$O' = O^{-1},$$

that is, the transpose of O is equal to its inverse. Thus we can write

$$O \cdot O' = I_m. \tag{2.9}$$

The matrix

$$O = \begin{bmatrix} 1/\sqrt{2} & -1/\sqrt{2} \\ 1/\sqrt{2} & 1/\sqrt{2} \end{bmatrix}$$

is an example of an orthogonal matrix since

$$O \cdot O' = \begin{bmatrix} 1/\sqrt{2} & -1/\sqrt{2} \\ 1/\sqrt{2} & 1/\sqrt{2} \end{bmatrix} \begin{bmatrix} 1/\sqrt{2} & 1/\sqrt{2} \\ -1/\sqrt{2} & 1/\sqrt{2} \end{bmatrix} = \begin{bmatrix} 1 & 0 \\ 0 & 1 \end{bmatrix}.$$

A second example is given by the matrix

$$\begin{bmatrix} 1/2 & 3/\sqrt{12} & 0 & 0 \\ 1/2 & -1/\sqrt{12} & 2/\sqrt{6} & 0 \\ 1/2 & -1/\sqrt{12} & -1/\sqrt{6} & 1/\sqrt{2} \\ 1/2 & -1/\sqrt{12} & -1/\sqrt{6} & -1/\sqrt{2} \end{bmatrix}.$$

Given the vector **x** containing, e.g. n elements, suppose the transformation is made to the vector **y** through the equation

$$\mathbf{y} = P\mathbf{x} \qquad (2.10)$$

where P is an n-square orthogonal matrix. The transformation given by Eq. 2.10 is called an orthogonal transformation. It is interesting to note that

$$\mathbf{y}'\mathbf{y} = \mathbf{x}'P'P\mathbf{x}$$
$$= \mathbf{x}'\mathbf{x}$$

due to the orthogonality of P.

2.6 | idempotent matrix

A square matrix B is said to be idempotent if $B^2 = B$. The concept of an idempotent matrix becomes quite important in the development of distributional properties of certain statistics which pertain to the material in regression analysis. An example of an idempotent matrix is given by

$$B = \begin{bmatrix} 2 & -2 & -4 \\ -1 & 3 & 4 \\ 1 & -2 & -3 \end{bmatrix}.$$

2.7 | characteristic roots of a matrix

Let A be an m-square matrix and λ be a scalar variable. $A - \lambda I_m$ is called the *characteristic matrix* of A. This characteristic matrix is merely A with λ

subtracted from each main diagonal element. The determinant $|A - \lambda I_m| = f(\lambda)$ is called the *characteristic function* of A, and the roots of the equation $f(\lambda) = 0$ are called the *characteristic roots* or *latent roots* of A.

The square matrix

$$A = \begin{bmatrix} 1 & 2 \\ 2 & 2 \end{bmatrix} \qquad (2.11)$$

has as its characteristic equation

$$\begin{vmatrix} 1 - \lambda & 2 \\ 2 & 2 - \lambda \end{vmatrix} = 0,$$

which reduces to

$$\lambda^2 - 3\lambda - 2 = 0.$$

The above equation has roots $\lambda_1 = 3/2 + \sqrt{17}/2$ and $\lambda_2 = 3/2 - \sqrt{17}/2$.

Suppose the m-square matrix A has the value λ as a characteristic root. Then an *eigenvector* associated with the characteristic root λ is defined as a column vector $\mathbf{x}$, which is a solution to the equation

$$A\mathbf{x} = \lambda\mathbf{x}$$

or

$$(A - \lambda I_m)\mathbf{x} = 0.$$

For the matrix given by Eq. 2.11, an eigenvector associated with the root $\lambda_1 = 3/2 + \sqrt{17}/2$ is given by any solution to the equation

$$\begin{bmatrix} 1 - 3/2 - \sqrt{17}/2 & 2 \\ 2 & 2 - 3/2 - \sqrt{17}/2 \end{bmatrix}\begin{bmatrix} x_1 \\ x_2 \end{bmatrix} = \begin{bmatrix} 0 \\ 0 \end{bmatrix}.$$

An important use of response surface technology is in the application to problems of finding optimum experimental conditions, that is, systematic searching for operating conditions which are optimum in some sense. Considerable discussion of techniques which are often used is given in Chapter 5, at which stage the reader will make use of characteristic roots of symmetric matrices. The following theorem pertains to the nature of these roots.

THEOREM 2.1. The characteristic roots of a *real* symmetric matrix are all real.

2.8 | real quadratic forms

In the application of the principle of least squares and the general linear model, extensive use is made of the *quadratic form*. The quadratic form in k variables $x_1, x_2, \ldots, x_k$ is a scalar expression of the type

$$Q = \sum_{i=1}^{k} a_{ii}x_i^2 + 2\sum_{i<j}\sum a_{ij}x_i x_j \qquad (2.12)$$

where it is assumed that the elements a_{ij} $(i, j = 1, 2, \ldots, k)$ are real. In matrix notation the algebraic expression in Eq. 2.12 can be conveniently written as $\mathbf{x}' A \mathbf{x}$ where

$$\mathbf{x} = \begin{bmatrix} x_1 \\ x_2 \\ \ldots \\ x_k \end{bmatrix}$$

and A is the symmetric matrix

$$\begin{bmatrix} a_{11} & a_{12} & \cdots & a_{1k} \\ & a_{22} & \cdots & a_{2k} \\ & & \cdots & \cdots \\ \text{sym} & & & a_{kk} \end{bmatrix}.$$

The matrix A is called the matrix of the quadratic form Q, and the determinant $|A|$ is called the *discriminant* of the quadratic form.

Consider the following simple illustration of a quadratic form:

$$\begin{bmatrix} x_1 & x_2 & x_3 \end{bmatrix} \begin{bmatrix} 2 & 1 & 4 \\ 1 & 6 & 3 \\ 4 & 3 & 2 \end{bmatrix} \begin{bmatrix} x_1 \\ x_2 \\ x_3 \end{bmatrix} = \begin{aligned} & 2x_1^2 + 6x_2^2 + 2x_3^2 + 2x_1x_2 \\ & \quad + 8x_1x_3 + 6x_2x_3. \end{aligned}$$

reduction of quadratic form to canonical form

A manipulation which is extremely useful in describing the nature of a response surface and locating regions of optimum conditions is the reduction of a quadratic form to *canonical form*. The following theorem describes the nature of this important transformation.

THEOREM 2.2. If $\lambda_1, \lambda_2, \ldots, \lambda_k$ are the characteristic roots (all real) of the real symmetric matrix A, there exists an *orthogonal* transformation

$$\mathbf{x} = P\mathbf{w}$$

such that the real quadratic form $Q = \mathbf{x}'A\mathbf{x}$ is transformed to the *canonical* expression

$$\lambda_1 w_1^2 + \lambda_2 w_2^2 + \cdots + \lambda_k w_k^2. \tag{2.13}$$

That is, the quadratic form Q is transformed to one whose matrix is diagonal, the diagonal elements being the characteristic roots of the matrix A. Much use is made of this theorem in the material presented in Chapter 5.

types of real quadratic forms

The rank r of a quadratic form $Q = \mathbf{x}'A\mathbf{x}$ is the rank of the matrix A. As it turns out, r is the number of nonzero roots of the characteristic equation of A. The *index u* of a quadratic form Q is the number of positive roots of the characteristic equation of A. For the matrix

$$A = \begin{bmatrix} 1 & 2 \\ 2 & 2 \end{bmatrix}$$

given in a previous illustration in Section 2.7, $\lambda_1 = 3/2 + \sqrt{17}/2$ and $\lambda_2 = 3/2 - \sqrt{17}/2$; the rank of the corresponding quadratic form $Q = \mathbf{x}'A\mathbf{x}$ is 2 and the index u is 1.

An *indefinite quadratic form* $Q = \mathbf{x}'A\mathbf{x}$ in k variables is one whose canonical form, given by Eq. 2.13, contains both positive and negative coefficients. That is, the characteristic equation of A contains both positive and negative roots; in terms of r and u,

$$1 \leq u < r.$$

If Q is of rank $r = k$ and furthermore if all characteristic roots of A are positive, that is, if

$$u = r = k,$$

then the quadratic form is said to be *positive definite*; if $r = k$ and all characteristic roots are negative, that is, $u = 0$, then the quadratic form is said to be *negative definite*. If the rank r is less than k, and furthermore if $u = r$, the quadratic form is said to be *positive semidefinite*; if $r < k$ and $u = 0$, Q is said to be *negative semidefinite*. Consider the matrix

$$A = \begin{bmatrix} 1 & 2 \\ 2 & 2 \end{bmatrix}.$$

The rank of A is 2, and it was seen in the section on types of quadratic forms (p. 16), that the index u is 1. Thus, the quadratic form $Q = \mathbf{x}'A\mathbf{x}$ is an indefinite quadratic form. For the matrix

$$B = \begin{bmatrix} 2 & 1 \\ 1 & 3 \end{bmatrix},$$

the two characteristic roots are $\lambda_1 = 5/2 + \sqrt{5}/2$ and $\lambda_2 = 5/2 - \sqrt{5}/2$. The two roots are positive and thus the quadratic form $\mathbf{x}'B\mathbf{x}$ is positive definite.

The following is an important theorem which links the sign of the quadratic form with the quadratic form type (*i.e.*, positive definite, negative definite, etc.).

THEOREM 2.3. An indefinite quadratic form is positive for some real values of the variables, negative for others. A positive semidefinite quadratic form is ≥ 0 for all real values of the variables; for a positive definite quadratic form, the above is a strict inequality (>0), except when all the variables are zero. A negative semidefinite quadratic form is ≤ 0 for all real values of the variables, with the inequality being strict in the case of a negative definite quadratic form, except for zero values of the variables.

To this point, the discussion on indefiniteness or semidefiniteness has been restricted to quadratic forms. These definitions also apply to real symmetric matrices; in fact a real symmetric matrix B is indefinite or semidefinite when the associated quadratic form $\mathbf{x}'B\mathbf{x}$ is indefinite or semidefinite.

In the case where a minor matrix of a matrix A is the square matrix which contains the $i_1, i_2, \ldots, i_s$ rows and $i_1, i_2, \ldots, i_s$ columns of A, this array is called a *principal minor matrix* of A and its determinant a *principal minor determinant* of A. For example, the 2×2 principal minor matrices of

$$A = \begin{bmatrix} 30 & 17 & 15 \\ 17 & 10 & 10 \\ 16 & 7 & 15 \end{bmatrix} \tag{2.14}$$

are

$$P_1 = \begin{bmatrix} 30 & 17 \\ 17 & 10 \end{bmatrix}, \quad P_2 = \begin{bmatrix} 30 & 15 \\ 16 & 15 \end{bmatrix}, \quad P_3 = \begin{bmatrix} 10 & 10 \\ 7 & 15 \end{bmatrix}.$$

In addition, other principal minor matrices for this case are the scalar diagonal elements 30, 10, 15, and the entire 3×3 matrix A. The *leading principal minor matrices* of an n-square matrix are the n principal minor matrices of order $1, 2, \ldots, n$, each being a submatrix of the next. For the matrix of Eq. 2.14, the leading principal minor matrices are

$$[30] \quad \begin{bmatrix} 30 & 17 \\ 17 & 10 \end{bmatrix} \quad \begin{bmatrix} 30 & 17 & 15 \\ 17 & 10 & 10 \\ 16 & 7 & 15 \end{bmatrix}.$$

THEOREM 2.4. A necessary and sufficient condition that a real quadratic form $\mathbf{x}'A\mathbf{x}$ be positive definite is that every leading principal minor determinant of the matrix A be > 0.

THEOREM 2.5. Suppose one begins with an $n \times p$ matrix A which has rank $p < n$, then the matrix $A'A$ is positive definite and the matrix AA' is positive semidefinite.

2.9 | trace of a matrix

The trace of an m-square matrix A, denoted by tr A, is merely the sum of the elements in the main diagonal of A.

It is easy to see that for two m-square matrices $A = (a_{ij})$ and $B = (b_{ij})$, $\text{tr}(A \pm B) = \text{tr } A \pm \text{tr } B$. The (i, i) element of $A \pm B$ is $a_{ii} \pm b_{ii}$, and thus

$$\text{tr } (A \pm B) = \sum_{i=1}^{m} (a_{ii} \pm b_{ii}); \text{tr } A = \sum_{i=1}^{m} a_{ii} \text{ and tr } B = \sum_{i=1}^{m} b_{ii}.$$

Thus

$$\text{tr } A \pm \text{tr } B = \sum_{i=1}^{m} a_{ii} \pm \sum_{i=1}^{m} b_{ii} = \sum_{i=1}^{m} (a_{ii} \pm b_{ii}) = \text{tr } (A \pm B).$$

A second important result is concerned with the trace of the product of two matrices. Given an $m \times n$ matrix A and an $n \times m$ matrix B, then

$$\text{tr } (AB) = \text{tr } (BA).$$

For the proof of this result let the matrix $C = AB$ and $D = BA$.

$$c_{ii} = \sum_{k=1}^{n} a_{ik}b_{ki},$$

and thus tr $C = \text{tr } AB$ is given by

$$\sum_{i=1}^{m} \left[\sum_{k=1}^{n} a_{ik}b_{ki} \right].$$

Reversing the order of the summation,

$$\text{tr } (AB) = \sum_{k=1}^{n} \left[\sum_{i=1}^{m} b_{ki} a_{ik} \right]$$

$$= \text{tr } (BA)$$

$$= \text{tr } D.$$

2.10 | differentiation using matrices

It is often helpful when one encounters the problem of differentiating some mathematical function, e.g. f, with respect to several variables, to express the derivative in matrix notation. This device is used in this text, not only in the review sections but also in several developments in the response surface methodology.

Suppose it is required to differentiate $f(z_1, z_2, \ldots, z_k)$ with respect to $z_1, z_2, \ldots, z_k$. Consider the z's in vector form, that is,

$$\mathbf{z} = \begin{bmatrix} z_1 \\ z_2 \\ \ldots \\ z_k \end{bmatrix}.$$

By the derivative $\partial f / \partial \mathbf{z}$, we mean the column vector

$$\begin{bmatrix} \partial f / \partial z_1 \\ \partial f / \partial z_2 \\ \ldots \\ \partial f / \partial z_k \end{bmatrix},$$

that is, the column vector of partial derivatives. On the other hand $\partial f / \partial \mathbf{z}'$ is the *row* vector of partial derivatives. With this convention at our disposal, we note the following rules.

RULE 2.1. Given a column vector $\mathbf{a}$ containing k constants, and a vector $\mathbf{z}$ also with k elements, consider the scalar $\mathbf{a}'\mathbf{z}$;

$$\frac{\partial \mathbf{a}'\mathbf{z}}{\partial \mathbf{z}} = \mathbf{a} = \begin{bmatrix} a_1 \\ a_2 \\ \ldots \\ a_k \end{bmatrix}$$

$$\frac{\partial \mathbf{a}'\mathbf{z}}{\partial \mathbf{z}'} = \mathbf{a}' = \begin{bmatrix} a_1 & a_2 & \ldots & a_k \end{bmatrix}.$$

These results are very simple to prove.

$$\frac{\partial \mathbf{a}'\mathbf{z}}{\partial z_i} = a_i \qquad (i = 1, 2, \ldots, k),$$

and from the convention cited earlier,

$$\frac{\partial \mathbf{a}'\mathbf{z}}{\partial \mathbf{z}} = \mathbf{a} \quad \text{and} \quad \frac{\partial \mathbf{a}'\mathbf{z}}{\partial \mathbf{z}'} = \mathbf{a}'.$$

RULE 2.2. Given the vector $\mathbf{z}$ with k elements. Consider the scalar $\mathbf{z}'\mathbf{z}$;

$$\frac{\partial \mathbf{z}'\mathbf{z}}{\partial \mathbf{z}} = 2\mathbf{z}; \quad \text{and} \quad \frac{\partial \mathbf{z}'\mathbf{z}}{\partial \mathbf{z}'} = 2\mathbf{z}'.$$

This result is likewise very simple to prove. $\mathbf{z}'\mathbf{z}$ is the sum of squares of the elements in the vector $\mathbf{z}$. Thus

$$\frac{\partial \mathbf{z}'\mathbf{z}}{\partial z_i} = 2z_i \qquad (i = 1, 2, \ldots, k),$$

and from the convention, the result is easily seen.

RULE 2.3. Consider the vector $\mathbf{z}' = \begin{bmatrix} z_1 & z_2 & \ldots & z_k \end{bmatrix}$ and the k-square matrix A. The derivative of the scalar $\mathbf{z}'A\mathbf{z}$ with respect to the column vector $\mathbf{z}$ is given by

$$\frac{\partial(\mathbf{z}'A\mathbf{z})}{\partial \mathbf{z}} = A\mathbf{z} + A'\mathbf{z} = (A + A')\mathbf{z}.$$

This rule is best illustrated by the following simple case. Consider

$$A = \begin{bmatrix} a_{11} & a_{12} \\ a_{21} & a_{22} \end{bmatrix}.$$

The scalar $\mathbf{z}'A\mathbf{z}$ is given by $a_{11}z_1^2 + a_{22}z_2^2 + (a_{12} + a_{21})z_1z_2$.

$$\frac{\partial \mathbf{z}'A\mathbf{z}}{\partial z_1} = 2a_{11}z_1 + (a_{12} + a_{21})z_2$$

$$\frac{\partial \mathbf{z}'A\mathbf{z}}{\partial z_2} = 2a_{22}z_2 + (a_{12} + a_{21})z_1$$

Thus it can be seen that

$$\frac{\partial \mathbf{z}'A\mathbf{z}}{\partial \mathbf{z}} = \left\{ \begin{bmatrix} a_{11} & a_{12} \\ a_{21} & a_{22} \end{bmatrix} + \begin{bmatrix} a_{11} & a_{21} \\ a_{12} & a_{22} \end{bmatrix} \right\} \begin{bmatrix} z_1 \\ z_2 \end{bmatrix} \qquad (2.15)$$

$$= (A + A')\mathbf{z}.$$

It is of particular interest to note this result when A is symmetric; the application of this derivative rule in the text is usually made for this special case. Thus consider the quadratic form $z'Az$ (i.e., $a_{ij} = a_{ji}$). From Eq. 2.15 it can be seen that

$$\frac{\partial z'Az}{\partial z} = 2Az. \qquad (2.16)$$

2.11 | use of matrix notation for means and variances of random vectors

In the balance of this chapter, a digression is made from the basic concepts of matrices and matrix algebra to its use in simplifying the notation in certain aspects of statistical methodology. Just as the rules given in Section 2.10 for forming vectors of partial derivatives are helpful in simplifying certain developments, so are other notational conventions and definitive rules which apply to means and variances of vectors of random variables.

Suppose one is concerned with k random variables, referred to as $y_1, y_2, \ldots, y_k$, where the means of these variables are given by $E(y_i) = \mu_i (i = 1, 2, \ldots, k)$. (Here, the E notation refers to *expectation*.) Then it becomes convenient to refer to the collection of variables as a vector of random variables and to use the notation

$$E(\mathbf{y}) = E \begin{bmatrix} y_1 \\ y_2 \\ \ldots \\ y_k \end{bmatrix} = \boldsymbol{\mu} = \begin{bmatrix} \mu_1 \\ \mu_2 \\ \ldots \\ \mu_k \end{bmatrix},$$

the expectation of a vector being the vector of expectations. The same applies more generally for matrices, namely, the expectation of a matrix of random variables is a matrix containing the means or expected values of the random variables. Likewise, we can use matrix notation to refer to the *variances* and *covariances* of the elements in a random vector. Suppose the variances of the y_i are given by

$$\text{var}(y_i) = E(y_i - u_i)^2$$
$$= \sigma_i^2 \qquad (i = 1, 2, \ldots, k), \qquad (2.17)$$

and the covariances by

$$\text{cov}(y_i, y_j) = E(y_i - \mu_i)(y_j - \mu_j)$$
$$= \sigma_{ij} \qquad (i < j; i, j = 1, 2, \ldots, k).$$

Then it becomes convenient to define the *variance–covariance* matrix Σ as a symmetric matrix which contains the variances on the main diagonal and the covariances as the off-diagonal elements. That is,

$$\Sigma = E(\mathbf{y} - \boldsymbol{\mu})(\mathbf{y} - \boldsymbol{\mu})' = \begin{bmatrix} \sigma_1^2 & \sigma_{12} & \cdots & \sigma_{1k} \\ & \sigma_2^2 & \cdots & \sigma_{2k} \\ & & \cdots & \cdots \\ & & & \sigma_k^2 \end{bmatrix}. \tag{2.18}$$

Notationally, the matrix given in Eq. 2.18 is often referred to as cov $\mathbf{y}$ or var $\mathbf{y}$. One can make use of these conventions to describe the vector of random variables $\mathbf{y}' = [y_1, y_2, \ldots, y_k]$, where the variables are jointly normally distributed with mean vector $\boldsymbol{\mu}$ and variance–covariance matrix Σ, that is,

$$\mathbf{y} \cap N(\boldsymbol{\mu}, \Sigma).$$

For the special case where the random variables are uncorrelated and have equal variances, e.g. σ^2,

$$\mathbf{y} \cap N(\boldsymbol{\mu}, \sigma^2 \cdot I_k).$$

some rules for finding means and variances

The following are three important rules which pertain to the use of matrix notation in writing expectation and variance of certain random vectors and scalars that appear rather naturally in the development in the text.

RULE 2.4. Given a vector $\mathbf{y}$ containing k random variables and having mean $\boldsymbol{\mu}$, then $E(A\mathbf{y}) = A\boldsymbol{\mu}$ where $A = (a_{ij})$ is some $n \times k$ matrix of constants.

The proof of the result in Rule 2.4 is quite simple. One merely forms the vector $A\mathbf{y}$, the ith element of which is $\sum_{j=1}^k a_{ij}y_j$.

$$E \sum_{j=1}^k a_{ij}y_j = \sum_{j=1}^k a_{ij}\mu_j,$$

where $\mu_j = E(y_j)$. $\sum_{j=1}^k a_{ij}\mu_j$ is clearly the ith element of $A\boldsymbol{\mu}$.

A similar rule applies more generally in the case of a matrix of random variables. That is, given $X = (x_{ij})$, a $k \times p$ matrix of random variables having $E(X) = M$, where the (i, j) element of M is $E(x_{ij})$,

$$E(AX) = AE(X)$$

$$= AM.$$

RULE 2.5. Given a vector y which has mean 0, variance–covariance matrix $\sigma^2 I$, and a real symmetric matrix B, then

$$E(y'By) = \sigma^2 \operatorname{tr} B.$$

The proof of the result is given in Graybill on page 87. There are other extremely important and interesting theorems in Graybill's text which pertain to distributional properties of quadratic forms.

RULE 2.6. If y is a vector of k random variables with mean μ, and cov y $= \Sigma$, and A is an $n \times k$ matrix of constants, then, defining z $= A$y,

$$\operatorname{cov} z = A \sum A'.$$

Rule 2.6 is proven as follows:

$$\begin{aligned}
\operatorname{cov} z &= E[z - \mu_z][z - \mu_z]' \\
&= EA[y - \mu][A(y - \mu)]'.
\end{aligned} \tag{2.19}$$

From the elementary properties of the transpose of a product, Eq. 2.19 is written

$$\begin{aligned}
\operatorname{cov} z &= AE[y - \mu][y - \mu]'A' \\
&= A \sum A'.
\end{aligned}$$

A special application of Rule 2.6 is the situation where one requires the variance of a linear combination of random variables; the variance is written conveniently in matrix notation as the quadratic form

$$\operatorname{var} (a'y) = a' \sum a, \tag{2.20}$$

where y contains k random variables and has variance–covariance matrix Σ and $a' = [a_1, a_2, \ldots, a_k]$. Equation 2.20 yields the following result in scalar notation:

$$\operatorname{var} (a'y) = \sum_{i=1}^{k} a_i^2 \sigma_i^2 + 2 \sum \sum_{\substack{ij \\ i<j}} a_i a_j \sigma_{ij}.$$

2.12 | further remarks

As has been indicated, it has not been the aim of this chapter to give sufficient material for a complete study of the use of matrices and matrix algebra. In fact, it is hoped that the student has had at least a practical exposure to the subject before he embarks upon the task of reading this text. If, in the course of the reader's education in the area of basic and applied statistics, he has had no experience in the use of matrices, he should supplement his reading with a basic textbook on matrix algebra. It would prove expedient to put particular emphasis on the general topics which are discussed in this review.

exercises

2.1. Perform the following matrix multiplications:

a) $\begin{bmatrix} 2 \\ 2 \\ 4 \end{bmatrix} [4 \quad 4 \quad 1 \quad 8]$.

b) $\begin{bmatrix} 1 & 8 & 7 \\ 2 & 4 & 1 \\ 4 & 4 & 9 \end{bmatrix} \begin{bmatrix} 2 & 1 \\ 1 & 3 \\ 5 & 3 \end{bmatrix}$.

c) $[2 \quad 3] \begin{bmatrix} 4 & 1 \\ 1 & 4 \end{bmatrix} \begin{bmatrix} 2 \\ 3 \end{bmatrix}$.

2.2. Solve the system of equations

$$\begin{bmatrix} 4 & 1 & 5 \\ 1 & 3 & 2 \\ 5 & 2 & 1 \end{bmatrix} \begin{bmatrix} x_1 \\ x_2 \\ x_3 \end{bmatrix} = \begin{bmatrix} 1 \\ 3 \\ 2 \end{bmatrix}.$$

2.3. Give the rank of the matrices

a) $\begin{bmatrix} 2 & 1 & 3 & 8 \\ 5 & 4 & 1 & 1 \end{bmatrix}$.

b) $\begin{bmatrix} 6 & 12 & 5 \\ 1 & 2 & 1 \\ 3 & 6 & 3 \end{bmatrix}$.

2.4. Show that the matrix

$$\begin{bmatrix} 1/\sqrt{3} & 0 & -2/\sqrt{6} \\ 1/\sqrt{3} & 1/\sqrt{2} & 1/\sqrt{6} \\ 1/\sqrt{3} & -1/\sqrt{2} & 1/\sqrt{6} \end{bmatrix}$$

is orthogonal. Construct an orthogonal matrix containing five rows and five columns.

2.5. Given the matrix

$$A = \begin{bmatrix} 2 & 1 & 2 \\ 2 & 3 & 5 \\ 3 & 3 & 1 \\ 5 & 1 & 3 \end{bmatrix},$$

show that the matrix $A'A$ is positive definite.

2.6. Given the $n \times 1$ vector $\mathbf{y}$, an $n \times k$ matrix A, and a $k \times 1$ vector $\mathbf{b}$; show that

$$L = (\mathbf{y} - A\mathbf{b})'(\mathbf{y} - A\mathbf{b}) = \mathbf{y}'\mathbf{y} - 2\mathbf{b}'A'\mathbf{y} + \mathbf{b}'A'A\mathbf{b}.$$

2.7. For the expression L in Problem 2.6, show that

$$\frac{\partial L}{\partial \mathbf{b}} = -2A'\mathbf{y} + 2(A'A)\mathbf{b}.$$

references

Browne, E. T.: *Introduction to the Theory of Determinants and Matrices,* University of North Carolina Press, Chapel Hill, North Carolina, 1958.

Graybill, F. A.: *Introduction to Linear Statistical Models,* Vol. 1, McGraw-Hill, Inc., New York, 1961.

Li, J. C. R.: *Statistical Inference,* Vol. 2, Statistics, Inc., distributed by Edwards Brothers, Inc., Ann Arbor, Michigan, 1964.

3 | review: least squares and experimental design

Before the reader can be completely prepared for the discussion of analysis and design in response surface studies, it is necessary that he review such important topics as the method of least squares, multiple regression, and factorial experimental designs. The basic response surface methodology (*both* analysis *and* design) relies heavily on these devices. Fundamentally, the response surface problem usually centers around an interest in some response η which is a function of k independent variables $x_1, x_2, \ldots, x_k$, that is,

$$\eta = f(x_1, x_2, \ldots, x_k). \tag{3.1}$$

The actual form of f in Eq. 3.1 is often unknown, but it is assumed that it can be approximated by a polynomial function of low order. For example, for $k = 2$ one might assume a model of the type

$$y = \beta_0 + \beta_1 x_1 + \beta_2 x_2 + \beta_{11} x_1^2 + \beta_{22} x_2^2 + \beta_{12} x_1 x_2 + \varepsilon$$

where $\beta_0, \beta_1, \beta_2, \beta_{11}, \ldots$ are constant coefficients, y is the *measured* response, and ε is a random error used primarily to account for one's inability to describe the true model. The variables $x_1, x_2, \ldots, x_k$ are quantitative and measured on some continuous scale. An insight into the utility of response surface methods, and a discussion of its drawbacks and limitations are given in succeeding chapters. It is the purpose of the present chapter to review more fundamental topics, those with which the reader should already be somewhat familiar. Emphasis is also placed on the introduction of notation which is used throughout the text. The first topic that is reviewed is the method of least squares.

3.1 | method of least squares

Suppose that the function f in Eq. 3.1 is approximated by a model linear in the x's. We shall assume for our discussion that this approximation is adequate, although the general discussion that follows can easily be altered to be consistent with an approximation of higher order. Suppose that n experimental runs are taken on various combinations of the x's, the combinations determined by the experimenter. The data is written in the form

$$
\begin{array}{ccccc}
y_1 & x_{11} & x_{21} & \cdots & x_{k1} \\
y_2 & x_{12} & x_{22} & \cdots & x_{k2} \\
\cdots & \cdots & \cdots & \cdots & \cdots \\
y_n & x_{1n} & x_{2n} & \cdots & x_{kn}
\end{array}
$$

where $n > k$. The actual plan of experimental levels in the x's (if there is a plan) is called the *experimental design*. The model which was assumed by the experimenter can be written

$$
y_i = \beta_0 + \beta_1 x_{1i} + \beta_2 x_{2i} + \cdots + \beta_k x_{ki} + \varepsilon_i \qquad (i = 1, 2, \ldots, n)
$$

$$(3.2)$$

where ε_i is a random variable. It is assumed that the ε_i is independent from run to run with zero mean and variance σ^2. That is, in terms of the following vector of errors

$$
\varepsilon = \begin{bmatrix} \varepsilon_1 \\ \varepsilon_2 \\ \cdots \\ \varepsilon_n \end{bmatrix},
$$

$$(3.3)$$

$E(\varepsilon) = \mathbf{0}$, and cov $(\varepsilon) = \sigma^2 I$. The model of Eq. 3.1 can be written very conveniently in the form.

$$
\mathbf{y} = X\boldsymbol{\beta} + \varepsilon.
$$

$$(3.4)$$

Here, of course,

$$
\mathbf{y} = \begin{bmatrix} y_1 \\ y_2 \\ \cdots \\ y_n \end{bmatrix}, \qquad \boldsymbol{\beta} = \begin{bmatrix} \beta_0 \\ \beta_1 \\ \beta_2 \\ \cdots \\ \beta_k \end{bmatrix},
$$

and

$$
X = \begin{bmatrix}
1 & x_{11} & x_{21} & \cdots & x_{k1} \\
1 & x_{12} & x_{22} & \cdots & x_{k2} \\
\cdots & \cdots & \cdots & \cdots & \cdots \\
1 & x_{1n} & x_{2n} & \cdots & x_{kn}
\end{bmatrix}.
$$

The model of Eq. 3.4 is referred to as the *general linear model*. The reader can readily see that the general linear model is easily applied to polynomial models of degree higher than one. For example, suppose the model assumed is a quadratic in two variables, that is, the response for the ith run, involving the levels (x_{1i}, x_{2i}) is given by

$$y_i = \beta_0 + \beta_1 x_{1i} + \beta_2 x_{2i} + \beta_{11} x_{1i}^2 + \beta_{22} x_{2i}^2 + \beta_{12} x_{1i} x_{2i} + \varepsilon_i \quad (3.5)$$

where $i = 1, 2, \ldots, n \geq 6$. It is seen that the X matrix and β vector can be written

$$X = \begin{bmatrix} 1 & x_{11} & x_{21} & x_{11}^2 & x_{21}^2 & x_{11}x_{21} \\ 1 & x_{12} & x_{22} & x_{12}^2 & x_{22}^2 & x_{12}x_{22} \\ \cdots & \cdots & \cdots & \cdots & \cdots & \cdots \\ 1 & x_{1n} & x_{2n} & x_{1n}^2 & x_{2n}^2 & x_{1n}x_{2n} \end{bmatrix}$$

and

$$\beta = \begin{bmatrix} \beta_0 \\ \beta_1 \\ \beta_2 \\ \beta_{11} \\ \beta_{22} \\ \beta_{12} \end{bmatrix}.$$

Suppose we focus our attention toward the general problem of estimating the parameters in the vector β. The method of *least squares* is a useful estimation procedure, particularly for models of the form in Eq. 3.4. Given the matrix X, a function of the preselected x levels, and the vector $\mathbf{y}$ of responses, the least squares method uses as an estimate of β, that vector which results in a minimum value for

$$L = \sum_{i=1}^{n} \varepsilon_i^2 = \varepsilon' \varepsilon,$$

the sum of squares of the *errors* or deviations from the observed response to the estimated value. L can be written

$$L = (\mathbf{y} - X\hat{\beta})'(\mathbf{y} - X\hat{\beta}). \quad (3.6)$$

Upon expanding the right-hand side of Eq. 3.6

$$\begin{aligned} L &= \mathbf{y}'\mathbf{y} - (X\hat{\beta})'\mathbf{y} - \mathbf{y}'X\hat{\beta} + (X\hat{\beta})'X\hat{\beta} \\ &= \mathbf{y}'\mathbf{y} - \hat{\beta}'X'\mathbf{y} - \mathbf{y}'X\hat{\beta} + \hat{\beta}'X'X\hat{\beta} \\ &= \mathbf{y}'\mathbf{y} - 2\hat{\beta}'X'\mathbf{y} + \hat{\beta}'X'X\hat{\beta}. \end{aligned} \quad (3.7)$$

One can find the $\hat{\beta}$ which results in L being a minimum by using the rules of differentiation reviewed in Chapter 2.

$$\frac{\partial L}{\partial \hat{\beta}} = -2X'\mathbf{y} + 2(X'X)\hat{\beta}.$$

Setting the partial derivative to zero and solving for $\hat{\beta}$,

$$(X'X)\hat{\beta} = X'\mathbf{y}. \tag{3.8}$$

Assuming that $X'X$ is nonsingular, we have the following *least squares estimator*:

$$\hat{\beta} = (X'X)^{-1}X'\mathbf{y}. \tag{3.9}$$

The Equations given by Eq. 3.8 are called the "normal equations" for estimating $\hat{\beta}$. For the *first order regression* model of Eq. 3.2 these equations are

$$\begin{bmatrix} n & \sum x_{1i} & \sum x_{2i} & \cdots & \sum x_{ki} \\ & \sum x_{1i}^2 & \sum x_{1i}x_{2i} & \cdots & \sum x_{1i}x_{ki} \\ & & \sum x_{2i}^2 & \cdots & \sum x_{2i}x_{ki} \\ & & & \cdots & \\ & & & & \sum x_{ki}^2 \end{bmatrix} \begin{bmatrix} \hat{\beta}_0 \\ \hat{\beta}_1 \\ \hat{\beta}_2 \\ \cdots \\ \hat{\beta}_k \end{bmatrix} = \begin{bmatrix} \sum y_i \\ \sum x_{1i}y_i \\ \sum x_{2i}y_i \\ \cdots \\ \sum x_{ki}y_i \end{bmatrix}. \tag{3.10}$$

bias and variance of least squares estimators

In the brief section given here, material is presented which displays the bias and the covariance properties of the estimators in the vector $\hat{\beta}$. Since all polynomial response models discussed in this text can be put in the form of Eq. 3.4, the bias and precision results will be of considerable use later in the text. Suppose one considers the expectation of the vector $\hat{\beta} = (X'X)^{-1}X'\mathbf{y}$. Since $\mathbf{y} = X\beta + \varepsilon$,

$$E(\hat{\beta}) = E[(X'X)^{-1}[X'(X\beta + \varepsilon)]]$$

$$= I\beta + E[(X'X)^{-1}X'\varepsilon].$$

Since $E(\varepsilon_i) = 0$ for $i = 1, 2, \ldots, n$,

$$E[(X'X)^{-1}X'\varepsilon] = 0$$

and thus

$$E(\hat{\beta}) = \beta,$$

which implies, of course, that each element in the vector of estimators is *unbiased* for the parameter it is estimating.

In the development of the experimental designs for the response surface methodology, it often becomes important to investigate the effect of design on the variance–covariance matrix of $\hat{\beta}$.

$$\text{cov}(\hat{\beta}) = E[\hat{\beta} - \beta][\hat{\beta} - \beta]'$$
$$= \text{cov}(X'X)^{-1}X'\mathbf{y}.$$

Since the matrix $(X'X)^{-1}X'$ contains no random variables and $\text{cov }\mathbf{y} = \sigma^2 I_n$, Rule 2.6 (p. 23) can be used to obtain

$$\text{cov }\hat{\beta} = [(X'X)^{-1}X']\sigma^2 I_n[(X'X)^{-1}X']',$$

which after simplification reduces to

$$\text{cov }\hat{\beta} = \sigma^2(X'X)^{-1}. \qquad (3.11)$$

Eq. 3.11 represents an extremely important result. It implies that the variances of the estimators in $\hat{\beta}$ are given by the diagonal elements of $(X'X)^{-1}$, each multiplied by σ^2; and the covariances between elements in the estimate vector $\hat{\beta}$ are the off-diagonal elements of $(X'X)^{-1}$, likewise multiplied by σ^2. For the linear regression model of Eq. 3.5

$$\text{cov}\begin{bmatrix} \hat{\beta}_0 \\ \hat{\beta}_1 \\ \hat{\beta}_2 \\ \dots \\ \hat{\beta}_k \end{bmatrix} = \begin{bmatrix} n & \sum x_{1i} & \sum x_{2i} & \cdots & \sum x_{ki} \\ & \sum x_{1i}^2 & \sum x_{1i}x_{2i} & \cdots & \sum x_{1i}x_{ki} \\ & & \sum x_{2i}^2 & \cdots & \sum x_{2i}x_{ki} \\ & & & \cdots & \cdots \\ & & & & \sum x_{ki}^2 \end{bmatrix}^{-1} \sigma^2.$$

3.2 | hypothesis testing

One is often interested in following the estimation of β with a test of hypothesis on one or more of the β's. If the additional assumption is made that the ε_i follow a normal distribution, that is,

$$\varepsilon \cap N(\mathbf{0}, \sigma^2 I_n),$$

then the y's are merely linear functions of the ε's and thus are normally distributed. Recalling, then, results that were developed in the Section 3.1,

$$\hat{\beta} \cap N[\beta, \sigma^2(X'X)^{-1}].$$

It is not the purpose of this section to present formally complete details of the hypothesis testing procedure for the general linear model. An account of the theory is given in Graybill. Other texts, for example Li, and Draper and Smith, outline the proper methods for the type of models which are of interest here, namely, regression models such as those given by Eqs. 3.2 and 3.5. The reader should refer to one of these texts for the procedures.

For the case of the general linear model, we shall suppose that X is of rank p, where p is the number of parameters in the model. Table 3.1 gives the proper partitioning of *sum of squares* and *degrees of freedom* attributed to *regression* and *error* (assume $n > p$ observations are taken).

Table 3.1. Sum of Squares and Degrees of Freedom for
Regression and Error for Model of Eq. 3.4

Source	Sum of Squares	Degrees of Freedom	Mean Square
regression	$\hat{\beta}'X'y$	p	$\hat{\beta}'X'y/p$
error	$y'y - \hat{\beta}'X'y$	$n - p$	$(y'y - \hat{\beta}'X'y)/(n - p)$
total	$y'y$	n	

For the general polynomial regression problems, the experimenter is often interested in a further partitioning of the regression sum of squares. For example, suppose one were to fit a second order function as defined by Eq. 3.5. In order to determine whether or not the *quadratic* contribution is significant, it is necessary to conduct an *analysis of variance* using the usual F-tests, etc., in which the regression sum of squares is subdivided into two parts—that attributed to linear regression and that attributed to the quadratic contribution. This approach is particularly useful in exploratory response surface work, as will be illustrated by examples in this chapter and with other developments in later chapters.

As an illustration of the computations involved in constructing Table 3.1, consider the model of Eq. 3.2, rewritten in the form

$$y_i = \beta_0' + \beta_1(x_{1i} - \bar{x}_1) + \beta_2(x_{2i} - \bar{x}_2) + \cdots + \beta_k(x_{ki} - \bar{x}_k) + \varepsilon_i \quad (3.12)$$

where $\bar{x}_j$ is the average value of x_j in the sample data $(j = 1, 2, \ldots, k)$. Likewise, if one considers the normal equations given by Eq. 3.7 for the model as written in Eq. 3.12

$$
\begin{bmatrix} \hat{\beta}_0' \\ \hat{\beta}_1 \\ \hat{\beta}_2 \\ \cdots \\ \hat{\beta}_k \end{bmatrix} = \begin{bmatrix} n & 0 & 0 & \cdots & 0 \\ & S_{11} & S_{12} & \cdots & S_{1k} \\ & & S_{22} & \cdots & S_{2k} \\ & & & \cdots & \\ & & & & S_{kk} \end{bmatrix}^{-1} \begin{bmatrix} \sum y_i \\ S_{1y} \\ S_{2y} \\ \cdots \\ S_{ky} \end{bmatrix} \quad (3.13)
$$

where S_{ii} is the *corrected* sum of squares of the column of x_i's; for example

$$S_{11} = \sum_{i=1}^{n} (x_{1i} - \bar{x}_1)^2.$$

S_{ij} is the corrected sum of products between the x_i and x_j; for example, S_{12} is written

$$S_{12} = \sum_{i=1}^{n} (x_{1i} - \bar{x}_1)(x_{2i} - \bar{x}_2).$$

The term S_{iy} is the corrected sum of products between x_i and y; for instance

$$S_{1y} = \sum_{i=1}^{n} (x_{1i} - \bar{x}_1)(y_i - \bar{y}).$$

Solving this system of equations yields the estimate

$$\hat{\beta}_0' = \sum_{i=1}^{n} y_i / n$$

independently, and the estimators $\hat{\beta}_1, \hat{\beta}_2, \ldots, \hat{\beta}_k$ are obtained by

$$\begin{bmatrix} \hat{\beta}_1 \\ \hat{\beta}_2 \\ \cdots \\ \hat{\beta}_k \end{bmatrix} = \begin{bmatrix} S_{11} & S_{12} & \cdots & S_{1k} \\ & S_{22} & \cdots & S_{2k} \\ & & \cdots & \cdots \\ & & & S_{kk} \end{bmatrix}^{-1} \begin{bmatrix} S_{1y} \\ S_{2y} \\ \cdots \\ S_{ky} \end{bmatrix}.$$

The display of the partitioning of sum of squares and degrees of freedom attributable to regression and error for this case is given in Table 3.2.

Table 3.2. Sum of Squares and Degrees of Freedom for First Order Regression Model

Source	Sum of Squares	Degrees of Freedom
regression due to β_0'	$\left(\sum\limits_{i=1}^{n} y_i \right)^2 / n$	1
regression on $x_1, x_2, \ldots, x_k$	$\hat{\beta}_1 S_{1y} + \hat{\beta}_2 S_{2y} + \cdots + \hat{\beta}_k S_{ky}$	k
error	difference	$n - k - 1$
total	$\sum\limits_{i=1}^{n} y_i^2$	n

A similar table can be constructed for the case of a quadratic regression model.

3.3 | estimator for σ^2

Inherent in any problem involving a regression model is the task of estimating σ^2, the error variance. The problem is discussed here using the framework of the general linear model; the regression models can be considered as special cases. Recalling information from the previous section, the quantity $\mathbf{y'y} - \hat{\boldsymbol{\beta}}'X'\mathbf{y}$ is referred to as the error sum of squares or, notationally, SS_E.

$$
\begin{aligned}
SS_E &= \mathbf{y'y} - [(X'X)^{-1}X'\mathbf{y}]'X'\mathbf{y} \\
&= \mathbf{y'y} - \mathbf{y}'X(X'X)^{-1}X'\mathbf{y} \\
&= \mathbf{y}'[I_n - X(X'X)^{-1}X']\mathbf{y}.
\end{aligned}
\tag{3.14}
$$

One notices that SS_E is a quadratic form in the y's, with matrix

$$
P = I_n - X(X'X)^{-1}X'.
$$

Consider the expectation of SS_E. Substituting

$$
\mathbf{y} = X\boldsymbol{\beta} + \boldsymbol{\varepsilon}
$$

into Eq. 3.14 and simplifying, yields

$$
E[\mathbf{y}'P\mathbf{y}] = E[\boldsymbol{\varepsilon}'P\boldsymbol{\varepsilon}].
\tag{3.15}
$$

At this point we can make use of Rule 2.5 (p. 23) in Chapter 2;

$$
E[\boldsymbol{\varepsilon}'P\boldsymbol{\varepsilon}] = \sigma^2 \operatorname{tr} P.
$$

The trace of I_n is n and since

$$
\begin{aligned}
\operatorname{tr} X(X'X)^{-1}X' &= \operatorname{tr} X'X(X'X)^{-1} \\
&= \operatorname{tr} I_p \\
&= p,
\end{aligned}
$$

the result is

$$
E(SS_E) = \sigma^2(n - p).
$$

Therefore, the quantity

$$
MS_E = \frac{SS_E}{n - p}
\tag{3.16}
$$

is an unbiased estimator of σ^2. The term MS_E refers to the *error mean square* in the analysis of the general linear model, that is, the error sum of

squares divided by the error degrees of freedom. For example, in the
multiple first order regression case, MS_E is written

$$MS_E = \frac{\sum y_i^2 - (\sum y_i)^2/n - [\hat{\beta}_1 S_{1y} + \hat{\beta}_2 S_{2y} + \cdots + \hat{\beta}_k S_{ky}]}{n - k - 1}.$$

Example. A field experiment was conducted to determine the second order
regression equation which relates the amount (parts per million, ppm) of
water soluble boron in the soil (y) with the concentration (weight percent,
wt %) of clay (x_1) and the soil pH (x_2). Twenty observations were taken and
the readings recorded as shown in Table 3.3.

Table 3.3. Amount of Water Soluble Boron at Various Levels
of Clay Concentration and Soil pH

Run	y (ppm)	x_1 (wt %)	x_2 (pH)
1	0.62	37	5.3
2	0.69	37	5.3
3	0.63	37	5.5
4	0.61	37	5.7
5	0.28	29	5.6
6	0.33	29	5.7
7	0.31	29	5.7
8	0.37	29	5.9
9	0.66	29	6.0
10	0.70	29	6.3
11	0.74	29	6.0
12	0.63	29	6.0
13	0.52	27	5.5
14	0.47	27	5.6
15	0.45	27	5.6
16	0.42	27	5.7
17	0.41	27	5.5
18	0.42	27	5.5
19	0.42	27	5.5
20	0.41	27	5.5

A model was postulated of the type

$$y_i = \beta_0 + \beta_1 x_{1i} + \beta_2 x_{2i} + \beta_{12} x_{1i} x_{2i} + \beta_{11} x_{1i}^2 + \beta_{22} x_{2i}^2 + \varepsilon_i$$

$$(i = 1, 2, \ldots, 20). \quad (3.17)$$

The data of Table 3.3 can be used to form the X and $X'X$ matrices as well
as the vector $X'y$. The elements of the symmetric matrix $X'X$ are given in
Table 3.4.

Table 3.4. Elements of the $X'X$ Matrix for Model of Eq. 3.17

Element	Value	Element	Value
$(1, 1) = n$	20	$(3, 3) = \sum x_{2i}^2$	644.22
$(1, 2) = \sum x_{1i}$	596.00	$(3, 4) = \sum x_{1i}x_{2i}^2$	19,140.82
$(1, 3) = \sum x_{2i}$	113.40	$(3, 5) = \sum x_{1i}^2 x_{2i}$	101,907.00
$(1, 4) = \sum x_{1i}x_{2i}$	3,374.20	$(3, 6) = \sum x_{2i}^3$	3,667.05
$(1, 5) = \sum x_{1i}^2$	18,036.00	$(4, 4) = \sum x_{1i}^2 x_{2i}^2$	576,975.24
$(1, 6) = \sum x_{2i}^2$	644.22	$(4, 5) = \sum x_{1i}^3 x_{2i}$	3,129,321.31
$(2, 2) = \sum x_{1i}^2$	18,036.00	$(4, 6) = \sum x_{1i}x_{2i}^3$	108,802.42
$(2, 3) = \sum x_{1i}x_{2i}$	3,374.20	$(5, 5) = \sum x_{1i}^4$	17,406,420.25
$(2, 4) = \sum x_{1i}^2 x_{2i}$	101,907.00	$(5, 6) = \sum x_{1i}^2 x_{2i}^2$	576,975.25
$(2, 5) = \sum x_{1i}^3$	555,188.00	$(6, 6) = \sum x_{2i}^4$	20,916.25
$(2, 6) = \sum x_{1i}x_{2i}^2$	19,140.82		

The elements of the $X'y$ vector are given by

$$\begin{bmatrix} \sum y_i & = & 10.09 \\ \sum y_i x_{1i} & = & 305.97 \\ \sum y_i x_{2i} & = & 57.41 \\ \sum y_i x_{1i} x_{2i} & = & 1,736.90 \\ \sum y_i x_{1i}^2 & = & 9,437.85 \\ \sum y_i x_{2i}^2 & = & 327.43 \end{bmatrix}$$

The normal equations were solved and the estimates of the regression coefficients were found to be the following:

$$\hat{\beta} = \begin{bmatrix} \hat{\beta}_0 & = & 7.0043 \\ \hat{\beta}_1 & = & -0.3620 \\ \hat{\beta}_2 & = & -0.7331 \\ \hat{\beta}_{12} & = & -0.0613 \\ \hat{\beta}_{11} & = & 0.0113 \\ \hat{\beta}_{22} & = & 0.2680 \end{bmatrix}$$

3.4 | use of orthogonal polynomials in fitting regression model

It was indicated earlier that a polynomial regression model can be handled by applying very generally the principles of the general linear model. However, if the experimenter chooses the levels of x variables so that they are *evenly spaced,* certain computational simplifications can be made by the use of *orthogonal polynomials.* One merely replaces the term x^j in the regression by a *particular* polynomial of order j. For example, suppose one assumes the following polynomial regression model for the case of a single independent variable:

$$y = \beta_0 + \beta_1 x + \beta_2 x^2 + \cdots + \beta_q x^q + \varepsilon. \tag{3.18}$$

Suppose further that one has experimental data of the form

y	x
y_1	x_1
y_2	x_2
...	...
y_n	x_n

where $n > q$ and the levels $x_1, x_2, \ldots, x_n$ are evenly spaced. That is, $x_2 = x_1 + d; x_3 = x_2 + d; \ldots$. One can rewrite the model of Eq. 3.18 in the form

$$y_i = \alpha_0 + \alpha_1 p_1(x_i) + \alpha_2 p_2(x_i) + \cdots + \alpha_q p_q(x_i)$$
$$+ \varepsilon_i \quad (i = 1, 2, \ldots, n) \tag{3.19}$$

where $p_j(x)$ is a polynomial in x of order j. The p's are chosen so that they are *orthogonal,* that is,

$$\sum_{i=1}^{n} p_j(x_i) = 0 \quad (j = 1, 2, \ldots, q)$$

$$\sum_{i=1}^{n} p_j(x_i)p_k(x_i) = 0 \quad \begin{array}{l}(j, k = 1, 2, \ldots, q) \\ (j \neq k)\end{array}$$

$$\sum_{i=1}^{n} p_j^2(x_i) \neq 0 \quad (j = 1, 2, \ldots, q).$$

With these restrictions on the p's, the determination of the least squares estimates of the coefficients in the model of Eq. 3.19 is greatly simplified. This is easily seen by applying the techniques of the general linear model. For Eq. 3.19

$$X = \begin{bmatrix} 1 & p_1(x_1) & p_2(x_1) & \cdots & p_q(x_1) \\ 1 & p_1(x_2) & p_2(x_2) & \cdots & p_q(x_2) \\ \cdots & \cdots & \cdots & \cdots & \cdots \\ 1 & p_1(x_n) & p_2(x_n) & \cdots & p_q(x_n) \end{bmatrix},$$

and from the orthogonality conditions on the polynomials, the sum of products of any two of the polynomials is zero, resulting in

$$X'X = \text{diag}\left[n, \sum_{i=1}^{n} p_1^2(x_i), \sum_{i=1}^{n} p_2^2(x_i), \ldots, \sum_{i=1}^{n} p_q^2(x_i) \right] \quad (3.20)$$

and the *right-hand side* vector in the normal equations

$$X'\mathbf{y} = \begin{bmatrix} \sum_i y_i \\ \sum_i p_1(x_i)y_i \\ \sum_i p_2(x_i)y_i \\ \ldots \\ \sum_i p_q(x_i)y_i \end{bmatrix}.$$

The estimates of the parameters in Eq. 3.19 are then simply

$$\hat{\alpha}_0 = \sum_i y_i/n$$

$$\hat{\alpha}_1 = \sum_i p_1(x_i)y_i/\sum_i p_1^2(x_i)$$

$$\hat{\alpha}_2 = \sum_i p_2(x_i)y_i/\sum_i p_2^2(x_i)$$

$$\ldots \qquad \ldots$$

$$\hat{\alpha}_q = \sum_i p_q(x_i)y_i/\sum_i p_q^2(x_i).$$

Thus, through the use of the p's in the redefinition of the model, the $X'X$ matrix is made diagonal, thereby reducing the computational procedure considerably.

determination of the polynomials

Let $\bar{x}$ be the average of the evenly spaced x levels, where the value d is the spacing. The first three orthogonal polynomials are

$$p_1(x) = \left[\frac{x - \bar{x}}{d} \right]$$

$$p_2(x) = \left[\left(\frac{x - \bar{x}}{d}\right)^2 - \left(\frac{n^2 - 1}{12}\right) \right] \quad (3.21)$$

$$p_3(x) = \left[\left(\frac{x - \bar{x}}{d}\right)^3 - \left(\frac{3n^2 - 7}{20}\right)\left(\frac{x - \bar{x}}{d}\right) \right].$$

A recursive scheme for obtaining $p_{r+1}(x)$ in terms of $p_r(x)$ is given by

$$p_{r+1}(x) = p_r(x)p_1(x) - \frac{r^2(n^2 - r^2)}{4(4r^2 - 1)} p_{r-1}(x) \qquad (r = 1, 2, \ldots,)$$

where $p_0(x)$ is taken to be unity.

Example. The data shown in Table 3.5 represent repeated measurements on some dependent variable (y) at specified levels of a single independent variable (x).

Table 3.5. Data on Reaction Yield for
Various Temperature Levels

y	x
82.0	180
89.2	200
94.5	220
99.6	240
102.5	260
103.2	280
103.8	300

A quadratic was assumed, that is, a model of the type

$$y_i = \alpha_0 + \alpha_1 p_1(x_i) + \alpha_2 p_2(x_i) + \varepsilon_i.$$

Using p_1 and p_2 as given by Eq. 3.21, one can easily construct a table giving the value of p_1 and p_2 for each of the levels of the variable x. These values are given in Table 3.6. It is easily seen that the orthogonality conditions hold.

Table 3.6. Values of p_1 and p_2 Using Eq. 3.21 for
Data of Table 3.5

x	$p_1(x)$	$p_2(x)$
180	-3	5
200	-2	0
220	-1	-3
240	0	-4
260	1	-3
280	2	0
300	3	5

The $X'X$ matrix and $X'y$ vector are

$$X'X = \text{diag} (7,28,84)$$

$$X'y = \begin{bmatrix} 674.8 \\ 101.4 \\ -60.4 \end{bmatrix},$$

and the estimates of the coefficients in the regression model are

$$\hat{a}_0 = 676.8/7 = 96.4$$

$$\hat{a}_1 = 101.4/28 = 3.621$$

$$\hat{a}_2 = -60.4/84 = -0.719.$$

Thus, the resulting estimating equation is given by

$$\hat{y} = 96.4 + 3.621 \, p_1(x) - 0.719 \, p_2(x).$$

The fundamental principles regarding the general linear model can be applied further for the case of this example; logically, one may be interested in estimates of the variances and covariances of the model coefficients and an estimate of the error variance σ^2. The total sum of squares is given by

$$y'y = \sum y_i^2 = 65,461,980,$$

and the regression sum of squares is given by

$$[\hat{a}_0 \quad \hat{a}_1 \quad \hat{a}_2] \, X'y = [96.4 \quad 3.621 \quad -0.719] \begin{bmatrix} 674.8 \\ 101.4 \\ -60.4 \end{bmatrix}.$$

$$= 65,461.317$$

Thus, the error sum of squares is found by difference

$$SS_E = 65,461.980 - 65,461.317 = 0.663,$$

and the estimate of σ^2 (4 degrees of freedom) is given by

$$MS_E = \frac{0.663}{4} = 0.166.$$

From this we compute estimates of the elements in the variance–covariance matrix of the vector $[\hat{a}_0, \hat{a}_1, \hat{a}_2]$.
    This matrix of estimates is given by

$$MS_E(X'X)^{-1} = 0.166 \begin{bmatrix} 1/7 & 0 & 0 \\ 0 & 1/28 & 0 \\ 0 & 0 & 1/84 \end{bmatrix}. \qquad (3.22)$$

The sum of squares due to regression, computed in this example to be 65,461.317 (with 3 degrees of freedom) can very easily be partitioned into single degree of freedom components—one component each for $\hat{\alpha}_0$, $\hat{\alpha}_1$, and $\hat{\alpha}_2$. In this case, *since the estimates are orthogonal* to each other, the components are simply the individual terms in the expression

$$SS_{reg} = [\hat{\alpha}_0, \hat{\alpha}_1, \hat{\alpha}_2] \, X'y.$$

That is,

$$\text{Sum of squares regression on } p_1(x) = 367.169;$$

$$\text{Sum of squares regression on } p_2(x) = \quad 43.428.$$

Individual F-tests can be made, indicating the significance of the linear and quadratic polynomial in the model, with $MS_E = 0.166$ as the denominator mean square in the F-ratio. The reader should be reminded that, in general, the individual sum of squares contributions are computed in this manner *only* when the estimators are orthogonal, one to another.

3.5 | factorial experiments

While it is assumed that the reader has been exposed to a first course in experimental design, a brief treatment is nevertheless given in this section on certain aspects of classical factorial experimental design. Much emphasis is placed on estimation of polynomial regression functions, since this will be the main concern in later chapters. As was the case in the previous sections, we shall not dwell on hypothesis testing, although certainly this topic is an important phase of the complete statistical analysis.

In many experimental situations where the scientist is interested in learning how some response is influenced by certain factors $x_1, x_2, \ldots, x_k$, a well-chosen experimental layout or experimental design can result in a savings of time and expense. In fact, if a polynomial relationship is to be estimated, a proper choice of the design can provide a certain "efficiency" in estimating the model coefficients. The array given by

$$D = \begin{bmatrix} x_{11} & x_{21} & \cdots & x_{k1} \\ x_{12} & x_{22} & \cdots & x_{k2} \\ \cdots & \cdots & \cdots & \cdots \\ x_{1n} & x_{2n} & \cdots & x_{kn} \end{bmatrix}, \tag{3.23}$$

which indicates the combinations of levels chosen, characterizes the experimental plan and is called the *design matrix*. The uth row,

$$[x_{1u}x_{2u}, \ldots, x_{ku}],$$

represents one experimental run. The reader should begin to understand as more treatment is given in future chapters to experimental designs, that the problem of choosing the proper design is not a simple one; the experimental levels are chosen in some systematic fashion which depends on the knowledge and interests of the experimenter.

The type of experiment to be reviewed in this section is the *factorial experiment*. The class of designs is characterized by the fact that the effect of changing one variable can be assessed independently of the others. The factorial experiment is accomplished by using as the design, each of the possible combinations of the levels (preselected by the experimenter) of each factor. For example, suppose one decides to carry out trials on factors

$$x_1: \text{temperature in reaction kettle, } °C$$

and

$$x_2: \text{concentration of one reactant, wt\%}$$

where the response y is the reaction time in seconds, and the experimenter decides on the following levels:

$$x_1: 150, \quad 200, \quad 250;$$
$$x_2: \quad 8, \quad 10, \quad 12.$$

The design matrix for this factorial experiment is

$$D = \begin{bmatrix} x_1 & x_2 \\ 150 & 8 \\ 150 & 10 \\ 150 & 12 \\ 200 & 8 \\ 200 & 10 \\ 200 & 12 \\ 250 & 8 \\ 250 & 10 \\ 250 & 12 \end{bmatrix}. \tag{3.24}$$

The nine *treatment combinations* are of course, not necessarily run in the order given in Eq. 3.24; rather, the order should be *randomized*. The design is referred to as a completely randomized design, and the experimental array is called a factorial experiment. One can, however, use the factorial experiment in conjunction with designs in which randomization is restricted, such as in cases where blocking of extraneous sources of variation is required.

The factorial experiment enjoys definite advantages over the one-factor-at-a-time experimental technique which is still used by some practitioners. In a factorial experiment, all factors are varied simultaneously, whereas the somewhat simpler one-factor-at-a-time procedure would involve, as the name implies, varying the levels of one factor at a time. An important advantage of the factorial approach is that it lends itself to assessing the "joint effect" of two or more variables, that is, the interaction among factors can be measured. Another advantage centers around the precision with which the effect of a factor can be measured. For example, suppose we consider three factors each at two levels. A one-factor-at-a-time experiment might be conducted with the following four treatment combinations:

factor	1	2	3	
	L	L	L	(1)
	H	L	L	(2)
	L	H	L	(3)
	L	L	H	(4)

The H notation refers to high level of the factor and the L notation refers to the low level. On the other hand, the factorial experiment would involve $2^3 = 8$ treatment combinations as follows:

factor	1	2	3	
	L	L	L	(1)
	H	L	L	(2)
	L	H	L	(3)
	L	L	H	(4)
	L	H	H	(5)
	H	L	H	(6)
	H	H	L	(7)
	H	H	H	(8)

Suppose that the observations are independent with equal variance σ^2. The effect of the first factor can be assessed as the difference between the response at low level and the response at high level, that is, (2)—(1) for the one-factor-at-a-time experiment and

$$\frac{(2) + (6) + (7) + (8) - (1) - (3) - (4) - (5)}{4}$$

for the factorial experiment. The variances of these two quantities are $2\sigma^2$ for the one-factor-at-a-time plan and $\sigma^2/2$ for the factorial plan, clearly indicating the superiority of the factorial experiment.

factorial experiments with each factor at two levels

The most elementary class of factorial experiments is the 2^k factorial, that is, k factors are of interest and each is taken at two levels. This type of design can be extremely useful in cases where the experimental situation is adequately represented by a first order relationship. Classical notation will be used here as far as the treatment combinations are concerned. For example, in a three-factor experiment (factors A, B, and C), the notation (1) is the observation or sum of the observations for which all three factors are at the low level. The presence of a lower case letter in the notation implies that the factor in question is at the high level, absence of a letter implies that the factor is at the low level.

(1) $- A, B, C$ at low level.

a $- A$ at high level; B and C at low level.

b $- B$ at high level; A and C at low level.

c $- C$ at high level; A and B at low level.

ab $- A$ and B at high level; C at low level.

ac $- A$ and C at high level; B at low level.

bc $- B$ and C at high level; A at low level.

abc $- A$, B, and C at high level.

When one fits a first order equation to a 2^k factorial experiment, it is often convenient to "code" the independent variables, with -1 representing the low level of a variable and $+1$ the high level. This, of course, corresponds to the transformation

$$x_i = 2 \left(\frac{\xi_i - \bar{\xi}_i}{d_i} \right),$$

where ξ_i is the actual reading in the original units and d_i is the spacing between the low and high level on the variable ξ_i. Suppose, for example, that the experiment is a 2^3 factorial with the fixed levels

$$\xi_1 : 150, 200$$

$$\xi_2 : 8, 12$$

$$\xi_3 : 30, 40$$

the following is the design matrix (in terms of the coded variables):

$$D = \begin{array}{c} \begin{array}{ccc} x_1 & x_2 & x_3 \end{array} \\ \begin{bmatrix} -1 & -1 & -1 \\ 1 & -1 & -1 \\ -1 & 1 & -1 \\ -1 & -1 & 1 \\ 1 & 1 & -1 \\ 1 & -1 & 1 \\ -1 & 1 & 1 \\ 1 & 1 & 1 \end{bmatrix} \begin{array}{l} (1) \\ a \\ b \\ c \\ ab \\ ac \\ bc \\ abc \end{array} \end{array} . \qquad (3.25)$$

Notice the treatment combination designation in the margin of the matrix in Eq. 3.25. For example, for the third data point only factor B is at the high level; then of course

$$x_2 = 2 \left(\frac{12 - 10}{4} \right) = +1,$$

and the value of x_3 is easily seen to be

$$x_3 = 2 \left(\frac{30 - 35}{10} \right) = -1.$$

Similarly, x_1 takes on a value of -1. If the design given by the matrix D of Eq. 3.25 is used to fit a model of the type

$$y_i = \beta_0 + \beta_1 x_1 + \beta_2 x_2 + \beta_3 x_3 + \varepsilon_i \qquad (i = 1, 2, \dots, 8), \qquad (3.26)$$

with the usual assumptions on the ε_i, then one can apply the principles of the general linear model to estimate the β_i and, if needed, make further inferences on these coefficients. It should be noted, of course, that since each factor is applied at only two levels, one cannot include *quadratic terms* such as $x_1^2, x_2^2, \dots$, in the model. Interaction terms such as $x_1 x_2, x_1 x_3, \dots$, *can be included* however. This will be discussed later in this chapter. For the model of Eq. 3.26 one has, for the X matrix of the general linear model,

$$X = \begin{array}{c} \begin{array}{cccc} & x_1 & x_2 & x_3 \end{array} \\ \begin{bmatrix} 1 & -1 & -1 & -1 \\ 1 & 1 & -1 & -1 \\ 1 & -1 & 1 & -1 \\ 1 & -1 & -1 & 1 \\ 1 & 1 & 1 & -1 \\ 1 & 1 & -1 & 1 \\ 1 & -1 & 1 & 1 \\ 1 & 1 & 1 & 1 \end{bmatrix} \end{array}$$

and

$$X'X = \begin{bmatrix} 8 & 0 & 0 & 0 \\ & 8 & 0 & 0 \\ & & 8 & 0 \\ & & & 8 \end{bmatrix}. \tag{3.27}$$

Using the previously defined notation for the observations, the $\mathbf{y}$ and $X'\mathbf{y}$ vectors are given by

$$\mathbf{y} = \begin{bmatrix} (1) \\ a \\ b \\ c \\ ab \\ ac \\ bc \\ abc \end{bmatrix} \quad X'\mathbf{y} = \begin{bmatrix} (1) + a + b + c + ab + ac + bc + abc \\ a + ab + ac + abc - (1) - b - c - bc \\ b + ab + bc + abc - (1) - a - c - ac \\ c + ac + bc + abc - (1) - a - b - ab \end{bmatrix}.$$

Therefore, the estimates $\hat{\beta}_0$, $\hat{\beta}_1$, $\hat{\beta}_2$, and $\hat{\beta}_3$ are merely the corresponding element of $X'\mathbf{y}$ divided by 8; for example,

$$\hat{\beta}_1 = (a + ab + ac + abc - (1) - b - c - bc)/8.$$

Actually the estimates of the model coefficients are *contrasts* in the observations divided by the total number of observations. Also note that due to the nature of the experimental design, the regression coefficients are uncorrelated. That is,

$$\text{cov } \hat{\boldsymbol{\beta}} = \text{cov} \begin{bmatrix} \hat{\beta}_0 \\ \hat{\beta}_1 \\ \hat{\beta}_2 \\ \hat{\beta}_3 \end{bmatrix} = \sigma^2(X'X)^{-1}$$

$$= (\sigma^2/8)I.$$

Thus, the covariance between any two distinct coefficients is zero. For the case where $r > 1$ observations are taken at each treatment combination, the principles of the general linear model still apply. One finds that for the 2^3 example given here, the symbols (1), a, b, $\ldots$, abc, formerly representing single observations, become the sum of r observations; the divisor 8 in the example becomes $8r$.

It should be noted at this stage that the 2^k factorial experimental design falls into a larger class of designs called *orthogonal designs*, that is, designs for which $X'X$ can be made diagonal, and thus, the model coefficients are uncorrelated. In some instances the class of orthogonal designs plays an important role in the development of schemes for choosing optimum designs in the area of response surface analysis.

Example. Four variables x_1, x_2, x_3, and x_4 are assumed to have an influence on some response according to the model

$$y = \beta_0 + \sum_{i=1}^{4} \beta_i x_i + \varepsilon.$$

A 2^4 factorial experimental design is used and the observation vector and the X matrix are given by

$$
\mathbf{y} =
\begin{bmatrix}
(1) = & 3.0 \\
a = & 5.0 \\
b = & 7.0 \\
c = & 2.0 \\
d = & 4.0 \\
ab = & 12.0 \\
ac = & 4.0 \\
ad = & 6.0 \\
bc = & 5.0 \\
bd = & 9.0 \\
cd = & 3.0 \\
abc = & 14.0 \\
abd = & 11.0 \\
acd = & 5.0 \\
bcd = & 7.0 \\
abcd = & 13.0
\end{bmatrix}
\quad
X =
\begin{array}{ccccc}
& x_1 & x_2 & x_3 & x_4 \\
\begin{bmatrix}
1 & -1 & -1 & -1 & -1 \\
1 & 1 & -1 & -1 & -1 \\
1 & -1 & 1 & -1 & -1 \\
1 & -1 & -1 & 1 & -1 \\
1 & -1 & -1 & -1 & 1 \\
1 & 1 & 1 & -1 & -1 \\
1 & 1 & -1 & 1 & -1 \\
1 & 1 & -1 & -1 & 1 \\
1 & -1 & 1 & 1 & -1 \\
1 & -1 & 1 & -1 & 1 \\
1 & -1 & -1 & 1 & 1 \\
1 & 1 & 1 & 1 & -1 \\
1 & 1 & 1 & -1 & 1 \\
1 & 1 & -1 & 1 & 1 \\
1 & -1 & 1 & 1 & 1 \\
1 & 1 & 1 & 1 & 1
\end{bmatrix}
\end{array}.
$$

The levels of the x's in the X matrix are, of course, coded to -1 and $+1$ in the usual fashion. It is easily seen that $X'X = 16\, I_5$ and thus the estimates of the coefficients in the model are simply contrasts, with a divisor of 16. For example,

$$
\hat{\beta}_1 = \frac{\begin{array}{l} a + ab + ac + ad + abc + abd + acd + abcd \\ \quad - (1) - b - c - d - bc - bd - cd - bcd \end{array}}{16}
$$

$$
= \frac{30}{16} = 1.875.
$$

$\hat{\beta}_2$, $\hat{\beta}_3$, and $\hat{\beta}_4$ are obtained in a similar manner. $\hat{\beta}_0$ is the average of all of the observations. The numerical results are given by

$$\begin{aligned}
\hat{\beta}_0 &= 110/16 = 6.875 \\
\hat{\beta}_2 &= 46/16 = 2.875 \\
\hat{\beta}_3 &= -4/16 = -0.25 \\
\hat{\beta}_4 &= 6/16 = 0.375.
\end{aligned}$$

SIGNIFICANCE TESTS ON MODEL COEFFICIENTS

It has been mentioned that an important feature of the 2^k factorial experimental designs (and more generally the class of orthogonal designs) is that the estimators of the model coefficients are uncorrelated with one another. This leads to a simple partitioning of the regression sum of squares, SS_{reg}, into independent components, each component expressing the amount of regression explained by an individual variable x_i in the model. One recalls from the discussion of the general linear model that

$$SS_{reg} = \hat{\beta}' X' \mathbf{y}.$$

For the case of the 2^k factorial designs used in the fitting of a linear regression model, it is seen that SS_{reg} takes the form

$$\hat{\beta}' X' \mathbf{y} = [\hat{\beta}_0 \quad \hat{\beta}_1 \quad \cdots \quad \hat{\beta}_k] \begin{bmatrix} \sum_{i=1}^{n} y_i \\ g_1 \\ g_2 \\ \cdots \\ g_k \end{bmatrix},$$

where we are taking n to be the total number of observations. Here the $g_i (i = 1, 2, \ldots, k)$ represent the contrasts in the observations. The sum of squares associated with the variable x_i is $\hat{\beta}_i g_i = (g_i)^2/n$ since from the normal equations, $\hat{\beta}_i = g_i/n$.

If one makes the additional assumption that the residual errors in the regression model follow a normal distribution, the 2^k factorial design lends itself to simple significance tests of the type

$$H_0: \beta_i = 0$$

$$H_1: \beta_1 \neq 0 \quad (i = 1, 2, \ldots, k),$$

through the analysis of variance procedure. This is best illustrated by extending the example given on page 46. The analysis of variance table with the significance test on each coefficient is shown in Table 3.7.

Table 3.7. Analysis of Variance for Example

Source	Sum of Squares	Degrees of Freedom	Mean Square	F
regression	$\hat{\beta}'X'y = 948.0$	5		
on mean	$(\sum y_i)^2/16 = (110)^2/16$	1	756.25	
on x_1	$\hat{\beta}_1 g_1 = (30)^2/16$	1	56.25	23.8
on x_2	$\hat{\beta}_2 g_2 = (46)^2/16$	1	132.25	56.0
on x_3	$\hat{\beta}_3 g_3 = (-4)^2/16$	1	1.00	< 1
on x_4	$\hat{\beta}_4 g_4 = (6)^2/16$	1	2.25	< 1
error	$974.0 - 948.0 = 26.0$	11	2.36	
total	$\sum y_i^2 = 974.0$	16		

The usual analysis of variance conclusions are made; for this case the coefficients β_3 and β_4 are not found to differ significantly from zero, whereas the contribution of x_1 and x_2 is found to be significant.

INCLUSION OF INTERACTION INTO THE MODEL

The 2^k factorial design can be used in cases where interaction or *cross product* terms are included in the regression model. If the complete factorial is used, the interaction coefficients are orthogonal to each other and to the first order coefficients. For example, suppose that at levels x_{1i} and x_{2i}, the measured response y_i is given by

$$y_i = \beta_0 + \beta_1 x_{1i} + \beta_2 x_{2i} + \beta_{12} x_{1i} x_{2i} + \varepsilon_i. \tag{3.28}$$

That is, the term $\beta_{12} x_1 x_2$, representing a deviation from linearity, is included. This is equivalent to assuming that the effect of x_1 on the response y depends on the operating level of x_2. For the case of three independent variables, terms such as $x_1 x_2$, $x_1 x_3$, $x_2 x_3$ and $x_1 x_2 x_3$ can appear. In fact, for k independent variables, there will be exactly $2^k - k - 1$ such terms possible. This corresponds exactly to the number of *error degrees of freedom* which are present if one uses a 2^k factorial experiment with one observation per treatment combination to fit a model which involves no interaction terms. Thus, for example, the error sum of squares with 11 degrees of freedom in the example on page 46 actually represents the contribution from the terms $x_1 x_2$, $x_1 x_3$, ..., and *not pure experimental error* variation. This is often referred to as *lack-of-fit* sum of squares, namely, that variation which represents other than contribution from first order terms. In cases where all of the interaction terms are included in the model, one must of course have $r > 1$ observations per treatment combination (same number at each combination in order to maintain orthogonality) in order to have an estimate of σ^2 and thus be able to make significance tests. The resulting $2^k(r - 1)$ degree of freedom mean square estimate would then represent variation within treatment combinations and becomes the pure experimental error contribution.

Consider a model given by Eq. 3.28 with the experiment containing two observations per treatment combination, the X matrix and corresponding observation vector being given as follows:

$$
y = \begin{bmatrix} 2.0 \\ 2.3 \\ 5.7 \\ 4.8 \\ 4.5 \\ 4.2 \\ 5.3 \\ 5.5 \end{bmatrix} \quad
X = \begin{matrix} \begin{matrix} x_1 & x_2 & x_1 x_2 \end{matrix} \\ \begin{bmatrix} 1 & -1 & -1 & 1 \\ 1 & -1 & -1 & 1 \\ 1 & 1 & -1 & -1 \\ 1 & 1 & -1 & -1 \\ 1 & -1 & 1 & -1 \\ 1 & -1 & 1 & -1 \\ 1 & 1 & 1 & 1 \\ 1 & 1 & 1 & 1 \end{bmatrix} \end{matrix} .
\tag{3.29}
$$

Allowing (1), a, b, and ab to denote totals, for example, (1) $= 2.0 + 2.3 = 4.3$, the vector of estimates is given by

$$
\hat{\beta} = \begin{bmatrix} \hat{\beta}_0 \\ \hat{\beta}_1 \\ \hat{\beta}_2 \\ \hat{\beta}_{12} \end{bmatrix} = (X'X)^{-1} \begin{bmatrix} (1) + a + b + ab \\ a + ab - (1) - b \\ b + ab - (1) - a \\ (1) + ab - a - b \end{bmatrix}
$$

$$
= \begin{bmatrix} 34.3/8 \\ 8.3/8 \\ 4.7/8 \\ -4.1/8 \end{bmatrix}
$$

$$
= \begin{bmatrix} 4.29 \\ 1.04 \\ 0.59 \\ -0.51 \end{bmatrix} .
$$

The analysis of variance is illustrated very simply. The regression sum of squares is partitioned into four orthogonal components. An estimate of σ^2 based on 4 degrees of freedom is obtained. Table 3.8 gives the analysis of variance for the example given by E.q 3.29.

Table 3.8. Analysis of Variance for Data of Eq. 3.29
Fit to Model of Eq. 3.28

Source	Sum of Squares	Degrees of Freedom	Mean Square	F
regression	$\hat{\beta}'X'\mathbf{y} = 160.6$	4	40.15	308.9
mean	$(34.3)^2/8 = 147.1$	1	147.1	
x_1	$(8.3)^2/8 = 8.6$	1	8.6	66.1
x_2	$(4.7)^2/8 = 2.8$	1	2.8	21.5
$x_1 x_2$	$(-4.1)^2/8 = 2.1$	1	2.1	16.2
error	0.5	4	0.13	
total	161.1	8		

The estimate of σ^2 is found to be 0.13. The F-ratios indicate that β_1, β_2, and β_{12} do differ significantly from zero. It can be seen from the $(X'X)^{-1}$ matrix that the covariances among the coefficients are zero, indicating that the interaction contribution has been included in the model with the orthogonality preserved.

factorial experiments at three levels

A factorial experiment involving k factors each at three levels is notationally referred to as a 3^k *factorial*. As in the 2^k case, the review will be confined to the case of a completely randomized design in which the variables are quantitative and the primary goal of the experimenter is to fit a regression function.

The class of 3^k factorial experimental designs can be useful when the regression model is best represented by a *second order* relationship, that is, where first and second order terms are included in the model. An obvious disadvantage of this type of design arises when a large number of factors are involved since it necessitates a relatively large experiment (3^k treatment combinations). Like the 2^k factorial, the 3^k factorial design falls into the class of orthogonal designs; with suitable coding of the independent variables, the $X'X$ matrix can be made diagonal. For the estimation procedure, the methods of the general linear model still apply.

Suppose the experimenter assumes a second order model of the type

$$\eta = \gamma_0 + \gamma_1 \xi_1 + \gamma_2 \xi_2 + \gamma_{11} \xi_1^2 + \gamma_{22} \xi_2^2 + \gamma_{12} \xi_1 \xi_2 \qquad (3.30)$$

in the variables ξ_1 and ξ_2. Coding ξ_1 to x_1 and ξ_2 to x_2, where the variables take on a *zero* value in the *center* of the design and -1 and $+1$ at the low and high level, respectively, the levels of the ζ's being spaced evenly, the design matrix is given by

$$D = \begin{matrix} & x_1 & x_2 \\ & \begin{bmatrix} -1 & -1 \\ -1 & 0 \\ -1 & 1 \\ 0 & -1 \\ 0 & 0 \\ 0 & 1 \\ 1 & -1 \\ 1 & 0 \\ 1 & 1 \end{bmatrix} \end{matrix}. \qquad (3.31)$$

For example, suppose the levels of the uncoded variables are $\zeta_1 = 10, 20, 30$; $\zeta_2 = 100, 150, 200$. The design points are given geometrically in Figure 3.1.

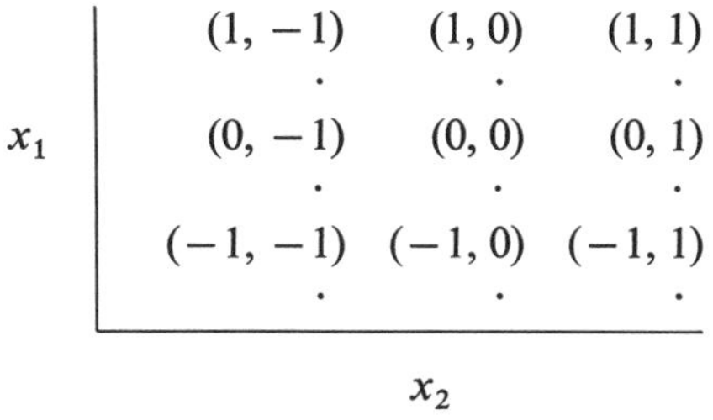

$$
\begin{array}{c}
x_1 \\

\end{array}
\begin{array}{ccc}
(1, -1) & (1, 0) & (1, 1) \\
\cdot & \cdot & \cdot \\
(0, -1) & (0, 0) & (0, 1) \\
\cdot & \cdot & \cdot \\
(-1, -1) & (-1, 0) & (-1, 1) \\
\cdot & \cdot & \cdot
\end{array}
$$

$$x_2$$

Fig. 3.1. Treatment Combinations for a 3^2 Factorial Experimental Design.

In terms of the coded variables, the x's, the X matrix is written

$$X = \begin{matrix} & x_1 & x_2 & x_1^2 & x_2^2 & x_1 x_2 \\ & \begin{bmatrix} 1 & -1 & -1 & 1 & 1 & 1 \\ 1 & -1 & 0 & 1 & 0 & 0 \\ 1 & -1 & 1 & 1 & 1 & -1 \\ 1 & 0 & -1 & 0 & 1 & 0 \\ 1 & 0 & 0 & 0 & 0 & 0 \\ 1 & 0 & 1 & 0 & 1 & 0 \\ 1 & 1 & -1 & 1 & 1 & -1 \\ 1 & 1 & 0 & 1 & 0 & 0 \\ 1 & 1 & 1 & 1 & 1 & 1 \end{bmatrix} \end{matrix}. \qquad (3.32)$$

The matrix $X'X$ is not diagonal when the model is written in this form. However, one can rewrite the model as

$$\eta = \beta_0 + \beta_1 x_1 + \beta_2 x_2 + \beta_{11}(x_1^2 - \overline{x_1^2}) + \beta_{22}(x_2^2 - \overline{x_2^2}) + \beta_{12} x_1 x_2$$

$$(3.33)$$

where $\overline{x_1^2}$ and $\overline{x_2^2}$ are average values of x_1^2 and x_2^2. Using the model of Eq. 3.33, the X and $X'X$ matrices are

$$X = \begin{array}{c} \quad\quad x_1 \quad\; x_2 \quad x_1^2 - \overline{x_1^2} \quad x_2^2 - \overline{x_2^2} \quad x_1 x_2 \\ \begin{bmatrix} 1 & -1 & -1 & 1/3 & 1/3 & 1 \\ 1 & -1 & 0 & 1/3 & -2/3 & 0 \\ 1 & -1 & 1 & 1/3 & 1/3 & -1 \\ 1 & 0 & -1 & -2/3 & 1/3 & 0 \\ 1 & 0 & 0 & -2/3 & -2/3 & 0 \\ 1 & 0 & 1 & -2/3 & 1/3 & 0 \\ 1 & 1 & -1 & 1/3 & 1/3 & -1 \\ 1 & 1 & 0 & 1/3 & -2/3 & 0 \\ 1 & 1 & 1 & 1/3 & 1/3 & 1 \end{bmatrix} \end{array}$$

$$X'X = \begin{bmatrix} 9 & 0 & 0 & 0 & 0 & 0 \\ & 6 & 0 & 0 & 0 & 0 \\ & & 6 & 0 & 0 & 0 \\ & & & 2 & 0 & 0 \\ & & & & 2 & 0 \\ \text{sym} & & & & & 4 \end{bmatrix}. \qquad (3.34)$$

The model of Eq. 3.33 is used only to simplify the computations in obtaining the estimates of the model coefficients. After the observations are taken, one can apply the usual normal equations and obtain estimates of the coefficients. The error mean square MS_E is computed in the usual way; namely, if the vector $X'y$ is written as

$$X'y = [g_0, g_1, g_2, g_3, g_4, g_5]',$$

then the error sum of squares with 3 degrees of freedom is

$$SS_E = \sum_{i=1}^{9} y_i^2 - [g_0, g_1, g_2, g_3, g_4, g_5] \begin{bmatrix} \hat{\beta}_0 \\ \hat{\beta}_1 \\ \hat{\beta}_2 \\ \hat{\beta}_{11} \\ \hat{\beta}_{22} \\ \hat{\beta}_{12} \end{bmatrix}.$$

Considerable attention is given to the class of 3^k factorial designs in Chapter 7, where the development of candidates for designs which are useful for fitting second order response surfaces is presented.

fractional factorial experimental designs

A fractional factorial is, as the name implies, a design consisting of a *fraction* of a complete factorial experiment. It can be particularly useful when the amount of experimentation required by the complete factorial is more than the experimenter can afford. For a complete account of fractional factorial designs, the reader is referred to Davies or other texts on experimental design. The brief review here will be confined to *fractional 2^k factorial design* which is used in response surface work for fitting regression models, when k is large and few or no interactions are considered to be important. The reduction in experimentation is accomplished at the expense of one or more interactions while the *main effects*, i.e., first order coefficients in the fitted model, are still independently estimated. As an example, consider a four factor experiment in which the assumed model is

$$\eta = \beta_0 + \beta_1 x_1 + \beta_2 x_2 + \beta_3 x_3 + \beta_4 x_4,$$

and instead of conducting a complete 2^4 factorial experiment, the following runs are made: *a, b, c, d, abc, abd, bcd, acd*. The X matrix (with the x's coded as usual and the treatment combinations written in the order above) is given by

$$X = \begin{bmatrix} x_1 & x_2 & x_3 & x_4 \\ 1 & 1 & -1 & -1 & -1 \\ 1 & -1 & 1 & -1 & -1 \\ 1 & -1 & -1 & 1 & -1 \\ 1 & -1 & -1 & -1 & 1 \\ 1 & 1 & 1 & 1 & -1 \\ 1 & 1 & 1 & -1 & 1 \\ 1 & -1 & 1 & 1 & 1 \\ 1 & 1 & -1 & 1 & 1 \end{bmatrix}. \tag{3.35}$$

For the first order model as written here, the design is orthogonal since $X'X = 8 I_5$; thus the estimates $\hat{\beta}_0, \hat{\beta}_1, \hat{\beta}_2, \hat{\beta}_3$, and $\hat{\beta}_4$, obtained in the usual fashion, are uncorrelated. The sacrifice that one has made in using the eight experimental points rather than the complete $2^4 = 16$ is very simple to illustrate. Suppose we consider the X matrix, now augmented with the terms

$x_1x_2, x_1x_3, x_1x_4, x_2x_3, \ldots, x_1x_2x_3x_4$. The following is that portion added to the X matrix

x_1x_2	x_1x_3	x_1x_4	x_2x_3	x_2x_4	x_3x_4
-1	-1	-1	1	1	1
-1	1	1	-1	-1	1
1	-1	1	-1	1	-1
1	1	-1	1	-1	-1
1	1	-1	1	-1	-1
1	-1	1	-1	1	-1
-1	-1	-1	1	1	1
-1	1	1	-1	-1	1

$x_1x_2x_3$	$x_1x_2x_4$	$x_1x_3x_4$	$x_2x_3x_4$	$x_1x_2x_3x_4$
1	1	1	-1	-1
1	1	-1	1	-1
1	-1	1	1	-1
-1	1	1	1	-1
1	-1	-1	-1	-1
-1	1	-1	-1	-1
-1	-1	-1	1	-1
-1	-1	1	-1	-1

To fit such a model with eight design points is completely out of the question since one needs at least sixteen points. However, the additional columns of the X matrix are given to show the consequence of using a 1/2 fraction of a 2^4. The reader should notice that the "contrast" calculated in assessing the effect of the term x_1 is identical, except for sign, to that which would be used in assessing the effect of $x_2x_3x_4$. That is, the corresponding elements in $X'y$ are equal (except for sign). As a result if the term $x_2x_3x_4$ were included in the model, the effects of x_1 and $x_2x_3x_4$ would be confused or *confounded* with each other. The effect of x_1 is said to be *aliased* with $x_2x_3x_4$. It is not difficult to observe that the other first order terms also have aliases. One can write (the $\equiv$ sign implies *aliased with*)

$$x_2 \equiv -x_1x_3x_4$$
$$x_3 \equiv -x_1x_2x_4$$
$$x_4 \equiv -x_1x_2x_3.$$

It can be seen that the two factor interactions also have aliases. In fact,

$$x_1x_2 \equiv -x_3x_4$$
$$x_1x_3 \equiv -x_2x_4$$
$$x_1x_4 \equiv -x_2x_3.$$

As far as the interaction term $x_1x_2x_3x_4$ is concerned, its effect is completely sacrificed. In fact, the column in the *augmented* X matrix attributed to $x_1x_2x_3x_4$ is identical, except for sign, to the column of 1's which represent the multiple in the general linear model of the intercept term β_0. The interaction which is completely sacrificed, usually a high order interaction, is termed the *defining contrast*.

The sacrifices made, *in this case*, by using a 1/2 fraction is not disastrous, as one can easily observe. The coefficients $\hat{\beta}_0$, $\hat{\beta}_1$, $\hat{\beta}_2$, $\hat{\beta}_3$, and $\hat{\beta}_4$ are aliased with effects that are not considered to be contributing in the model. It is obvious that in general one should construct the fractional factorial so that no two important effects are aliased.

CONSTRUCTING THE 1/2 FRACTION OF A 2^k

The variables x_1, x_2, ... are to be referred to notationally as A, B, ... The interactions are denoted by AB, AC, ..., ABC, ... A defining contrast $A^{\gamma_1}B^{\gamma_2}C^{\gamma_3}$... is chosen, where γ_i is either 0 or 1. Define a new set of variables $z_1, z_2, \ldots, z_k$, associated with the lower case letters $a, b, c, \ldots$, respectively. For a particular treatment combination, z_j will be *one* if its corresponding lower case letter appears in the treatment combination and *zero* otherwise. For example, for $k = 4$, $z_1 = 1$, $z_2 = 1$ and all other z's are zero for the treatment combination ab. One then evaluates

$$L = \gamma_1 z_1 + \gamma_2 z_2 + \gamma_3 z_3 + \cdots + \gamma_k z_k$$

for the 2^k treatment combinations (1), a, b, ... Then for the 2^k values of L,

$$s = L(\text{modulo } 2)$$

is computed. This involves evaluating $L/2$ and taking s as the remainder (either 0 or 1). The procedure will result in 2^{k-1} treatment combinations with $s = 0$ and a like number with $s = 1$. Either set suffices as the 1/2 fraction, the fraction actually used in the experiment being selected at random from this pair.

ALIASES IN THE 1/2 FRACTION

In the 1/2 fraction of the 2^k, each effect has one alias, the alias determined by multiplying the effect in question by the previously selected defining contrast, with the exponents reduced modulo 2. For example, in the 2^4 factorial it was earlier shown that with the defining contrast $ABCD$ ($x_1x_2x_3x_4$ interaction), the effect A was aliased with BCD; that is,

$$A(ABCD) = A^2BCD = BCD,$$

the exponent 2 on A being reduced to 0 (modulo 2). The effect BCD is said to be the *generalized interaction* of A and the defining contrast $ABCD$. In general, in the 2^k factorial system, *the alias of an effect is the generalized interaction between the effect and the defining contrast.*

It is obvious then that care should be taken in choosing the defining contrast, since it determines what the alias structure is for the terms in the model.

Examples. Consider the 2^4 example cited earlier. We shall illustrate the method of construction which led to the design which has the X matrix given by Eq. 3.35. With $x_1 x_2 x_3 x_4$ as the defining contrast,

$$L = z_1 + z_2 + z_3 + z_4$$

since $\gamma_1 = \gamma_2 = \gamma_3 = \gamma_4 = 1$. The values of s are given in Table 3.9.

Table 3.9. Values of s for a 1/2 Fraction of a 2^4 Factorial
With Defining Contrast *ABCD*

Treatment Combination	s
(1)	0
a	1
b	1
c	1
d	1
ab	0
ac	0
ad	0
bc	0
bd	0
cd	0
abc	1
abd	1
acd	1
bcd	1
$abcd$	0

The design chosen consists of the treatment combinations having $s = 1$. If the treatment combinations with $s = 0$ are chosen, the same alias structure would result. However, an effect would have identically the same contrast as its alias, rather than being the negative of it.

As a second example, consider the problem of constructing a 1/2 fraction with four factors, using the defining contrast *ACD*. In this case we have

$$L = z_1 + z_3 + z_4.$$

Table 3.10 gives the value of s for each of the sixteen treatment combinations.

Table 3.10. Values of s for a 1/2 Fraction of a 2^4 Factorial
With Defining Contrast ACD

Treatment Combination	s
(1)	0
a	1
b	0
c	1
d	1
ab	1
ac	0
ad	0
bc	1
bd	1
cd	0
abc	0
abd	0
acd	1
bcd	0
$abcd$	1

Once again, either the set having $s = 0$ or the set having $s = 1$ would suffice as the 1/2 fraction. For this example, the main effects A, C, and D are aliased with two factor interactions, while B is aliased with $ABCD$.

THE 1/4 FRACTION OF THE 2^k

In the case where k is large, the experimenter may be forced to a design which is smaller than the 1/2 fraction. The 1/4, 1/8 fractions, etc., are very simple to construct. However, it must be kept in mind that as the fractionation becomes more drastic, more and more information is sacrificed in the experiment. Unless a large number of variables are involved, reduction of the size of the design may defeat the entire purpose of the experiment.

Suppose an experimenter wishes to fit a first order regression of the type

$$y = \beta_0 + \sum_{i=1}^{6} \beta_i x_i + \varepsilon. \tag{3.63}$$

A complete 2^6 factorial might yield interaction degrees of freedom that are of little interest to the experimenter. He may be seeking an estimating equation for a narrow range of the variables and he is quite sure that the true model involves no interactions. A 1/4 fraction would require $2^{6-2} = 16$ observations which would be satisfactory as long as no two main effects are aliased with each other and the defining contrast is an interaction. This leaves 9 degrees of freedom for error, or lack-of-fit in this case. An appropriate design will be constructed and the alias structure shown following a brief outline of the general procedure for constructing a 1/4 fraction.

The 1/4 fraction requires that the experimenter choose *two* defining contrasts, $A^{\gamma_1}B^{\gamma_2}\ldots$ and $A^{\omega_1}B^{\omega_2}\ldots$. As in the case of the 1/2 fraction, the effects of these defining contrasts are completely sacrificed. It is important to note that a *third* defining contrast results and it is determined by multiplying the initial two and reducing the exponents modulo 2. That is, the third defining contrast is the generalized interaction of the initial two. One then determines

$$L_1 = \gamma_1 z_1 + \gamma_2 z_2 + \cdots + \gamma_k z_k$$
$$L_2 = \omega_1 z_1 + \omega_2 z_2 + \cdots + \omega_k z_k \tag{3.37}$$

and the corresponding $s_1 = L_1$ modulo 2, and $s_2 = L_2$ modulo 2 for each of the 2^k treatment combinations. This results in *four sets* of treatment combinations:

$$\begin{Bmatrix} s_1 = 0 \\ s_2 = 0 \end{Bmatrix}, \begin{Bmatrix} s_1 = 0 \\ s_2 = 1 \end{Bmatrix}, \begin{Bmatrix} s_1 = 1 \\ s_2 = 1 \end{Bmatrix}, \begin{Bmatrix} s_1 = 1 \\ s_2 = 0 \end{Bmatrix}$$

each containing 2^{k-2} treatment combinations. Any one of these sets would suffice as the 1/4 fraction. The aliases for a particular effect, or correspondingly, a particular term in the fitted model are determined by multiplying by the defining contrasts (three of them) and reducing the exponents modulo 2, resulting in *three aliases for each effect*.

Returning to the problem posed earlier, suppose it was decided that the defining contrasts should be $ABDE$ and $CDEF$. The third defining contrast is then

$$(ABDE)(CDEF) = ABCF.$$

A quick inspection reveals that the first order terms in the regression model will be aliased with interactions of third order and higher. For example, x_1 is aliased with $x_2 x_4 x_5$, $x_1 x_3 x_4 x_5 x_6$, and $x_2 x_3 x_6$. Therefore, if the assumption that the interactions are negligible is valid, that is, if the model of Eq. 3.36 is correct, it would seem that the 1/4 fraction would be an appropriate design. The design which results in $s_1 = 0$ and $s_2 = 0$ for the expression given by

$$L_1 = z_1 + z_2 + z_4 + z_5$$
$$L_2 = z_3 + z_4 + z_5 + z_6$$

contains the following treatment combinations:

(1), *de, ab, cdef, abde, cf, abcdef, abcf,*

aef, adf, bef, acd, bdf, ace, bcd, bce.

It can easily be verified that the above is an orthogonal design for fitting the first order model of Eq. 3.36.

Further fractionation of the 2^k can be accomplished by merely extending the procedures outlined here. In general, for a 2^{-p} fraction of a 2^k factorial design $(k \geq p)$, p defining contrasts are selected by the experimenter and $2^p - p - 1$ additional effects are sacrificed. For example, for a 1/8 fraction, three defining contrasts are chosen and four additional ones result. The initial three are selected in such a way that no single defining contrast is a generalized interaction of the other two. Expressions for L_1, L_2, and L_3 are used to construct the design, these expressions corresponding to the three chosen defining contrasts. Eight sets of 2^{k-3} treatment combinations each are constructed, corresponding to the $2^3 = 8$ combinations of s_1, s_2, and s_3 with $s_i = L_i$ modulo 2. The procedures are illustrated in Hicks and other experimental design texts.

exercises

3.1. The following experimental data (coded) is taken on a system involving two independent variables and a single response.

Run	y	x_1	x_2
1	13.9	-1	-1
2	13.1	-1	1
3	12.9	1	-1
4	13.6	1	1
5	15.7	0	0
6	11.8	-1.5	0
7	12.7	1.5	0
8	12.0	0	-1.5
9	12.4	0	1.5

a) Give the least squares estimates of the coefficients in the model

$$y_i = \beta_0 + \beta_1 x_{1i} + \beta_2 x_{2i} + \beta_{11} x_{1i}^2 + \beta_{22} x_{2i}^2 + \beta_{12} x_{1i} x_{2i} + \varepsilon_i \quad (i = 1, 2, \ldots, 9).$$

b) Assuming that the errors are independent with zero mean and variance σ^2, give numerical estimates of
1. σ^2,
2. variance $(\hat{\beta}_{ii})$ $(i = 1, 2)$,
3. covariance $(\hat{\beta}_{11} \hat{\beta}_{22})$.

3.2. It is assumed that three variables, x_1, x_2, and x_3, have an influence on a particular important response. A completely randomized 2^3 factorial experimental design with two observations at each treatment combination is used (sixteen total observations). The model assumed is given by

$$y_i = \beta_0 + \sum_{p=1}^{3} \beta_p x_{pi} + \sum_{p=1}^{3} \sum_{\substack{q=1 \\ p<q}}^{3} \beta_{pq} x_{pi} x_{qi} + \varepsilon_i \qquad (i = 1, 2, \ldots, 16).$$

That is, main effects and interactions involving two factors are considered important. The levels of the variables are coded in the usual manner, that is -1 and $+1$ assigned to low level and high level, respectively.
a) Write down the X matrix for the model above.
b) What is the $(X'X)^{-1}$ matrix?
c) How many degrees of freedom are attributed to lack-of-fit
d) How many degrees of freedom are attributed to pure experimental error?
e) Write down an expression, using the usual (1), $a, b, \ldots$, notation, for the least squares estimator of β_{13}.

3.3. In a pilot study it is desired to fit a first order regression model involving five factors. It is decided that eight observations should be sufficient. A 1/4 fraction of a 2 factorial experimental design is sought.
a) Using the usual -1, $+1$ coding system, write down the design matrix for an appropriate experiment.
b) Write down the *aliases* for each main effect.
c) Using the usual notation for the treatment combinations, write down the least squares estimates of each of the coefficients in the model.

references

Davies, O. L.: *Design and Analysis of Industrial Experiments,* 2nd ed., Hafner Publishing Company, Inc. New York, 1956.

Draper, N. R. and H. Smith: *Applied Regression Analysis*, John Wiley & Sons, Inc., New York, 1966.

Graybill, F. A.: *Introduction to Linear Statistical Models,* Vol. 1, McGraw-Hill, Inc., New York, 1961.

Hicks, C. R.: *Fundamental Concepts In The Design Of Experiments,* Holt, Rinehart & Winston, Inc., New York, 1964.

Li, J. C. R.: *Statistical Inference II,* Statistics, Inc., distributed by Edwards Brothers, Inc., Ann Arbor, Michigan, 1964.

4 | fundamentals of response surface technology

In this chapter, we attempt to emphasize some of the very fundamental assumptions involved in the use of the response surface approach to problem solving. At the same time, it is hoped that the reader can gain a further insight into the actual goal of response surface methods and understand the kind of problems to which the procedures can be applied.

4.1 | basic concepts

It is assumed that the experimenter is concerned with a system involving some response η which depends on the input variables $\xi_1, \xi_2, \ldots, \xi_k$. A distinction should be made at this stage between the *natural variables* (ξ's) and the coded or *design variables* (x's), the latter normally being simple linear functions of the former. It is further assumed that the ξ's can be controlled by the experimenter with negligible error. As an example, consider a situation where a chemist or chemical engineer is interested in the yield, η, of a chemical reaction. The yield depends on the reaction temperature (ξ_1), reaction pressure (ξ_2), concentration of one of reactants (ξ_3), etc. In general, we have

$$\eta = f(\xi_1, \xi_2, \ldots, \xi_k)$$

where the form of f is unknown and perhaps extremely complicated. The success of the RSM depends on the approximation of f by a low order polynomial in some region of the independent variables. For example, if the approximating function is linear in the variables, then we write, in terms of the design variables,

$$\eta = \beta_0 + \beta_1 x_1 + \beta_2 x_2 + \cdots + \beta_k x_k. \qquad (4.1)$$

This *first order model* is often useful when the experimenter is interested in studying f in narrow regions of $x_1, x_2, \ldots, x_k$, that is, where little curvature in f is present. Otherwise, the experimenter might use the *second order* approximating function

$$\eta = \beta_0 + \sum_{i=1}^{k} \beta_i x_i + \sum_{i=1}^{k} \beta_{ii} x_i^2 + \sum_{\substack{ij \\ i<j}} \beta_{ij} x_i x_j. \qquad (4.2)$$

At times, models of order greater than two are used. The rationale for the polynomial approximation of f is based on the Taylor series expansion of f around the point $x_1 = x_2 = x_3 = \cdots = x_k = 0$. For example, the first order model is developed from the first order expansion

$$f = f_{\mathbf{x}=0} + \left(\frac{\partial f}{\partial x_1}\right)_{\mathbf{x}=0} x_1 + \left(\frac{\partial f}{\partial x_2}\right)_{\mathbf{x}=0} x_2 + \cdots + \left(\frac{\partial f}{\partial x_k}\right)_{\mathbf{x}=0} x_k \qquad (4.3)$$

where $\mathbf{x}$ refers to the vector of independent variables. One can, of course, arrive at the second order approximation by further expansion.

There are a few fundamental assumptions on which much of the work in this text is based. These are summarized as follows:

1. A structure $\eta = f(x_1, x_2, \ldots, x_k)$ exists and is either very complicated or unknown. The variables involved are quantitative and continuous.
2. The function f can be approximated in the region of interest by a low-order polynomial such as Eq. 4.1 or 4.2.
3. The independent variables $x_1, x_2, \ldots, x_k$ are controlled in the observational process and measured with negligible error.

4.2 | goal of response surface methods

The types of industrial problems for which RSM is most effectively used are as old as industry itself. The experimenter is often interested in (1) finding a suitable approximating function for the purpose of predicting future response, and (2) determining what values of the independent variables are optimum as far as the response is concerned. The latter or *optimization phase* of the problem very often involves finding the values of $x_1, x_2, \ldots, x_k$ which *maximize* the response. This is particularly true in chemical situations where the response in question is often some type of yield variable which one desires to have as large as possible. It should be noted here that the response surface procedures are *not* primarily used for the purpose of allowing the experimenter to understand the *mechanism* of the underlying system or process, though the use of the procedures may, in some cases, aid in determining the underlying mechanism. Rather, its purpose is to determine what the *optimum operating conditions* are, or determine a *region* of the total space of the factors in which certain operating specifications are met.

Although the eventual goal in the response surface analysis is usually to answer certain questions regarding operating conditions in the system, it is extremely important that the decision be made, at the outset, regarding what experimental "design points" are to be used, that is, what factor levels should be considered in the experimental process. The coefficients β_0, β_1, ... in the models given by Eqs. 4.1 and 4.2 are estimated from data taken by the experimenter. This estimation can be accomplished with maximum effectiveness if proper thought is given to the question of what experimental design is to be used. As is the case in any statistical inference where experimentation is involved, it is important that the reader clearly understand the analysis before he can intelligently choose a proper experimental plan. For this reason, the analysis is considered in the early chapters and design in the latter part of the text.

4.3 | other considerations in the study of RSM

The reader might wonder why the term "Response Surface" was coined. It can be seen that for $k = 1$, that is, if only one independent variable, x, is under consideration in the system, a second order response function can be illustrated in two dimensions, as in Fig. 4.1.

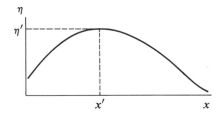

Fig. 4.1. Graphical illustration of a second order response function for $k = 1$.

The point x' represents the value of x where the maximum response η' is obtained. However, if $k = 2$, and if one wishes to characterize a second order response function graphically, a convenient procedure is to plot *contours of constant response*. An illustration is given in Fig. 4.2.

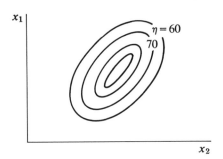

Fig. 4.2. Graphical illustration of a second order
response function for $k = 2$.

One can see that the response function for $k > 2$ is characterized by *surfaces* of constant response. The analysis of the estimated response function is often called the analysis of the *fitted surface*. This analysis is accomplished through use of least squares estimation procedures, augmented by mathematical techniques that are illustrated in Chapter 5. If the model equation is an adequate representation in the region of interest, the analysis of the fitted surface will approximate the analysis of the physical system. In the case of a second order system, one can think of a response surface study as being one in which the topography of an area is being explored, where the top of a "hill" or "mound" represents the point of maximum response. In a case where the region explored contains a point of minimum response, this condition can be likened to a valley, and the bottom of the valley is the point where the response is at its minimum.

It seems appropriate at this stage to present a few expository remarks concerning what model is to be assumed and what experimental design is to be used. (The two questions are, of course, not unrelated). The first order model is often used in situations where the experimenter does not feel as if the curvature in the model is significant. For example, as was mentioned earlier, the region in the x's which is of interest may be very "narrow" so that the curvature present in that region is negligible; the first order model is also used in circumstances where small *pilot experiments* are used preliminary to a more elaborate exploration involving additional experimentation. These preliminary procedures are often sequential in nature, where the procedure "leads" the experimenter toward the general region of the optimum values of $(x_1, x_2, \ldots, x_k)$. This procedure is usually followed with an analysis of a fitted surface, where the response function is of an order greater than 1.

Often the underlying theory of the process, if it is known at all by the experimenter, can help dictate the model to be used; actually models other than the polynomial type can often be used in response surface studies.

Whenever possible, the experimenter should attempt to incorporate known theory of the system into the model. Often, however, these theoretical models are nonlinear in nature (nonlinear in the parameters) and hence lack simplicity.

The decision regarding which experimental design is used is often a very critical one. To use a simple example as an illustration, suppose it is known that a response function is well represented by a simple first order model of the type

$$\eta = \beta_0 + \beta_1(x - \bar{x})$$

or, in terms of the observed response y,

$$y = \beta_0 + \beta_1 (x - \bar{x}) + \varepsilon \qquad (4.4)$$

for some interval $[a, b]$ in x; $\bar{x}$ is taken as the average of the x values in the experiment. It is decided that n experimental points are to be spaced in some fashion over $[a, b]$, the resulting distribution of points being the experimental design. What design should be chosen? That is, how should the points be spaced over the interval? It is well known that the least squares estimators for the parameters are

$$\hat{\beta}_0 = \bar{y} \text{ (average value of observed } y'\text{s)}$$

$$\hat{\beta}_1 = \frac{\sum\limits_{i=1}^{n} y_i(x_i - \bar{x})}{\sum\limits_{i=1}^{n} (x_i - \bar{x})^2}$$

and, making the usual general linear model assumptions on the model error of Eq. 4.4, $\hat{\beta}_0$ and $\hat{\beta}_1$ are unbiased for β_0 and β_1, respectively (independent of design), and

$$\text{var} (\hat{\beta}_0) = \sigma^2/n$$

$$\text{var} (\hat{\beta}_1) = \sigma^2 \bigg/ \sum\limits_{i=1}^{n} (x_i - \bar{x})^2.$$

Thus, var $\hat{\beta}_1$ is dependent on the design and is minimized when the "spread" in the design points is greatest; that is, the variance of the estimated slope is minimized when the design is chosen for which

$$\sum\limits_{i=1}^{n} (x_i - \bar{x})^2$$

is as large as possible.

The choice of experimental design, in many respects, depends on the experimenter's ability to postulate a proper model. Such was the case in the above illustration. The experimenter knew that the model was first order in the important interval of x. In many cases, a model is assumed but it is not an adequate approximation of the true system mechanism. As a result, the model coefficients are *biased* by terms that are of order higher than the order of the assumed model. The extent of these biases (present only because an improper model has been chosen) can be altered by the choice of the design; therefore, if bias is of primary consideration, a design should be chosen which results in relatively light biasing. Researchers interested in the design problem in RSM have devised several *design criteria* to aid the experimenter in choosing appropriate designs, depending on the situations. Through the use of these criteria, which take into consideration *variance of the predicted response* or *bias of the predicted response*, various classes of experimental designs having properties which are desirable (depending on the circumstance) have been developed in the statistics literature and are presented in this text. When the design problem is not a simple one, the experimenter might find himself faced with the prospect of choosing among several designs. He then attempts to weigh the appropriateness of the various design types from which he is to choose, against cost of experimentation, ease of analysis, or any other pertinent scientific or engineering consideration.

The early chapters in this text are devoted to discussion of analysis of the response surface, whereas the latter portion is devoted to developments which are pertinent to the design problem.

5 | determination of optimum operating conditions

Often in experimental work, the researcher is called upon to seek the conditions of experimentation which are most desirable, depending upon some preselected criterion. For example, being able to sell a product with high purity (high concentration of primary component) is certainly of importance to a chemical manufacturer. A metallurgy researcher might be interested in the percentage of certain alloys which result in minimum corrosion. As was related in earlier chapters, the approach to this problem is often made with the use of response surface methods. Often *more than one response* is of interest. For example, the purpose of the research may be to maximize one response, η_1, while holding a second response, η_2, as small as possible. In practice, the multiresponse problem often necessitates a compromise in the final determination of operating conditions.

In this chapter, attention is given to methods for locating optima. Two distinct situations are considered: (1) the case in which the experimental region used is in the general vicinity of the optimum, and (2) the actual optimum is remote from the experimental region. Of course, in practice the experimenter hopes that the latter is not the situation. A prudent researcher would certainly plan his investigation so that the experimental runs he makes are in the region in which he *thinks* the optimum is located. However, he may begin his work with complete ignorance with regard to the proper region, in which case his experimental plan may develop into a "sequential" determination, where he begins in a region remote from the optimum and systematically works his way toward the desirable conditions.

5.1 | analysis of a fitted surface

In this section we consider the situation in which the experimenter has selected a region of experimentation—a region that he feels confident contains the optimum. He is then prepared to embark on a full scale set of runs, leading to the analysis of a second order response function.

Suppose that for k variables, a second order response model of the type

$$\eta = \beta_0 + \sum_{j=1}^{k} \beta_j x_j + \sum_{\substack{j=1 \\ j<m}}^{k} \sum_{m=1}^{k} \beta_{jm} x_j x_m + \sum_{j=1}^{k} \beta_{jj} x_j^2 \qquad (5.1)$$

is assumed for some region of the x's. Once an appropriate experimental design has been chosen and the experiment has been conducted, one can use the techniques of the general linear model as described in Chapter 3 to estimate the coefficients in Eq. 5.1. Hereafter, the estimators will be denoted by $b_0, b_1, \ldots, b_k, b_{11}, \ldots, b_{kk}, b_{12}, \ldots, b_{k-1,k}$. The estimating equation (or *prediction equation*) often referred to as the *fitted response surface* is then given by

$$\hat{y} = b_0 + \sum_j b_j x_j + \sum_{\substack{jm \\ j<m}} \sum b_{jm} x_j x_m + \sum_j b_{jj} x_j^2. \qquad (5.2)$$

Equation 5.2 is used to predict the response for given values of x_1, $x_2, \ldots, x_k$. It should be emphasized here that, in general, it is not advisable to extrapolate outside of the experimental range (the range of the experimental design) in using the fitted surface. After obtaining Eq. 5.2, the experimenter is prepared to conduct the analysis of the fitted surface, the extent of the analysis depending on the experimenter's goal.

Suppose the goal of the experimenter is to *estimate* the conditions on $x_1, x_2, \ldots, x_k$ which *maximize* the response η. It is well known that if the experimenter fits a second order model in one variable, that is, he has as the estimated response function

$$\hat{y} = b_0 + b_1 x + b_{11} x^2,$$

and *if* a local maximum response exists, it is estimated by differentiating the response function with respect to x, equating to zero, and solving. That is,

$$\frac{\partial \hat{y}}{\partial x} = b_1 + 2b_{11} x = 0,$$

and the value of x which results in the maximum on the estimated response function is given by

$$x = -b_1/2b_{11}. \qquad (5.3)$$

One recalls from elementary work in calculus that Eq. 5.3 yields a maximum if the *second derivative* $\partial^2 \hat{y}/\partial x = 2b_{11}$ is negative. If the second derivative is positive, this value of x yields a *minimum*. The value of x given by Eq. 5.3 is referred to as the *stationary point* for the response function, that is, the point for which the derivative with respect to the independent variable is zero.

It is necessary at this stage to extend the discussion to the case where more than one independent variable is involved in the response system. The reader should observe that the fitted second order function in Eq. 5.2 is given in matrix notation by

$$y = b_0 + \mathbf{x}'\mathbf{b} + \mathbf{x}'B\mathbf{x} \tag{5.4}$$

where

$$\mathbf{x} = \begin{bmatrix} x_1 \\ x_2 \\ \cdots \\ x_k \end{bmatrix}, \quad \mathbf{b} = \begin{bmatrix} b_1 \\ b_2 \\ \cdots \\ b_k \end{bmatrix} \quad B = \begin{bmatrix} b_{11} & b_{12}/2 & \cdots & b_{1k}/2 \\ & b_{22} & \cdots & b_{2k}/2 \\ & & \cdots & \cdots \\ & & \cdots & b_{k-1,k}/2 \\ \text{sym} & & & b_{kk} \end{bmatrix}$$

Here, the $\mathbf{x}'\mathbf{b}$ portion in Eq. 5.4 gives the first order terms in the response function and the quadratic form $\mathbf{x}'B\mathbf{x}$ gives the quadratic contribution. The latter contains terms involving the *mixed quadratic* coefficients, b_{ij} $(i \neq j)$ and the *pure* quadratic coefficients b_{ii}. The maximum, if it exists, will be a set of conditions on $(x_1, x_2, \ldots, x_k)$ such that the derivatives $\partial \hat{y}/\partial x_1$, $\partial \hat{y}/\partial x_2, \ldots, \partial \hat{y}/\partial x_k$ are simultaneously zero. This value, say $\mathbf{x}_0' = [x_{1,0}, x_{2,0}, \ldots, x_{k,0}]$ is the stationary point of the fitted surface, and as in the case of a single variable, will not always be a point of maximum response.

In the following development, the rules outlined in Chapter 2 for differentiating a scalar with respect to a column vector can be applied to find a usable expression for the stationary point. This stationary point will in turn, be used to aid in describing the response surface system. The derivative of $\hat{y}$ with respect to the vector $\mathbf{x}$, equated to $\mathbf{0}$, gives

$$\frac{\partial \hat{y}}{\partial \mathbf{x}} = \frac{\partial}{\partial \mathbf{x}} [\mathbf{x}'\mathbf{b} + \mathbf{x}'B\mathbf{x}] = \mathbf{0}$$

$$= \mathbf{b} + 2B\mathbf{x} = \mathbf{0}.$$

Solving for $\mathbf{x}$ we have the stationary point $\mathbf{x}_0$ given by

$$\mathbf{x}_0 = -B^{-1}\mathbf{b}/2. \tag{5.5}$$

It must be emphasized again that this point is *not* necessarily that which maximizes the response. In fact, the $\mathbf{x}_0$ computed by Eq. 5.5 can be (1) a point at which the fitted surface attains a maximum, (2) a point at which the fitted surface attains a minimum, and (3) a *saddle point* of the fitted surface. The three conditions are illustrated by the contour plots given in Figs. 5.1, 5.2, and 5.3 for the case of two variables x_1 and x_2.

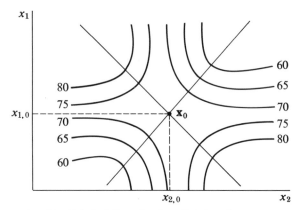

Fig. 5.1. Saddle point in a fitted surface.

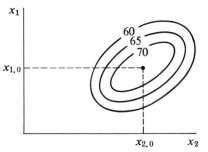

Fig. 5.2. Maximum point in a fitted surface.

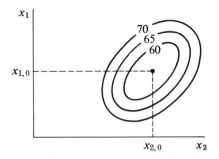

Fig. 5.3. Minimum point in a fitted surface.

Of course, if the stationary point is a maximum, "moving away" from x_0 results in a corresponding decrease in response (as far as the fitted surface is concerned). If x_0 is a minimum, a corresponding increase would result. However, in the case of a saddle point, the experimenter may get an increase *or* decrease in response when he moves away from the stationary point, depending on which direction he takes. If the experimenter is seeking the location of the greatest possible response and the stationary point turns out to be a saddle point, he would be extremely interested in knowing in which direction he must move to obtain an increase. Of course the experimenter does *not* learn the nature of the stationary point by merely computing it. In the special case of one or two variables, e.g. Figs. 5.1, 5.2, and 5.3, one can plot contours of constant response and get a clear indication of the nature of x_0. However, in general, it is necessary to conduct a further analysis. The development concerning *how* one determines the nature of the stationary point will be given shortly. Consider first, however, Figs. 5.4 and

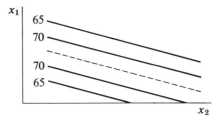

Fig. 5.4. Stationary ridge system in a fitted surface.

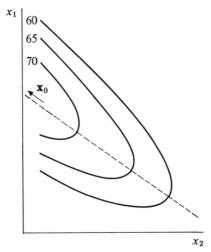

Fig. 5.5. Rising ridge system in a fitted surface.

5.5 which illustrate in two variables two important special situations which can occur in practice.

Figure 5.4 illustrates the *Stationary Ridge* System and Fig. 5.5 the *Rising Ridge* System. The stationary ridge indicates that there is a *region*, rather than a single point, where there is approximately maximum (or minimum) response. The region is a line in the case of two variables. This can tend to supply certain flexibility to the experimenter as far as operating conditions are concerned. For the case of the rising ridge, the actual stationary point is remote from the experimental region and the estimated response increases as one moves up the dotted line toward the stationary point as shown in Fig. 5.5. If the response decreases as one moves toward x_0, the system is termed a *Falling Ridge*. Actually, these ridge systems are special cases of the basic systems in Figs. 5.1, 5.2, and 5.3. The detection of existing ridge systems is obviously an important part of the total response surface analysis and will be discussed in detail later in this chapter.

canonical analysis

It is necessary that the second order response function, given by Eq. 5.2 and written in matrix notation in Eq. 5.4, be written in a somewhat different form, that which is more clearly interpreted by the researcher. The eventual goal is to be able to determine the nature of the stationary point and the entire response system. This analysis begins with a *translation* of the response function from the origin $(x_1 = 0, x_2 = 0, \ldots, x_k = 0)$ to the stationary point x_0; then the response function is expressed in terms of new variables, $w_1, w_2, \ldots, w_k$, the axes of which correspond to the principal axes of the contour system. This is illustrated for two variables in Fig. 5.6.

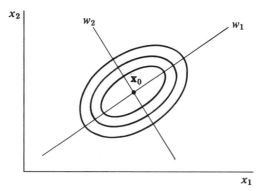

Fig. 5.6. Illustration of canonical form for a response surface in two variables.

The origin has been translated to the center of the response system, and axes for new variables w_1 and w_2 have been formed. The form of the function in terms of these variables is called the *canonical form* and is given by

$$\hat{y} = \hat{y}_0 + \lambda_1 w_1^2 + \lambda_2 w_2^2 + \cdots + \lambda_k w_k^2 \qquad (5.6)$$

where $\hat{y}_0$ is the estimated response at the stationary point $\mathbf{x}_0 = -B^{-1}\mathbf{b}/2$, and the λ_i are constants. It is of interest to the experimenter to know the sign and magnitude of these λ's; they aid in determining the nature of the stationary point and the response system. The relationship between the w's and the x's can also be a valuable piece of information. This expression of ten indicates to the experimenter the fruitful regions for further exploration when the stationary point is found to correspond to an unsatisfactory set of operating conditions. The reduction of the response surface to canonical form is called a *canonical analysis*. The method of canonical analysis is systematically developed in succeeding paragraphs, with an extensive discussion of interpretation being given in a later section.

The estimated response at the stationary point, $\hat{y}_0$, can actually be written in terms of b_0, the stationary point $\mathbf{x}_0$, and the vector $\mathbf{b}$ of first order coefficients. First we write, from Eq. 5.4,

$$\begin{aligned}
\hat{y}_0 &= b_0 + \mathbf{x}_0'\mathbf{b} + \mathbf{x}_0'B\mathbf{x}_0 \\
&= b_0 + [-B^{-1}\mathbf{b}/2]'\mathbf{b} + [-B^{-1}\mathbf{b}/2]'B[-B^{-1}\mathbf{b}/2] \\
&= b_0 - \mathbf{b}'B^{-1}\mathbf{b}/2 + \mathbf{b}'B^{-1}BB^{-1}\mathbf{b}/4 \\
&= b_0 - \mathbf{b}'B^{-1}\mathbf{b}/2 + \mathbf{b}'B^{-1}\mathbf{b}/4.
\end{aligned}$$

Now, by once again inserting $\mathbf{x}_0 = -B^{-1}\mathbf{b}/2$, we have

$$\begin{aligned}
\hat{y}_0 &= b_0 + \mathbf{x}_0'\mathbf{b} - \mathbf{x}_0'\mathbf{b}/2 \\
&= b_0 + \mathbf{x}_0'\mathbf{b}/2. \qquad (5.7)
\end{aligned}$$

Suppose we now turn our attention to the response function in Eq. 5.4 and translate it to the new origin $\mathbf{x}_0$. This is easily accomplished by defining the vector $\mathbf{z} = \mathbf{x} - \mathbf{x}_0$ and writing the response function in terms of $\mathbf{z}$. Equation 5.4 is equivalently given by

$$\begin{aligned}
\hat{y} &= b_0 + (\mathbf{z}' + \mathbf{x}_0')\mathbf{b} + (\mathbf{z}' + \mathbf{x}_0')B(\mathbf{z} + \mathbf{x}_0) \\
&= b_0 + \mathbf{x}_0'\mathbf{b} + \mathbf{x}_0'B\mathbf{x}_0 + \mathbf{z}'\mathbf{b} + \mathbf{z}'B\mathbf{x}_0 + \mathbf{x}_0'B\mathbf{z} + \mathbf{z}'B\mathbf{z}. \qquad (5.8)
\end{aligned}$$

Here, the order of the terms has conveniently been altered. Since $\mathbf{z}'B\mathbf{x}_0$ and $\mathbf{x}_0'B\mathbf{z}$ are equivalent, and since the first three terms represent the response function evaluated at the stationary point, Eq. 5.8 is written

$$\begin{aligned}
\hat{y} &= \hat{y}_0 + \mathbf{z}'(\mathbf{b} + 2B\mathbf{x}_0) + \mathbf{z}'B\mathbf{z} \\
&= \hat{y}_0 + \mathbf{z}'[\mathbf{b} - 2B(B^{-1}\mathbf{b}/2)] + \mathbf{z}'B\mathbf{z} \\
&= \hat{y}_0 + \mathbf{z}'B\mathbf{z}. \qquad (5.9)
\end{aligned}$$

Equation 5.9 represents the second order response surface, translated to the new origin $(x_{1,0}, x_{2,0}, \ldots, x_{k,0})$. In order that the canonical form of Eq. 5.6 be obtained, the quadratic form $z'Bz$ must be reduced to an expression involving only "squared terms" in the variables $w_1, w_2, \ldots, w_k$. The reader recalls from the section on the reduction of quadratic form to canonical form (p. 15) that there exists an *orthogonal* transformation,

$$z = Mw \tag{5.10}$$

such that

$$\begin{aligned} z'Bz &= w'M'BMw \\ &= \lambda_1 w_1^2 + \lambda_2 w_2^2 + \cdots + \lambda_k w_k^2 \end{aligned} \tag{5.11}$$

where $\lambda_1, \lambda_2, \ldots, \lambda_k$ are *characteristic roots of the matrix B*. The matrix M is a $k \times k$ orthogonal matrix—that is, $M'M = I_k$. The λ_i (all real since B is a real symmetric matrix) are the constants that appear in the important canonical form that is shown in Eq. 5.6.

Determination of the matrix M can often be quite important because the transformation

$$w = M'z, \tag{5.12}$$

obtained by premultiplying both sides of Eq. 5.10 by M', enables the experimenter to obtain the expression relating the *old* variables to the new. Suppose we partition M as follows

$$M = [\mathbf{M}_1 \, \mathbf{M}_2 \cdots \mathbf{M}_k]$$

where $\mathbf{M}_i$ is the ith column of M. $\mathbf{M}_i$ is obtained by finding an eigenvector associated with λ_i and normalizing it so that the sum of the squares of the elements in $\mathbf{M}_i$ is unity. In other words we seek the solution vector

$$\mathbf{M}_i = \begin{bmatrix} m_{1i} \\ m_{2i} \\ \ldots \\ m_{ki} \end{bmatrix}$$

to

$$(B - \lambda_i I_k)\mathbf{M}_i = 0 \tag{5.13}$$

for which $m_{1i}^2 + m_{2i}^2 + \ldots + m_{ki}^2 = \mathbf{M}_i'\mathbf{M}_i = 1$. A numerical illustration of the canonical analysis will be given subsequently. It is important for the reader to be able to make use of the canonical analysis, that is, the computation of the values $\lambda_1, \lambda_2, \ldots, \lambda_k$, as a part of the total analysis. The following section deals with the interpretation made of the response system through the canonical analysis.

interpretation of system

Upon performing the canonical analysis, the experimenter can determine the nature of the stationary point and the response surface system by observing the *sign* and *magnitude* of the λ's. It can be noted from the canonical Eq. 5.6 that if $\lambda_1, \lambda_2, \ldots, \lambda_k$ are all *negative*, a move in any direction from the stationary point results in a decrease in $\hat{y}$. Therefore, the stationary point x_0 represents a point of maximum response for the fitted surface, with the response estimate at that point being given by Eq. 5.7. On the other hand, if $(\lambda_1, \lambda_2, \ldots, \lambda_k)$ are all positive, x_0 is a *minimum* for the fitted surface. In the case where the λ's differ in sign, the stationary point is a *saddle point*. For example, suppose for two variables that $\lambda_1 < 0$ and $\lambda_2 > 0$; when one moves along the w_1 axis away from the stationary point in either direction, a corresponding decrease in estimated response is obtained, whereas movement along the w_2 axis away from x_0 results in an increase in response. This type of occurrence in practice could well imply the existence of a system containing two peaks, where two maxima are occurring in different regions.

The magnitude of the λ's can offer a great deal of information regarding the system. For example, suppose that for $k = 2$, λ_1 and λ_2 are both negative and that $|\lambda_2|$ is considerably greater than $|\lambda_1|$. This situation is illustrated in Fig. 5.7.

The stationary point is a maximum. However, an interesting and important feature of this system is the difference in sensitivity of the response with respect to the two variables w_1 and w_2. As one moves along the w_1

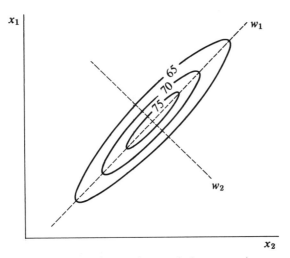

Fig. 5.7. Maximum elongated along w_1 axis.

axis away from the stationary point in either direction, there is little change in estimated response compared to the change incurred if one were to move away from the stationary point a similar distance along the w_2 axis. That is, the response contours are elongated in the w_1 direction. This can also occur for the case where the stationary point is a minimum or saddle point. The extreme in two variables for this situation is the stationary ridge which was shown in Fig. 5.4, where one of the λ's is zero. If in practice one of the λ values turns out to be very small, then the system approximates that of a stationary ridge. While it is unlikely that an exact stationary ridge condition would occur in practice, the practical implications of a *near-stationary ridge* are very important. For example, if the stationary point is found to be a maximum, and λ_1 is near zero, then for all practical purposes the maximum is not uniquely the stationary point; rather the experimenter has at his disposal a *range* of possible operating conditions along the w_1 axis, all of which give approximately optimum estimated response. Similar conditions can occur in quadratic response functions in *more* than two variables, although they are rather difficult to illustrate graphically. For example, suppose that for $k = 3$, λ_1 and λ_2 are both negative (not near zero) while λ_3 is very close to zero. Then essentially when one moves away from the stationary point $(x_{1,0}, x_{2,0}, x_{3,0})$, a decrease in estimated response results. However, moving away from $\mathbf{x}_0$ along the w_3 axis results in very small changes in $\hat{y}$; thus, one would expect that there is a region along w_3 for which the response incurred is close to the maximum value. An illustration of the extreme situation is given by the single surface of Fig. 5.8.

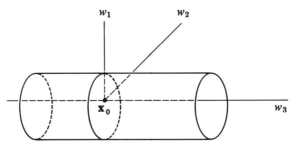

Fig. 5.8. A quadratic response surface with $(\lambda_1, \lambda_2, \lambda_3) = (-, -, 0)$.

The same graphical illustration applies for the case where λ_1 and λ_2 are *positive*, the w_3 axis representing the region of minimum response.

In the preceding development, we have considered the situation where the magnitudes of the λ's were quite different. The stationary ridge condition arises as a limiting case of a maximum, minimum, or saddle point condition.

In each of these cases, however, the stationary point is in the vicinity of the experimental design used to fit the second order response function. Suppose however that the point x_0 is far removed from the experimental region. For example for $k = 2$ suppose that λ_1 is negative, λ_2 is near zero, and the stationary point is *not* in the vicinity of the experimental region. The condition approaches that of a rising ridge. The extreme, that is, the limiting case representing the exact rising ridge condition is given by a negative λ_1, a λ_2 of zero, and a stationary point at infinity. As was the case for the stationary ridge, the exact rising ridge could hardly exist in practice. However, conditions which *approach* that of a rising ridge (or a falling ridge if λ_1 is positive) are quite common and certainly should be considered. Figure 5.9 illustrates a rising ridge in two variables where λ_1 is negative and λ_2 is zero.

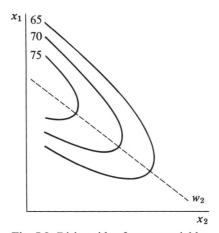

Fig. 5.9. Rising ridge for two variables.

Note that in the figure, the w_1 and w_2 axes intersect at infinity, representing the extreme of the more practical situation where x_0 is found to be remote from the design region. A wise researcher would certainly consider it poor practice to draw conclusions about the surface for a region outside the experimental area. As a result, nothing is inferred about the region containing the stationary point. In fact, one often finds $\hat{y}_0$ to be completely unrealistic—e.g., a yield response exceeding 100%. Inferences can be made, however, about the experimental region. For example, in the case of Fig. 5.9, an increase in response would certainly be expected as one moved up the w_2 axis, that is, with $w_1 = 0$. This gives a ready indication as to possible locations for future observations in one's search for the maximum. The equation relating the variables w_1 and w_2 to the x's given by Eq. 5.12 can be used to ascertain locations for possible future runs.

The rising (or falling) ridge in more than two variables warrants consideration. Suppose, for example, that $k = 3$ and λ_1 and λ_2 are negative, while λ_3 is near zero and $\mathbf{x}_0$ is remote from the experimental region. The condition then approaches a rising ridge in three variables, the exact *limiting* condition given by $(\lambda_1, \lambda_2, \lambda_3) = (-, -, 0)$ and $\mathbf{x}_0$ at infinity as illustrated in Fig. 5.10.

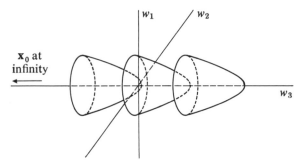

Fig. 5.10. Rising ridge in three variables.

For the practical situation which would approach that given in Fig. 5.10, no inferences are made concerning the condition of the system in the vicinity of the stationary point.

Examples. Two examples are given, showing the canonical analysis and interpretation of the response system. The first involves an experiment from which the researcher attempts to gain an insight into the influence of sealing temperature (x_1), cooling bar temperature (x_2), and % polyethylene additive (x_3) on the seal strength in grams per inch of a breadwrapper stock. The actual levels of the variables are coded for the computations with the formulas used in the coding being given by

$$x_1 = \frac{\text{seal temp.} - 255}{30}$$

$$x_2 = \frac{\text{cooling temp.} - 55}{9}$$

$$x_3 = \frac{\% \text{ polyethylene} - 1.1}{0.6}$$

Five levels of the variables were used in the experimental design. The coded and the measured levels for the variables are given by the following:

	−1.682	−1.000	0.000	+1.000	1.682
(x_1)	204.5	225	255	285	305.5
(x_2)	39.9	46	55	64	70.1
(x_3)	0.09	0.5	1.1	1.7	2.11

The design matrix* (in terms of the coded variables) and the corresponding vector $\mathbf{y}$ of observations are

$$
D = \begin{array}{ccc} x_1 & x_2 & x_3 \end{array}
\begin{bmatrix}
-1 & -1 & -1 \\
1 & -1 & -1 \\
-1 & 1 & -1 \\
1 & 1 & -1 \\
-1 & -1 & 1 \\
1 & -1 & 1 \\
-1 & 1 & 1 \\
1 & 1 & 1 \\
-1.682 & 0 & 0 \\
1.682 & 0 & 0 \\
0 & -1.682 & 0 \\
0 & 1.682 & 0 \\
0 & 0 & -1.682 \\
0 & 0 & 1.682 \\
0 & 0 & 0 \\
0 & 0 & 0 \\
0 & 0 & 0 \\
0 & 0 & 0 \\
0 & 0 & 0 \\
0 & 0 & 0
\end{bmatrix}
\qquad
\mathbf{y} = \begin{bmatrix}
6.6 \\
6.9 \\
7.9 \\
6.1 \\
9.2 \\
6.8 \\
10.4 \\
7.3 \\
9.8 \\
5.0 \\
6.9 \\
6.3 \\
4.0 \\
8.6 \\
10.1 \\
9.9 \\
12.2 \\
9.7 \\
9.7 \\
9.6
\end{bmatrix} .
\qquad (5.14)
$$

For the second order fitted response model

$$\hat{y} = b_0 + \sum_{i=1}^{3} b_i x_i + \sum_{i=1}^{3} b_{ii} x_i^2 + \sum_{\substack{ij \\ i<j}} b_{ij} x_i x_j,$$

---

*This type of experimental design, called a *central composite design*, is considered in detail in Chapter 7.

Example data courtesy of *Tappi* **41** (6), 295–300 (June 1958).

the X matrix is given by

x_1	x_2	x_3	x_1^2	x_2^2	x_3^2	x_1x_2	x_1x_3	x_2x_3
1			1	1	1	1	1	1
1			1	1	1	-1	-1	1
1			1	1	1	-1	1	-1
1			1	1	1	1	-1	-1
1			1	1	1	1	-1	-1
1			1	1	1	-1	1	-1
1			1	1	1	-1	-1	1
1			1	1	1	1	1	1
1	D		2.828	0	0	0	0	0
1			2.828	0	0	0	0	0
1			0	2.828	0	0	0	0
1			0	2.828	0	0	0	0
1			0	0	2.828	0	0	0
1			0	0	2.828	0	0	0
1			0	0	0	0	0	0
1			0	0	0	0	0	0
1			0	0	0	0	0	0
1			0	0	0	0	0	0
1			0	0	0	0	0	0
1			0	0	0	0	0	0

By using the procedures which were reviewed in Chapter 3, we have the normal equations

$$(X'X)\hat{\beta} = X'\mathbf{y}$$

where

$$\hat{\beta} = \begin{bmatrix} b_0 \\ b_1 \\ b_2 \\ b_3 \\ b_{11} \\ b_{22} \\ b_{33} \\ b_{12} \\ b_{13} \\ b_{23} \end{bmatrix}$$

$$X'X = \begin{array}{c} \begin{array}{cccccccccc} b_0 & b_1 & b_2 & b_3 & b_{11} & b_{22} & b_{33} & b_{12} & b_{13} & b_{23} \end{array} \\ \left[\begin{array}{cccccccccc} 20 & 0 & 0 & 0 & 13.658 & 13.658 & 13.658 & 0 & 0 & 0 \\ 0 & 13.658 & 0 & 0 & 0 & 0 & 0 & 0 & 0 & 0 \\ & & 13.658 & 0 & 0 & 0 & 0 & 0 & 0 & 0 \\ & & & 13.658 & 0 & 0 & 0 & 0 & 0 & 0 \\ & & & & 24 & 8 & 8 & 0 & 0 & 0 \\ & & & & & 24 & 8 & 0 & 0 & 0 \\ & & & & & & 24 & 0 & 0 & 0 \\ & & & & & & & 8 & 0 & 0 \\ & & & & & & & & 8 & 0 \\ & & & & & & & & & 8 \end{array}\right] \end{array}$$

$$X'y = \begin{bmatrix} g_0 & = & 163.0000 \\ g_1 & = & -15.0736 \\ g_2 & = & 1.1908 \\ g_3 & = & 13.9372 \\ g_{11} & = & 103.0544 \\ g_{22} & = & 98.5296 \\ g_{33} & = & 96.8328 \\ g_{12} & = & -2.8000 \\ g_{13} & = & -4.0000 \\ g_{23} & = & 1.2000 \end{bmatrix}$$

The normal equations are solved and the second order response function is given by

$$\hat{y} = 10.1657 - 1.1038x_1 + 0.0872x_2 + 1.0206x_3 - 0.7602x_1^2$$
$$- 1.430x_2^2 - 1.1491x_3^2 - 0.3500x_1x_2$$
$$- 0.5000x_1x_3 + 0.1500x_2x_3. \tag{5.15}$$

An analysis of variance is conducted at this point, with tests made on the significance of regression due to the model variables and lack-of-fit. In this case the sum of squares attributed to regression (including the constant term b_0) is given by

$$\hat{\beta}'X'y = b_0g_0 + b_1g_1 + b_2g_2 + \cdots + b_{23}g_{23}$$
$$= 1398.7556.$$

The sum of squares which accounts for regression on the variables in the model (i.e. $x_1, x_2, x_3, x_1^2, \ldots$) is given by

$$1398.7556 - (g_0)^2/20$$
$$= 1398.7556 - 132.8450$$
$$= 70.3056.$$

Notice that the experimental design in this case involved taking six observations in the *center* of the design, the center being $(0, 0, 0)$ in the coded variables, resulting in $6 - 1 = 5$ degrees of freedom for "pure error." The corresponding sum of squares is computed by obtaining the corrected sum of squares for these six observations. The result is given by

$$SS_E = \sum_{j=1}^{6} y_{0j}^2 - \left(\sum_{j=1}^{6} y_{0j} \right)^2 \Big/ 6 = 4.960$$

where y_{0j} $(j = 1, 2, \ldots, 6)$ refers to the jth observation at the design center. The analysis of variance is given in Table 5.1.

Table 5.1. Analysis of Data Variance Given by Eq. 5.14

Source	Sum of Squares	Degrees of Freedom	Mean Square	F
regression				
(linear and quadratic)	70.3056	9	7.8117	7.87
lack-of-fit	6.9044	5	1.3809	1.39
error	4.9600	5	0.9920	
total	82.1700	19		

The lack-of-fit does not appear to be significant. Using Eq. 5.5 the stationary point is found to be

$$\mathbf{x}_0 = \begin{bmatrix} x_{1,0} = -1.0098 \\ x_{2,0} = 0.2602 \\ x_{3,0} = 0.6808 \end{bmatrix}, \tag{5.16}$$

while the estimated response at $\mathbf{x}_0$ is $\hat{y}_0 = 11.08$.

The next logical step in the reduction of the data is to perform the canonical analysis. This requires values of λ_1, λ_2, and λ_3, the characteristic roots of the matrix B. We need, then, to solve the determinantal equation

$$\begin{vmatrix} (-0.7602 - \lambda) & -0.1750 & -0.2500 \\ -0.1750 & (-1.0430 - \lambda) & 0.0750 \\ -0.2500 & 0.0750 & (-1.1491 - \lambda) \end{vmatrix} = 0,$$

the elements in the determinant being taken from the fitted Eq. 5.15. Expanding the determinant, we have

$$\lambda^3 + 2.9523\lambda^2 + 2.7662\lambda + 0.7999 = 0,$$

with the solution to the cubic equation yielding the roots

$$\lambda_1 = -0.5630, \quad \lambda_2 = -1.2712, \quad \lambda_3 = -1.1172.$$

The canonical form, demonstrating the nature of the response system, is then given by

$$\hat{y} = 11.08 - 0.5630w_1^2 - 1.2712w_2^2 - 1.1172w_3^2. \tag{5.17}$$

Equation 5.17 shows *negative* signs for all λ-values, indicating that the stationary point given by Eq. 5.16 is in fact a *maximum*. Notice that the stationary point is well inside the experimental region, and the response surface is elongated along the w_1 axis. The response seems to be approximately equally sensitive to changes in w_2 and w_3.

It could be of interest to the experimenter to know the relationship between the w variables and the x's. We can use Eq. 5.13 to obtain the columns of the M matrix and Eq. 5.12 to obtain the transformation needed. If we call m_{ij} the element in the ith row and jth column of M, we have for $\lambda_1 = -0.5630$,

$$\begin{bmatrix} (b_{11} + 0.5630) & b_{12}/2 & b_{13}/2 \\ b_{12}/2 & (b_{22} + 0.5630) & b_{23}/2 \\ b_{13}/2 & b_{23}/2 & (b_{33} + 0.5630) \end{bmatrix} \begin{bmatrix} m_{11} \\ m_{21} \\ m_{31} \end{bmatrix} = \mathbf{0}.$$

Substituting the proper values for the b's, we have the simultaneous equations

$$-0.1972m_{11} - 0.1750m_{21} - 0.2500m_{31} = 0$$
$$-0.1750m_{11} - 0.4800m_{21} + 0.0750m_{31} = 0$$
$$-0.2500m_{11} + 0.0750m_{21} - 0.5861m_{31} = 0$$

At this point the solution vectors obtained must be normalized. That is, for $\mathbf{M}_1$ as illustrated here,

$$m_{11}^2 + m_{21}^2 + m_{31}^2 = 1.$$

The solutions to these equations are not unique, therefore we can arbitrarily assign some value to one of the unknowns and then normalize them. This is best accomplished by substituting $m'_{31} = 1$ in place of m_{31} into the above set and obtaining solutions $m'_{11} = -2.0791$ and $m'_{21} = 0.9142$. The values m_{11}, m_{21}, and m_{31} are obtained by dividing m'_{11}, m'_{21}, and m'_{31} by

$$\sqrt{(m'_{11})^2 + (m'_{21})^2 + (m'_{31})^2} = \sqrt{6.1584}.$$

The solutions obtained are

$$m_{11} = -0.8378, \quad m_{21} = 0.3684, \quad m_{31} = 0.4030.$$

The same procedure applies for $\lambda_2 = -1.2735$ and $\lambda_3 = -1.1159$, giving the additional two columns of the M matrix. The final result is given by

$$M = \begin{bmatrix} -0.8378 & 0.4535 & -0.3052 \\ 0.3684 & 0.0552 & -0.9281 \\ 0.4030 & 0.8895 & 0.2132 \end{bmatrix}.$$

The relationship between the w variables and the x's is then given by

$$\begin{bmatrix} w_1 \\ w_2 \\ w_3 \end{bmatrix} = \begin{bmatrix} -0.8378 & 0.3684 & 0.4030 \\ 0.4535 & 0.0552 & 0.8895 \\ -0.3052 & -0.9281 & 0.2132 \end{bmatrix} \begin{bmatrix} x_1 + 1.0098 \\ x_2 - 0.2602 \\ x_3 - 0.6808 \end{bmatrix}.$$

The second example involves a chemical process in which 1, 2-propanediol is being converted to 2, 5-dimethylpiperazine. The object is to examine the effect of several factors on the course of the reaction and to determine the conditions which give rise to maximum conversion. The following four variables were studied:

$$NH_3 = \text{amount of ammonia, grams}$$
$$T = \text{temperature, } °C$$
$$H_2O = \text{amount of water, grams}$$
$$P = \text{hydrogen pressure, psi}$$

It was decided that a second order model should be adequate. The design consisted of twenty-five points in the coded variables

$$x_1 = \frac{NH_3 - 102}{51}$$

$$x_2 = \frac{T - 250}{20}$$

$$x_3 = \frac{H_2O - 300}{200}$$

$$x_4 = \frac{P - 850}{350}$$

As in the previous example, the type of second order design used was a central composite design. The design matrix and the corresponding vector of response observations are given as follows†:

---

†Taken from C. D. Chang, O. K. Koncnenko, and R. E. Franklin, "Maximum Data Through a Statistical Design," *Ind. Eng. Chem.* **52** (11), 939–942 (1960). Reprinted by permission of the copyright owner.

$$D = \begin{bmatrix} x_1 & x_2 & x_3 & x_4 \\ -1 & -1 & -1 & -1 \\ +1 & -1 & -1 & -1 \\ -1 & +1 & -1 & -1 \\ +1 & +1 & -1 & -1 \\ -1 & -1 & +1 & -1 \\ +1 & -1 & +1 & -1 \\ -1 & +1 & +1 & -1 \\ +1 & +1 & +1 & -1 \\ -1 & -1 & -1 & +1 \\ +1 & -1 & -1 & +1 \\ -1 & +1 & -1 & +1 \\ +1 & +1 & -1 & +1 \\ -1 & -1 & +1 & +1 \\ +1 & -1 & +1 & +1 \\ -1 & +1 & +1 & +1 \\ +1 & +1 & +1 & +1 \\ 0 & 0 & 0 & 0 \\ -1.4 & 0 & 0 & 0 \\ +1.4 & 0 & 0 & 0 \\ 0 & -1.4 & 0 & 0 \\ 0 & +1.4 & 0 & 0 \\ 0 & 0 & -1.4 & 0 \\ 0 & 0 & +1.4 & 0 \\ 0 & 0 & 0 & -1.4 \\ 0 & 0 & 0 & +1.4 \end{bmatrix} \quad y = \begin{bmatrix} 58.2 \\ 23.4 \\ 21.9 \\ 21.8 \\ 14.3 \\ 6.3 \\ 4.5 \\ 21.8 \\ 46.7 \\ 53.2 \\ 23.7 \\ 40.3 \\ 7.5 \\ 13.3 \\ 49.3 \\ 20.1 \\ 32.8 \\ 31.1 \\ 28.1 \\ 17.5 \\ 49.7 \\ 49.9 \\ 34.2 \\ 31.1 \\ 43.1 \end{bmatrix} \qquad (5.18)$$

The actual measured factor levels, corresponding to levels of the coded values are the following:

Factor	-1.4	-1.0	0	1.0	1.4
ammonia, grams	30.6	51	102	153	173.4
temperature, °C	222	230	250	270	278
water, grams	20	100	300	500	580
hydrogen pressure, psi	360	500	850	1200	1340

The fitted second order surface, found by the method of least squares, is given by

$$\hat{y} = 40.198 - 1.511x_1 + 1.284x_2 - 8.739x_3 + 4.955x_4 - 6.332x_1^2$$
$$- 4.292x_2^2 + 0.020x_3^2 - 2.506x_4^2 + 2.194x_1x_2 - 0.144x_1x_3$$
$$+ 1.581x_1x_4 + 8.006x_2x_3 + 2.806x_2x_4 + 0.294x_3x_4.$$

Applying the formula of Eq. 5.5 to the response function, the coordinates of the stationary point are found to be $x_{1,0} = 0.265$, $x_{2,0} = 1.034$, $x_{3,0} = 0.291$, and $x_{4,0} = 1.668$, with $\hat{y}_0 = 43.53$. The canonical coefficients λ_1, λ_2, λ_3, λ_4 are found as the characteristic roots of the matrix

$$B = \begin{bmatrix} -6.332 & 1.0969 & -0.0720 & 0.7905 \\ & -4.292 & 4.0030 & 1.4030 \\ & & 0.020 & 0.1470 \\ & & & -2.506 \end{bmatrix}.$$

The canonical form is found to be

$$\hat{y} - 43.07 = -7.55w_1^2 - 6.01w_2^2 - 2.16w_3^2 + 2.60w_4^2, \qquad (5.19)$$

whereas the transformation relating the x's to the w's is given by

$$\mathbf{w} = M'(\mathbf{x} - \mathbf{x}_0),$$

$$\begin{bmatrix} w_1 \\ w_2 \\ w_3 \\ w_4 \end{bmatrix} = \begin{bmatrix} 0.5977 & -0.7025 & 0.3756 & 0.0908 \\ -0.7688 & -0.4568 & 0.2858 & 0.3445 \\ 0.2151 & 0.1374 & -0.3071 & 0.9168 \\ 0.0741 & 0.5282 & 0.8264 & 0.1803 \end{bmatrix} \begin{bmatrix} x_1 - 0.265 \\ x_2 - 1.034 \\ x_3 - 0.291 \\ x_4 - 1.668 \end{bmatrix}.$$

$$(5.20)$$

The M matrix was obtained in a fashion similar to that illustrated in the previous example.

Examination of Eq. 5.19 reveals that a decrease in estimated yield occurs upon moving away from the stationary point along the w_1, w_2, and w_3 axes. However, the estimated yield increases when one moves along the w_4 axis. It would seem reasonable that the experimenter might, at this stage, use Eq. 5.20 to find possible operating conditions, that is, conditions of high yield of 2,5-dimethylpiperazine, in the region of the designed experiment. It must be noted that the eventual operating conditions must be such that, in the coded variables,

$$x_3 \geq -1.5$$

since an x_3 of -1.5 represents the condition of *no water* in the process. Equation 5.19 was used to compute the conditions on x_1, x_2, x_3, and x_4 which give zero values for w_1, w_2, and w_3, and various values (positive and negative) for w_4. The results are presented in Table 5.2.

Notice that for positive w_4, the x values are out of the region of the designed experiment. It appears as though the most desirable conditions are those which result in $w_4 \cong -2.2$, that is, $x_1 = 0.102$, $x_2 = -0.128$, $x_3 = -1.50$ (no water), and $x_4 = 1.27$. Any point resulting in $w_1 = 0$,

Table 5.2. Values of Independent Variables Giving Rise to
Zero Values for (w_1, w_2, w_3) and Various w_4

w_4	1.0	1.5	2.0	−1.0	−1.5	−2.0	−2.5
x_1	0.339	0.376	0.413	0.191	0.154	0.117	0.080
x_2	1.562	1.826	2.090	0.506	0.242	−0.022	−0.287
x_3	1.117	1.531	1.944	−0.535	−0.949	−1.362	−1.775
x_4	1.848	1.938	2.028	1.488	1.398	1.307	1.217

$w_2 = 0$, $w_3 = 0$, and $|w_4| > 2.2$ is either far outside of the experimental region or is a condition requiring *negative* grams of water, which represents an experimental impossibility.

summary remarks concerning analysis of fitted surface

In the case of a second order response function, the techniques which are often used for examining the response function are (1) determination of location of stationary point, (2) canonical analysis to examine the nature of the stationary point, and (3) determination of the relationship between the "canonical variables" and the original independent variables of the experiment. The latter is used as an aid in determining location of operating conditions or location of future experimental runs in case the stationary point does not represent satisfactory conditions. For example, the stationary point may not be a point of maximum response, which is required; or it may be an optimum as far as the actual response is concerned, but yet may represent conditions which are economically unfeasible.

After the quadratic response function has been fitted by the method of least squares, the stationary point $\mathbf{x}_0$ is found by using Eq. 5.5. The nature of the stationary point is determined by writing the fitted response surface in canonical form, which expresses the function as

$$\hat{y} = \hat{y}_0 + \lambda_1 w_1^2 + \lambda_2 w_2^2 + \cdots + \lambda_k w_k^2$$

where $w_1, w_2, \ldots, w_k$ are the canonical variables which are linear combinations of the original variables $x_1, x_2, \ldots, x_k$. The values of $\lambda_1, \lambda_2, \ldots, \lambda_k$ are the characteristic roots of the symmetric matrix B, the latter defined by Eq. 5.4. The sign of the λ's determines whether the stationary point is a maximum, minimum, or saddle point:

1. If $\lambda_1, \lambda_2, \ldots, \lambda_k$ are all negative, $\mathbf{x}_0$ is a point of maximum response.
2. If $\lambda_1, \lambda_2, \ldots, \lambda_k$ are all positive, $\mathbf{x}_0$ is a point of minimum response.
3. If the signs of $\lambda_1, \lambda_2, \ldots, \lambda_k$ differ, $\mathbf{x}_0$ is a saddle point.

If one or more of the λ-values is near zero or considerably smaller in magnitude than the others, a type of ridge response system is indicated.

The relationship between the x variables and the w variables can be determined by using Eq. 5.12, with the columns of the matrix M being the normalized eigenvectors associated with the roots $\lambda_1, \lambda_2, \ldots, \lambda_k$ of the matrix B. The computation of these vectors is illustrated for a specific example on page 78.

5.2 | method of steepest ascent

In the presentation of Section 5.1, it is assumed that the experimenter has some prior notion (either through knowledge of the system or previous exploratory experimentation) concerning the general vicinity of the optimum. A rather elaborate experiment, with a carefully chosen experimental design, is run in the "region of the optimum" and a canonical analysis is performed as an aid in the interpretation of the response system. Of course, the canonical analysis may indicate that the experimenter's prior opinion about the region of the optimum is in error, as in the case where the analysis shows a rising or falling ridge system. Also, in the case of a saddle stationary point, the experimenter may learn that experimentation in a completely new region may be more fruitful. It is doubtful that he would invest in a rather large and perhaps costly experiment unless it is felt that the optimum is either inside the design region or very close to the design periphery. As a result, it is important that the user of response surface techniques include in his repertoire a procedure for *searching for the region of the maximum response*; the procedure can then be used when the experimenter has no prior information concerning the location of the maximum.

The *steepest ascent procedure* is a method whereby the experimenter proceeds *sequentially* along the path of steepest ascent, that is, along the path of maximum increase in response. The steps in the procedure can be generally described as follows:

1. The experimenter fits a first order response model in some restricted region of the variables $x_1, x_2, \ldots, x_k$.
2. The information from Step 1 is used to locate a path of steepest ascent.
3. A series of experiments is conducted along the path until no additional increase in response is evident.
4. Steps 1, 2, and 3 are repeated, using the *new* region, the one which seems to be promising as indicated by Step 2.
5. If curvature is evident and the experimenter is satisfied that he can obtain little or no additional information from the method, a more elaborate experiment is conducted, complete with canonical analysis, etc.

For Step (1) consider the first order response function

$$\hat{y} = b_0 + \sum_{i=1}^{k} b_i x_i. \tag{5.21}$$

It must be emphasized that Step (1) only represents a preliminary investigation. A simple 2^k factorial design, or fractional factorial can be used at this stage to estimate the coefficients. It is assumed that one wishes to advance from the origin of the preliminary design R units on the surface of a *hypersphere* such that maximum increase in response is obtained. That is, if the variables are coded, with the design center being $(0, 0, \ldots, 0)$, the experimenter wishes to find the values of $(x_1, x_2, \ldots, x_k)$ which maximize

$$b_0 + \sum_{i=1}^{k} x_i$$

subject to the restriction

$$\sum_{i=1}^{k} x_i^2 = R^2.$$

This can be done for various R, and the resulting path taken by the values of the variables describes the *path of steepest ascent*. Using Lagrange multipliers for restricted maximization, we equate to zero the partial derivatives

$$\frac{\partial Q(x_1, \ldots, x_k)}{\partial x_j} \qquad (j = 1, 2, \ldots, k)$$

and

$$\frac{\partial Q(x_1 \cdots x_k)}{\partial \mu},$$

where

$$Q(x_1, x_2, \ldots, x_k) = b_0 + \sum_{i=1}^{k} b_i x_i - \mu \left(\sum_{i=1}^{k} x_i^2 - R^2 \right).$$

It is observed that

$$\partial Q / \partial x_j = b_j - 2\mu x_j$$

and

$$\partial Q / \partial \mu = - \left[\sum_{i=1}^{k} x_i^2 - R^2 \right].$$

Equating $\partial Q / \partial x_j$ to zero, one obtains

$$x_j = b_j / 2\mu \qquad (j = 1, 2, \ldots, k). \tag{5.22}$$

The procedure is easier to carry out when one selects convenient values of μ, rather than determining the value of μ which corresponds to a particular R, that is, values are selected which correspond to a particular *increment* in one of the variables. After μ is selected, Eq. 5.22 is used to compute the first point on the path of steepest ascent. The experimenter then proceeds to Step 3 in the procedure. A numerical example illustrating the method is given in the following section.

Example. Suppose the goal of a response surface study is to find the conditions on x_1, x_2, x_3, and x_4 which maximize some response. It is decided that initially a 1/2 fraction of a 2^4 factorial should be used in the following region of the variables:

	-1	$+1$	
ξ_1:	10	15	(factor A)
ξ_2:	1	2	(factor B)
ξ_3:	25	35	(factor C)
ξ_4:	75	85	(factor D)

With $ABCD$ used as the defining contrast, the observations taken are given by

$$
\begin{bmatrix}
(1) = 62.0 \\
ab = 69.0 \\
cd = 57.0 \\
ac = 64.5 \\
ad = 61.8 \\
bc = 64.7 \\
bd = 62.2 \\
abcd = 66.3
\end{bmatrix}.
$$

The notation for the treatment combinations is consistent with that presented in Chapter 3. For the fitted model

$$
\hat{y} = b_0 + \sum_{i=1}^{4} b_i x_i,
$$

where the x's are the coded variables, the least squares estimates are found to be

$$
\begin{array}{lll}
b_0 = 63.44 & b_2 = 2.1125 \\
b_1 = 1.9625 & b_3 = -0.3125 & b_4 = -1.6125
\end{array}
$$

Suppose it is decided that it would be convenient to choose μ so that a change in one unit of the variable ξ_1 defines an increment along the path. In the coded variable this corresponds to $1/(2.5) = 0.4$ units. The coefficient b_1 is positive, so the value of x_1 for the first coordinate along the path is $+0.4$. As a result, using Eq. 5.22,

$$\mu = \frac{1.9625}{(0.4)2} = 2.453.$$

The values of x_2, x_3, and x_4 can easily be computed using Eq. 5.22. Table 5.3 gives several coordinates along the path using the increments as defined. Runs 9, 10, 11, and 12 are coordinates, out of the original experimental region, where additional observations on the response were made.

Note that the Δ increment is positive for variables 1 and 2 but negative for variables 3 and 4, as one would expect. Runs 9, 10, 11, and 12 indicate an increase followed by a leveling in response. This implies that there is no further advantage in proceeding along the present path. Thus, a new factorial experiment should probably be conducted with the factor levels having their *base* or zero (coded) values in the vicinity of trial 12. Essentially, it is hoped that the second experiment, and the resulting path of steepest ascent, will lead the experimenter to the vicinity of the optimum. It should be pointed out that the method will become less effective as the procedure continues; for as one approaches the region of the stationary point, the first order approximation will tend to deteriorate due to existence of curvature in the system. For our example, the path of steepest ascent which was taken after the first experiment indicated an increase in yield from 63.44 (average from first experiment) to 81.0 (trial 11). If a second experiment were conducted, one would expect a smaller gain in response, or perhaps none at all, as one sequentially experimented along the new path. If no progress is detected, further work should involve the inclusion of higher order terms in the response model.

further comments concerning method of steepest ascent

As indicated in previous discussion, steepest ascent for maximization is a method whereby the experimenter moves up the *fitted plane* in the direction of greatest slope or steepest ascent. The approximation by a first order model becomes more inadequate as the method progresses, so the procedure is eventually self-defeating. Also the experimenter, due to the mechanism in the system which he is exploring, may encounter one of a *number* of peaks which actually exist for the process. In this case, the peak approached will depend on the location of the initial experiment.

Table 5.3. Coordinates Along Path of Steepest Ascent (Uncoded Variables)

Run		ξ_1	ξ_2	ξ_3	ξ_4	Y
	base	12.5	1.5	30	80	
	Δ	1.0	$\left[\dfrac{b_2}{2\mu}\right][0.5] = 0.215$	$\left[\dfrac{b_3}{2\mu}\right][5.0] = -0.319$	$\left[\dfrac{b_4}{2\mu}\right][5.0] = -1.643$	
	base $+ \Delta$	13.5	1.715	29.681	78.357	
	base $+ 2\Delta$	14.5	1.930	29.362	76.714	
	base $+ 3\Delta$	15.5	2.145	29.043	75.071	
9	base $+ 4\Delta$	16.5	2.360	28.724	73.428	74.0
10	base $+ 6\Delta$	18.5	2.790	28.086	70.142	77.0
11	base $+ 8\Delta$	20.5	3.220	27.448	66.856	81.0
12	base $+ 9\Delta$	21.5	3.435	27.129	65.213	78.7

The procedure of steepest ascent is *not* invariant with respect to scale on the variables; that is, the path which is taken by the procedure depends on the units used. For most factors, one of many choices of units can be made. This is discussed and illustrated at length in a paper by Buehler, Shah, and Kempthorne. We shall proceed to illustrate here with a very simple example. Consider a two variable problem in which it is desired to fit locally a first order model and proceed along the path of steepest ascent to maximize the response. The response depends on variables x_1 and x_2, and initially two levels are used in a 2^2 factorial design as follows:

Run	ξ_1	ξ_2
1	10	60
2	10	80
3	20	60
4	20	80

Suppose the coding

$$x_1 = \frac{\xi_1 - 15}{5} \qquad x_2 = \frac{\xi_2 - 70}{10}$$

is used. The design origin is then $x_1 = 0$, $x_2 = 0$ corresponding to $\xi_1 = 15$, $\xi_2 = 70$. Suppose further that the fitted equation is given by

$$\hat{y} = 1 + 10x_1 + 2x_2$$

which means that the change in x_1 along the path is five times the change in x_2. For example, if the first increment is to be computed on the basis of a change of five units in ξ_1 (corresponding to a unit change in x_1), then the path is given by Table 5.4.

Table 5.4. Path of Steepest Ascent Using Variables x_1 and x_2

	x_1	x_2	ξ_1	ξ_2
base	0	0	15	70
Δ	1	0.2	5	2
base $+\ \Delta$	1	0.2	20	72
base $+\ 2\Delta$	2	0.4	25	74
base $+\ 3\Delta$	3	0.6	30	76
base $+\ 4\Delta$	4	0.8	35	78

Consider the same problem with the fitted equation being written in terms of the uncoded variables ξ_1 and ξ_2, that is,

$$\hat{y} = 1 + 10 \left[\frac{\xi_1 - 15}{5} \right] + 2 \left[\frac{\xi_2 - 70}{10} \right]$$

$$= -43 + 2\xi_1 + 0.2\xi_2. \tag{5.23}$$

Once again, the method is designed to search for coordinates ξ_1, ξ_2 that maximize the response on the surface of a sphere with the design origin at the center. Therefore, it is required to maximize $y = -43 + 2\xi_1 + 0.2\xi_2$ subject to the restriction that

$$(\xi_1 - 15)^2 + (\xi_2 - 70)^2 = R^2.$$

Using the Lagrange multipliers, we equate the derivatives of

$$-43 + 2\xi_1 + 0.2\xi_2 - \mu[(\xi_1 - 15)^2 + (\xi_2 - 70)^2 - R^2]$$

with respect to ξ_1 and ξ_2 to zero and solve. The result is given by

$$\xi_1 - 15 = 2/(2\mu) \qquad \xi_2 - 70 = 0.2/(2\mu).$$

The path of steepest ascent is given in Table 5.5.

Table 5.5. Path of Steepest Ascent Using Original Units

	ξ_1	ξ_2
base	15	70
Δ	5	0.5
base + Δ	20	70.5
base + 2Δ	25	71.0
base + 3Δ	30	71.5
base + 4Δ	35	72.0

Note the difference in the paths displayed by the two tables.

As was indicated earlier, one would expect the steepest ascent procedure to become less effective as he proceeds with it from one experiment to another. It is imperative that the experimenter "pause to take stock" of the situation in between experiments to be sure that the first order assumptions hold. There is a need then for a test for lack-of-fit to be sure that the first order terms are dominating. Although it would be impossible to estimate most of these second order effects (particularly if the experiment represents a fractional factorial), it is imperative that the *collection* of higher order terms *not show* a highly significant contribution. In particular suppose a fractional factorial design is used in a preliminary stage and one of the main effects, say x_1, is aliased with an important two factor interaction, say $x_2 x_3$. Actually the estimate b_1 is likely to be *heavily biased* by the coefficient β_{23}. (The analogy between aliasing and biasing is discussed at length in Chapter 6.) Since the coordinate for x_1 in the path of steepest ascent is directly proportional to the estimate of the slope parameter β_{23}, the experimenter could be completely misled with his new path of testing.

Although the method of steepest ascent (or descent) has several disadvantages, it is probably the most often used optimum seeking (or optimum region seeking) procedure. An extremely interesting and informative example of the use of the method is given in Box and Wilson.

There are other optimum seeking procedures which are often used in RSM work. One of the popular ones is called *method of parallel tangents*. A good exposition on this procedure is given in Buehler, Shah, and Kempthorne.

5.3 | method of ridge analysis

At times it becomes rather difficult to form decisions regarding optimum operating conditions even after a canonical analysis has been performed. As cases in point, in situations such as rising ridge or saddle point systems, the optimum has not been "pinpointed" and the condition may very well indicate the need either for further analysis of the existing data, or for additional experimental runs. For example, in the case of a rising ridge, the experimenter may wish to augment the canonical analysis by taking observations "along the ridge" in his quest for the optimum.

The estimated response function can be subjected to an additional analysis which can often serve as an aid to the experimenter in determining best conditions. This method is called *ridge analysis*. The term was first coined by Hoerl whose work was somewhat expository in nature. A rigorous development of the theory underlying the technique is given in a paper by Draper. The procedure itself involves techniques whereby the experimenter formulates a k-variable response surface problem in two dimensions. Consider a second order response function with canonical form given by Eq. 5.6. Suppose we concern ourselves with the stationary points of the second order model, (the notation being that of Section 5.1)

$$\hat{y} = b_0 + \mathbf{x}'\mathbf{b} + \mathbf{x}'B\mathbf{x}, \qquad (5.24)$$

restricting ourselves to spheres of varying radii. Using the usual coding of the variables, with the origin of the design at $(0, 0, \ldots, 0)$, for a point $(x_1, x_2, \ldots, x_k)$ on a sphere of radius R,

$$\sum_{i=1}^{k} x_i^2 = R^2. \qquad (5.25)$$

We should at this point attempt to find the conditions on the variables which *maximize* $\hat{y}$ subject to the constraint given by Eq. 5.25 for various R. After these conditions are found, R can be plotted against the appropriate coordinates $x_1, x_2, \ldots, x_k$, and $\hat{y}$. The experimenter can then observe the plots and determine for various distances from the design center, the value of the maximum estimated response, and where on the sphere the corresponding conditions are located, that is, what values of the variables give rise to the estimated response.

To maximize $\hat{y}$ subject to the constraint of Eq. 5.25, we consider the function

$$F = \hat{y} - \mu(\mathbf{x}'\mathbf{x} - R^2)$$

where μ is a Lagrangian multiplier and $\mathbf{x}' = [x_1, x_2, \ldots, x_k]$. Using Eq. 5.24, we have

$$\partial F/\partial \mathbf{x} = \mathbf{b} + 2B\mathbf{x} - 2\mu\mathbf{x}. \tag{5.26}$$

Equating Eq. 5.26 to zero, and solving for $\mathbf{x}$, we have

$$(B - \mu I_k)\mathbf{x} = -\mathbf{b}/2. \tag{5.27}$$

It should be noted that this procedure closely resembles the steepest ascent method. While the latter method is used *before* the canonical analysis, ridge analysis is designed to be used *after* canonical analysis as a tool to aid in the interpretation of the existing response system. One can insert predetermined values of μ into Eq. 5.27, solve for $x_1, x_2, \ldots, x_k$, compute R from Eq. 5.25, and $\hat{y}$ from Eq. 5.24. Of course, this method generates stationary points on *spheres of varying radii*. However, it is important to note that the nature of the stationary points depends on the value of μ chosen. It turns out that if care is not used in the choice of μ, one cannot be sure whether or not the various stationary points found are points of maximum (or minimum) response. Certain important theorems are given in the following section which pertain either directly or indirectly to the nature of these points found from Eq. 5.27. In some instances, proofs of the theorems are given.

results pertaining to the nature of stationary points

The reader should recall that the characteristic roots of the matrix B are vital to the canonical analysis as discussed on page 74. They also play an important role in the ridge analysis procedure. Denote the roots by λ_i $(i = 1, 2, \ldots, k)$. The λ_i are such that

$$|B - \lambda_i I_k| = 0.$$

In the use of the ridge analysis procedure, it may happen that different values of the Lagrangian multiplier μ used in Eq. 5.27 may lead to the same R values resulting for $\hat{y}$. Actually, though, one can make appropriate selections of values for μ, selections very much dependent on the λ_i, which will yield in the procedure, points which are *absolute* maxima, *absolute* minima, . . . , depending on what is required by the response surface problem.

To aid in the development of the properties of the stationary points, a well-known mathematical theorem is given here. Consider the stationary points of a function $f(x_1, x_2, \ldots, x_k)$ subject to restrictions

$$h_j(x_1, x_2, \ldots, x_k) = 0 \qquad (j = 1, 2, \ldots, n). \qquad (5.28)$$

Suppose we form the partial derivatives with respect to x_i ($i = 1, 2, \ldots, k$) of the function

$$F = f(x_1, x_2, \ldots, x_k) - \sum_{j=1}^{n} \mu_j h_j(x_1, x_2, \ldots, x_k) \qquad (5.29)$$

where the μ_j are Lagrange multipliers, and equate the derivatives to zero. The resulting set of equations will be

$$\partial F / \partial x_i = \frac{\partial f(x_1, x_2, \ldots, x_k)}{\partial x_i} - \sum_{j=1}^{n} \mu_j \frac{\partial h_j(x_1, x_2, \ldots, x_k)}{\partial x_i}$$

$$(i = 1, 2, \ldots, k). \qquad (5.30)$$

Equations 5.28 and 5.30 represent $n + k$ equations in a like number of unknowns. These equations can be solved for the x_i by first eliminating the μ_j and not actually solving for them. If $\mathbf{x}' = \mathbf{a}' = [a_1, a_2, \ldots, a_k]$ is a solution to Eqs. 5.28 and 5.30 after the *elimination* of the μ_j, then the properties of the symmetric matrix

$$M(\mathbf{x}) = \begin{bmatrix} \partial^2 F / \partial x_1^2 & \partial^2 F / \partial x_1 \partial x_2 & \cdots & \partial^2 F / \partial x_1 \partial x_k \\ & \partial^2 F / \partial x_2^2 & \cdots & \partial^2 F / \partial x_2 \partial x_k \\ & & \cdots & \cdots \\ & & & \partial^2 F / \partial x_k^2 \end{bmatrix}$$

evaluated at $x_1 = a_1, x_2 = a_2, \ldots, x_k = a_k$, determine the nature of the point $a_1, a_2, \ldots, a_k$. In particular,

1. If $M(\mathbf{a})$ is positive definite, then the solution is a local minimum for

$$f(x_1, x_2, \ldots, x_k).$$

2. If $M(\mathbf{a})$ is negative definite, then the solution is a local maximum for

$$f(x_1, x_2, \ldots, x_k).$$

The proof to this result is not given here, but can be found in many texts of advanced calculus, (e.g., see Widder). For the situation considered here, a second order response function, we have

$$F = \hat{y} - \mu(\mathbf{x'x} - R^2)$$
$$= b_0 + \mathbf{x'b} + \mathbf{x'}B\mathbf{x} - \mu(\mathbf{x'x} - R^2), \qquad (5.31)$$

and as we have shown, the appropriate partial derivatives equated to zero yield

$$(B - \mu I_k)\mathbf{x} = -1/2\mathbf{b}. \qquad (5.32)$$

Suppose we now turn our attention to the matrix $M(\mathbf{x})$.

$$\partial F/\partial \mathbf{x} = \mathbf{b} + 2B\mathbf{x} - 2\mu\mathbf{x}. \qquad (5.33)$$

Writing out the elements in Eq. 5.33, we have

$$
\begin{bmatrix} \partial F/\partial x_1 \\ \partial F/\partial x_2 \\ \cdots \\ \partial F/\partial x_k \end{bmatrix}
=
\begin{bmatrix} b_1 \\ b_2 \\ \cdots \\ b_k \end{bmatrix}
+ 2
\begin{bmatrix} b_{11} & b_{12}/2 & \cdots & b_{1k}/2 \\ & b_{22} & \cdots & b_{2k}/2 \\ & & \cdots & \cdots \\ & & & b_{kk} \end{bmatrix}
\begin{bmatrix} x_1 \\ x_2 \\ \cdots \\ x_k \end{bmatrix}
- 2\mu
\begin{bmatrix} x_1 \\ x_2 \\ \cdots \\ x_k \end{bmatrix}.
$$

The vector of pure second partials is written

$$
\begin{bmatrix} \partial^2 F/\partial x_1^2 \\ \partial^2 F/\partial x_2^2 \\ \cdots \\ \partial^2 F/\partial x_k^2 \end{bmatrix}
=
\begin{bmatrix} 2b_{11} - 2\mu \\ 2b_{22} - 2\mu \\ \cdots \\ 2b_{kk} - 2\mu \end{bmatrix}. \qquad (5.34)
$$

It is easily seen that the mixed partial $\partial^2 F/\partial x_i \partial x_j$ is written as

$$\partial^2 F/\partial x_i \partial x_j = b_{ij} \qquad (i \neq j). \qquad (5.35)$$

Therefore, combining Eqs. 5.34 and 5.35 we have

$$M(\mathbf{x}_i) = 2(B - \mu I_k). \qquad (5.36)$$

The result in Eq. 5.36 is very important. It is the nature of this matrix which determines what kind of stationary point has been found after a choice of μ has been made.

THEOREM 5.1. Consider two solutions of Eq. 5.32

$$\mathbf{x}_1' = [a_1, a_2, \ldots, a_k] \text{ for } \mu = \mu_1$$

and

$$\mathbf{x}_2' = [c_1, c_2, \ldots, c_k] \text{ for } \mu = \mu_2,$$

resulting in estimates $\hat{y}_1$ and $\hat{y}_2$ on spheres of radii R_1 and R_2, respectively. Then if $R_1 = R_2$ and $\mu_1 > \mu_2$, $\hat{y}_1 > \hat{y}_2$.

The proof of this theorem is not given here but can be found in the paper by Draper. The theorem essentially says that for two stationary points that are an equal distance from the design origin, the response estimate will be larger for that stationary point corresponding to the larger value of μ.

THEOREM 5.2. If $R_1 = R_2$, and $M(\mathbf{x}_1)$ and $M(\mathbf{x}_2)$ are positive definite and indefinite, respectively, then $\hat{y}_1 < \hat{y}_2$.

For the proof of this theorem, consider first Eq. 5.36 for the stationary point $\mathbf{x}'_i = [x_{1i}, x_{2i}, \ldots, x_{ki}]$ and some μ_i. Consider also any $k \times 1$ vector $\mathbf{u}$. Since $M(\mathbf{x}_2) = 2[B - \mu_2 I]$ is indefinite, its corresponding quadratic form is indefinite. Thus

$$\mathbf{u}'[B - \mu_2 I]\mathbf{u} \leq 0 \qquad (5.37)$$

for at least one $\mathbf{u} = \mathbf{q}$ ($\mathbf{q} \neq 0$). Since $M(\mathbf{x}_1)$ is positive definite

$$\mathbf{u}'[B - \mu_1 I]\mathbf{u} > 0$$

for all $\mathbf{u}$. Thus, from the above inequality, substituting $\mathbf{u} = \mathbf{q}$,

$$\mathbf{q}'[B - \mu_1 I]\mathbf{q} > 0. \qquad (5.38)$$

Then from the inequalities given in Eqs. 5.37 and 5.38

$$\mu_2 \mathbf{q}'\mathbf{q} > \mathbf{q}'B\mathbf{q} > \mu_1 \mathbf{q}'\mathbf{q},$$

which implies that $\mu_2 > \mu_1$. Recalling Theorem 5.1, it is easily seen that $\hat{y}_2 > \hat{y}_1$.

THEOREM 5.3. If $\mu_1 > \lambda_i$ (all i), where λ_i is the ith characteristic root of B, then $\mathbf{x}_1$ (point found using Eq. 5.27 with $\mu = \mu_1$) is a point at which $\hat{y}$ attains a local maximum on R_1 (radius associated with μ_1). On the other hand, when $\mu_1 < \lambda_i$ (all i), then $\mathbf{x}_1$ is a point at which $\hat{y}$ attains a local minimum on R_1.

The above is an extremely important theorem; the proof is not difficult and will be shown here. Suppose we once again indicate by $\mathbf{u}$ any $k \times 1$ vector. Then the quadratic form for $M(\mathbf{x}_1)$ is given by

$$\begin{aligned} \mathbf{u}'M(\mathbf{x}_1)\mathbf{u} &= \mathbf{u}'(B - \mu_1 I)\mathbf{u} \\ &= \mathbf{u}'B\mathbf{u} - \mu_1 \mathbf{u}'\mathbf{u}. \end{aligned} \qquad (5.39)$$

Now consider the quadratic form $\mathbf{u}'B\mathbf{u}$. We know that there exists an orthogonal transformation

$$\mathbf{u}' = \mathbf{v}'M'$$

so that

$$\mathbf{u}'B\mathbf{u} = \mathbf{v}'[\text{diag}\,(\lambda_1, \lambda_2, \ldots, \lambda_k)]\mathbf{v}.$$

In fact, we made use of this transformation earlier in this chapter in developing the canonical form of a second order response surface. Now since M is an orthogonal matrix,

$$\mu_1 \mathbf{u}'\mathbf{u} = \mu_1 \mathbf{v}'M'M\mathbf{v} = \mu_1 \mathbf{v}'\mathbf{v}.$$

The rest of the proof is quite simple. The quadratic form $\mathbf{u}'[M(\mathbf{x}_1)]\mathbf{u}$ in Eq. 5.39 can now be written

$$\mathbf{u}'[M(\mathbf{x}_1)]\mathbf{u} = \mathbf{v}' \left[\text{diag} \left(\lambda_1 - \mu_1, \lambda_2 - \mu_1, \ldots, \lambda_k - \mu_1 \right) \right]\mathbf{v}.$$

Thus, if μ_1 is *larger than* all of the characteristic roots of B, the quadratic form $\mathbf{u}'[M(\mathbf{x}_1)]\mathbf{u}$ is less than zero, which implies that $M(\mathbf{x}_1)$ is *negative definite*. Also, if μ_1 is *less than* all of the k characteristic roots, $\mathbf{u}'[M(\mathbf{x}_1)]\mathbf{u}$ is greater than zero, resulting in a *positive definite* $M(\mathbf{x}_1)$. Recalling the result from calculus, which was given earlier in this section, if $\mu_1 > \lambda_i$ $(i = 1, 2, \ldots, k)$, a local maximum is attained at $\mathbf{x}_1$ on R_1; if $\mu_1 < \lambda_i$ $(i = 1, 2, \ldots, k)$, a local minimum is attained at $\mathbf{x}_1$ on R_1.

Theorem 5.3 would imply that, in carrying out the ridge analysis procedure, in order for the experimenter to be insured that stationary points used for the ridge analysis plots are local maxima, the μ value should be *larger* than the largest characteristic root of B; if one is seeking local minima, values of μ should be selected which are *smaller* than the smallest characteristic root of B. We should actually strengthen the point regarding the practical application of values of the μ's; in fact, if one restricts himself to values of μ greater than the largest root, the values of $\mathbf{x}$ obtained will be points of absolute maxima, not merely local maxima; however, values smaller than the smallest root of B result in points $\mathbf{x}$ which give absolute minima for the estimated response. This will be illustrated subsequently.

Draper gives further theoretical development which can be used to indicate the general nature of plots of R, the radius in question, against μ, the chosen value of the Lagrange multiplier used in Eq. 5.27 for obtaining the values $(x_1, x_2, \ldots, x_k)$. Figure 5.11 gives an illustration of this plot, which enables the reader to determine why values of *absolute* maxima (or minima) are found by choosing μ in the fashion that was described earlier. In the figure the λ's are values of the characteristic roots of B, ranked in ascending order of magnitude.

Suppose we consider what occurs as the experimenter chooses various values of μ in the subintervals labeled in the figure. The λ's are ranked values of the characteristic roots, λ_1 being the smallest and λ_k the largest. It is easily seen that as many as $2k$ values of μ could result in the same R. The reader must keep in mind that all of the values of $\mathbf{x}$ that occur from the various choices of μ are stationary points. At $\mu = \pm \infty$, the value of $\mathbf{x}$ will be $(0, 0, \ldots, 0)$ from Eq. 5.27, yielding an R value of zero. Draper shows that for $R \neq 0$, the second derivative $\partial^2 R / \partial u^2 > 0$, so, between λ_i and λ_{i+1}, R "dips down" and then rises again, approaching infinity at λ_{i+1}. From Theorem 5.3, and upon observing the nature of Fig. 5.11, it is ap-

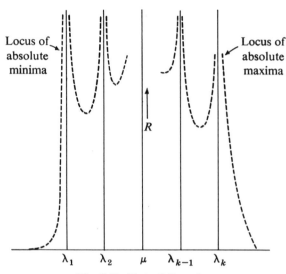

Fig. 5.11. Plot of R against μ.

parent that for a particular R, the value of μ which is larger than the largest characteristic root of B, namely λ_k, will give rise to a stationary point which yields an absolute maximum of the response surface on R. Likewise, the value of μ which is smaller than λ_1 will give rise to an x which gives an absolute minimum on R. This would imply that, in performing the ridge analysis, if one is interested in finding the locus of maximum $\hat{y}$ (in plotting against R as the procedure requires) values of μ *greater* than λ_k should be used. A similar statement would apply for the experimenter interested in minima, that is, values of μ smaller than λ_1 should be considered.

summary remarks

The ridge analysis procedure for a case of a second order response surface involves determining and plotting the absolute maximum (or minimum) of $\hat{y}$ on a sphere of radius R as a function of R. One can also find the various coordinates or operating conditions which give rise to each maximum or minimum. Essentially $k + 1$ curves with $y, x_1, x_2, \ldots, x_k$ plotted against R are prepared in order that the experimenter can observe, for a particular R, what is the maximum (or minimum) estimated response and what the operating conditions are that give rise to it. This is all accomplished by the following:

1. Obtain the characteristic roots of the B matrix. (This stage of the procedure has likely been accomplished earlier in the response surface procedure as part of the canonical analysis.
2. Choose values of μ greater than the largest characteristic root (case where maxima are sought) and use Eq. 5.34 to solve for $\mathbf{x}$ the vector of operating conditions.
3. The distance from the design center $(0, 0, \ldots, 0)$ is computed by $R = (\mathbf{x}'\mathbf{x})^{1/2}$. $\hat{y}$ is computed by substituting $\mathbf{x}$ into the fitted response function. This procedure is continued until a sufficient number of points have been plotted for the appropriate curves to be drawn. As a precaution, one must keep in mind that the portions of the curves which fall outside the experimental boundary should *not* be considered a display of reliable information.

Example. It is of interest to know the relationship between the yield of mercaptobenzothiazole (MBT) and the independent variables, time and temperature. A fitted second order response surface was found to be‡

$$\hat{y} = 82.17 - 1.01x_1 - 8.61x_2 + 1.40x_1^2 - 8.76x_2^2 - 7.20x_1x_2, \quad (5.40)$$

where

$$x_1 = \frac{\text{time (hr)} - 12}{8} \qquad x_2 = \frac{\text{temp. (°C)} - 250}{30}.$$

The contours of constant response are given in Fig. 5.12. The points on the figure represent locations of actual design points. As one can easily see, the stationary point of the system is a saddle point located at $\mathbf{x}_0' = (-0.439 - 0.311)$. The estimated response at the stationary point is $\hat{y}_0 = 83.73$.

The characteristic roots of B are the roots of the equation

$$\begin{vmatrix} 1.40 - \lambda & -3.60 \\ -3.60 & -8.76 - \lambda \end{vmatrix} = 0.$$

The results are $\lambda_1 = -9.9063$ and $\lambda_2 = 2.5463$. Assuming the experimenter is interested in maximum yield of the MBT, values of μ *greater* than 2.5463 are substituted into Eq. 5.27. It becomes necessary, then, to solve

$$\begin{bmatrix} 1.40 - \mu & -3.60 \\ -3.60 & -8.76 - \mu \end{bmatrix} \begin{bmatrix} x_1 \\ x_2 \end{bmatrix} = \begin{bmatrix} 0.505 \\ 4.305 \end{bmatrix}.$$

---

‡SOURCE: S. A. Frankel, "Statistical Design of Experiments for Process Development of MBT," *Rubber Age* **89**, 453 (1961).

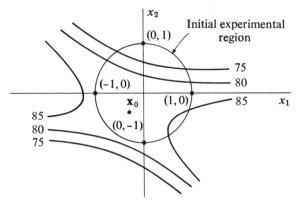

Fig. 5.12. Response system for yield of mercaptobenzothiazole as a function of time (x_1) and temperature (x_2).

Thus

$$x_1 = \frac{11.0742 - 0.505\mu}{\mu^2 + 7.36\mu - 25.224}$$

and

$$x_2 = \frac{7.845 - 4.305\mu}{\mu^2 + 7.36\mu - 25.224}.$$

These values give the location of points on the absolute maximum ridge for $\hat{y}$. For a particular point, R is computed by

$$R^2 = x_1^2 + x_2^2,$$

and the estimated response at that point is given by the response function of Eq. 5.40. As an example calculation, consider a value of $\mu = 4.0$. The corresponding coordinates are given by

$$x_1 = \frac{11.072 - (0.505)(4.0)}{(4.0)^2 + (7.36)(4.0) - 25.224} = 0.4479$$

$$x_2 = \frac{7.845 - (4.305)(4.0)}{20.216} = -0.4637.$$

Thus, the coordinate ($x_1 = 0.4479$, $x_2 = -0.4637$) represents a point on the locus of absolute maxima on $\hat{y}$. The radius R is given by

$$R = \sqrt{(0.4479)^2 + (-0.4637)^2} = 0.644.$$

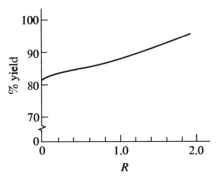

Fig. 5.13. Yield of MBT as a function of R for absolute maximum ridge.

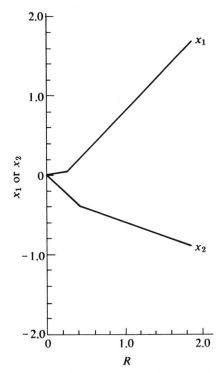

Fig. 5.14. Plots of x_1 and x_2 as a function of R for absolute maximum ridge.

At the point in question,

$$\hat{y} = 85.602.$$

Various values of $\mu > 2.5463$ were used to obtain the plot of $\hat{y}$ against R shown in Fig. 5.13 for the absolute maximum ridge. Figure 5.14 shows a plot of x_1 and x_2 against R. Notice that at the value $R = 1$, which is located at the periphery of the experimental region, the maximum estimated yield of MBT is approximately 88%, which is attained at $x_1 \cong 0.8$ and $x_2 \cong -0.6$.

exercises

5.1. Suppose the experimenter has the following experimental data at his disposal and he is interested in fitting a second order response surface in three variables. The levels of the variables are coded.

x_1	x_2	x_3	y
-1	-1	-1	52
1	-1	-1	45
-1	1	-1	30
1	1	-1	46
-1	-1	1	48
1	-1	1	55
-1	1	1	50
1	1	1	34
-2	0	0	47
2	0	0	52
0	-2	0	49
0	2	0	54
0	0	-2	36
0	0	2	44
0	0	0	42

a) Fit a second order response surface to the data of this designed experiment. Compute the stationary point of the response system.

b) Perform the canonical analysis, that is, compute the values of λ_1, λ_2, and λ_3 in the canonical form of the response function. Use these to interpret the nature of the response surface.

5.2. In a study to determine the nature of a response system which relates dry modulus of rupture (psi) in a certain ceramic material with three important independent variables, the following quadratic regression equation was determined (see Hackney and Jones):

$$\hat{y} \times 10^{-2} = 6.88 - 0.1466x_1^2 + 0.1875x_1x_2 + 0.2050x_1x_3$$
$$+ 0.0325x_1 - 0.0053x_2^2 - 0.1450x_2x_3 + 0.2588x_2$$
$$+ 0.1359x_3^2 - 0.1363x_3.$$

The independent variables represent ratios of concentration of various ingredients in the material.

a) Determine the stationary point.

b) Put the response surface into canonical form and determine the nature of the stationary point.

c) Find the appropriate expressions relating the canonical variables to the independent variables, x_1, x_2, and x_3.

5.3. Given the fitted response function

$$\hat{y} = 72.0 + 3.6x_1 - 2.5x_2,$$

which is found to fit well in a localized region of (x_1, x_2),

a) Plot on a graph, contours (lines in this case) of constant response, y, in the (x_1, x_2) plane.

b) Plot the path of steepest ascent generated from this response function.

references

Box, G. E. P. and K. B. Wilson: "On the Experimental Attainment of Optimum Conditions," *J. Roy. Statist. Soc.*, *B* **13**, 1 (1951).

Buehler, R. J., B. V. Shah, and O. Kempthorne: "Some Properties of Steepest Ascent and Related Procedures for Finding Optimum Conditions," *ONR Tech. Rept. No. 1*, Iowa State Univ., 1961.

————"Method of Parallel Tangents," *Chem. Eng. Progr.*, *Symp. Ser.* **60** (50), (1964).

Draper, N. R.: "Ridge Analysis of Response Surfaces," *Technometrics* **5** (4), 469 (1963).

Frankel, S. A.: "Statistical Design of Experiments for Process Development of MBT," *Rubber Age* **89**, 453 (1961).

Hackney, H. and P. R. Jones: "Response Surface for Dry Modulus of Rupture and Drying Shrinkage," *Am. Ceram. Soc. Bull.* **46** (8), (1967).

Hoerl, A. E.: "Optimum Solution of Many Variables Equations," *Chem. Eng. Progr.* **55** (11), 69 (1959).

Widder, D. V.: *Advanced Calculus*, 2nd ed., Prentice-Hall, Inc., Englewood Cliffs, N. J., 1961.

6 | designs for fitting first order models

At this stage of the text, the reader should be prepared to embark upon the second phase of response surface work—that part pertaining to the selection of an experimental design to use in the procedure leading to the response surface analysis. The first and second order response surface designs are treated separately. The present chapter is devoted to the discussion of designs for fitting first order models.

Suppose for k variables $\xi_1, \xi_2, \ldots, \xi_k$, in some region of interest for these factors, a response η is presumed to follow the model

$$\eta \cong \gamma_0 + \gamma_1\xi_1 + \gamma_2\xi_2 + \cdots + \gamma_k\xi_k. \qquad (6.1)$$

Consider an experiment with $N > k$ runs, the results of which will be used to estimate the parameters in Eq. 6.1 by the method of least squares. The question arises, "What combination of levels of the factors should be used in the experimental runs in order that parameters can be estimated with maximum precision?" Certain designs in the class of *orthogonal* designs, namely, the 2^k factorial and fractional factorial designs, have already been mentioned. Before these and other important designs are further discussed, we shall proceed to show the theoretical importance of the class of orthogonal designs.

6.1 | the orthogonal design

In order for the question posed in the previous paragraph to be answered, it becomes necessary to introduce a certain convention pertaining to the response surface experimental design. If for the N experimental runs we describe the uth observed response in the coded or design variables by

$$y_u = \beta_0 + \sum_{i=1}^{k} \beta_i x_{iu} + \varepsilon_u \, ;$$

then, in the general linear model

$$\mathbf{y} = X\boldsymbol{\beta} + \boldsymbol{\varepsilon},$$

the $N \times (k + 1)$ matrix X can be written

$$X = \left[\begin{array}{c|c} \begin{matrix} 1 \\ 1 \\ \ldots \\ 1 \end{matrix} & D \end{array} \right].$$

In this case,

$$\boldsymbol{\beta} = \begin{bmatrix} \beta_0 \\ \beta_1 \\ \beta_2 \\ \ldots \\ \beta_k \end{bmatrix} \qquad D = \begin{bmatrix} x_{11} & x_{21} & \cdots & x_{k1} \\ x_{12} & x_{22} & \cdots & x_{k2} \\ \ldots & \ldots & \ldots & \ldots \\ x_{1N} & x_{2N} & \cdots & x_{kN} \end{bmatrix},$$

where the matrix D is determined by the experimental runs and is called the design matrix. In some of the theoretical work that follows it is convenient to adopt the following convention for coding design levels:

$$\begin{aligned} \sum_{u=1}^{N} x_{iu}^2 &= N \\ \sum_{u=1}^{N} x_{iu} &= 0 \end{aligned} \qquad (i = 1, 2, \ldots, k). \qquad (6.2)$$

This coding is, of course, easily accomplished. If the actual value of the uth level of variable i is denoted by ξ_{iu}, then the corresponding coded value is

$$x_{iu} = \frac{\xi_{iu} - \bar{\xi}_i}{S_i}$$

where $\bar{\xi}_i$ is the average of the levels of the ith variable and

$$S_i^2 = \frac{\sum_{u=1}^{N} (\xi_{iu} - \bar{\xi}_i)^2}{N} .$$

With the convention stipulated by Eq. 6.2, if one chooses to use N experimental runs with an orthogonal design, then $X'X$ is the $(k + 1)$ by $(k + 1)$ matrix given by

$$X'X = \begin{bmatrix} N & 0 & 0 & \cdots & 0 \\ & N & 0 & \cdots & 0 \\ & & & \cdots & \cdots \\ & & & & 0 \\ & & & & N \end{bmatrix}. \tag{6.3}$$

Here,

$$\sum_{u=1}^{N} X_{iu}X_{ju} = 0 \qquad (i \neq j).$$

In other words, the columns of the X matrix are orthogonal to each other. As it turns out, for N runs, the experimental plan or design which *minimizes the variances of the coefficients* b_i $(i = 0, 1, 2, \ldots, k)$ is a design which is orthogonal, that is, for which $X'X$ takes the form given by Eq. 6.3. The proof that an orthogonal design minimizes var b_i for all i is not difficult and will be given here. The reader recalls that

$$\text{var}(b_i) = \sigma^2 c_{ii} \qquad (i = 0, 1, 2, \ldots, k)$$

where c_{ii} is the ith diagonal element of $(X'X)^{-1}$. Suppose we call a_{ij} the (i, j) element of $X'X$ and A_{pp} the *cofactor* of a_{pp}, the pth diagonal element of $X'X$. In addition, we shall denote by $A_{ij:pp}$ the cofactor of a_{ij} in A_{pp}, where $(i, j) \neq p$. The determinant of $X'X$ can be evaluated by the *Cauchy Expansion*:

$$|X'X| = a_{pp}A_{pp} - \sum_i \sum_j a_{pi}a_{pj}A_{ij:pp} \qquad (p = 0, 1, 2, \ldots, k); (i, j) \neq p$$

$$= a_{pp}A_{pp} - Q.$$

It can be seen that Q is a positive definite quadratic form in the a_{pi}. If we divide both sides of the above equation by $|X'X|$ and multiply by σ^2,

$$\sigma^2 = \frac{a_{pp}A_{pp}\sigma^2}{|X'X|} - \frac{Q\sigma^2}{|X'X|}.$$

By the convention set by Eq. 6.2, a_{pp} is the sum of the squares of the elements of the pth column of the X matrix, and thus $a_{pp} = N$. Also it should be noted that $A_{pp}/|X'X|$ is the pth diagonal element of $(X'X)^{-1}$. Therefore,

$$\sigma^2 A_{pp}/|X'X| = \text{var } b_p.$$

Thus

$$\sigma^2 = N \text{ var } b_p - Q\sigma^2/|X'X|,$$

and as a result,

$$\text{var } b_p = [\sigma^2/N][1 + Q/|X'X|]. \tag{6.4}$$

Here, the determinant $|X'X| > 0$, and since Q is positive definite, the term $Q/|X'X|$ can be no smaller than zero. In fact, it can only be zero when the a_{pi} for $p \neq i$ are all zero, that is, when $X'X$ is diagonal. Thus, var b_p for $p = 0, 1, 2, \ldots, k$ is minimized when $X'X$ is of the form in Eq. 6.3.

The orthogonal designs most often used for fitting first order models are the 2^k factorial and fractional factorial designs.

biases of regression coefficients in fractional factorial 2^k designs

The design construction and analysis for the class of fractional 2^k factorial designs were discussed in Chapter 3. However, it is interesting to observe the effect of fitting a first order model with a fractional factorial design when the actual response system contains interactions among the factors. Suppose a first order model is fitted as given by Eq. 6.1 when, in fact, the true situation (unknown to the experimenter) is best described by a response function involving both the first order contribution and certain interaction terms. For example, for $k = 3$ an experimenter may assume that the system contains no interactions when the true model is represented by

$$y = \beta_0 + \sum_{i=1}^{3} \beta_i x_i + \beta_{12} x_1 x_2 + \varepsilon, \tag{6.5}$$

the term $\beta_{12} x_1 x_2$ representing the interaction contribution between x_1 and x_2. The reader should recall that the concept of *aliasing* played a major role in the development given on fractional factorials in Chapter 3. It is essentially this same concept which prevails here. Just as each *main effect* has one or more aliases in the analysis of a fractional factorial experiment, each first order regression coefficient has aliases in the form of coefficients of higher order terms which act as *biases* in the presence of a system which is more complicated than the assumed first order model. For example, if the true response function is indicated by Eq. 6.5 and the first order model is fitted using a fractional factorial experimental design with defining contrast $ABC = I$, then the estimator b_3 will be biased by the coefficient β_{12}; that is,

$$E(b_3) = \beta_3 + f(\beta_{12}),$$

where $f(\beta_{12})$ implies that the bias is some function of the coefficient β_{12}. In this case, the estimated coefficients b_1 and b_2 are unbiased for β_1 and β_2, respectively. On the other hand, if a first order model is fitted in the presence of a response function containing *all second order cross product terms* as follows,

$$y = \beta_0 + \sum_{i=1}^{3} \beta_i x_i + \sum_{\substack{i=1 \\ i<j}}^{3} \sum_{j=1}^{3} \beta_{ij} x_i x_j + \varepsilon, \qquad (6.6)$$

then all first order coefficients are biased by the existing second order terms. Using the three factor interaction as the defining contrast, the expected values of the first order coefficients are given by

$$\begin{aligned}
E(b_1) &= \beta_1 + f(\beta_{23}) \\
E(b_2) &= \beta_2 + g(\beta_{13}). \\
E(b_3) &= \beta_3 + h(\beta_{12})
\end{aligned} \qquad (6.7)$$

As one can see, the fractional factorial which is used implies a particular alias structure, and thus a bias structure on the first order coefficients. When using a fractional factorial for fitting a first order model, the experimenter should keep the alias structure in mind to insure himself that a first order coefficient is not biased by an interaction that is likely to contribute. It should be apparent that heavy biasing can be particularly damaging when one uses fractional factorial designs in the latter stages of the method of steepest ascent.

Although the primary interest here is the bias of first order coefficients when a fractional factorial experimental design is used, a more general theory is given in this section. The results indicate the biases of coefficients in a response function when the *true model* is of an order higher than the one estimated by the experimenter. The development involves the usual framework of the general linear model. Suppose then, that the experimenter postulates the model

$$y = X_1 \beta_1 + \varepsilon, \qquad (6.8)$$

where y is the usual $N \times 1$ vector of responses, X_1 is an $N \times p_1$ matrix, and β_1 is the $p_1 \times 1$ vector of parameters postulated by the experimenter ($N \geq p_1$). Suppose, however, that the *true* response function involves the p_1 parameters in Eq. 6.8 *plus* p_2 additional ones. That is, we are interested in the biases of the coefficients in the vector

$$\hat{\beta}_1 = (X_1'X_1)^{-1} X_1' y \qquad (6.9)$$

in the presence of the existing model

$$y = X_1 \beta_1 + X_2 \beta_2 + \varepsilon \qquad (6.10)$$

where X_2 is $N \times p_2$ and β_2 is a $p_2 \times 1$ vector of additional parameters. Taking the expected value of $\hat{\beta}_1$ in Eq. 6.9, under the condition of Eq. 6.10,

$$E(\hat{\beta}_1) = E(X_1'X_1)^{-1}X_1'[X_1\beta_1 + X_2\beta_2 + \varepsilon]$$
$$= E[(X_1'X_1)^{-1}(X_1'X_1)\beta_1 + (X_1'X_1)^{-1}X_1'X_2\beta_2 + (X_1'X_1)^{-1}X_1'\varepsilon].$$

Upon making the usual assumption that $E(\varepsilon) = 0$,

$$E\hat{\beta}_1 = \beta_1 + (X_1'X_1)^{-1}X_1'X_2\beta_2$$
$$= \beta_1 + A\beta_2. \tag{6.11}$$

The extent of the bias is determined by the matrix A, the *alias matrix*. Each coefficient has as its bias a linear combination of the parameters in β_2. Equation 6.11 can then be used, for example, to determine the functions f, g, and h in Eq. 6.7.

Example. Suppose the researcher conducts an experiment using a $1/2$ fraction of a 2^3 factorial, with the defining contrast given by

$$ABC = -I.$$

The four treatment combinations in this fraction can be shown to be (1), ab, ac, and bc. The model postulated is a $k = 3$ first order function. How are the estimates b_0, b_1, b_2, and b_3 biased if the true model involves all possible two factor interaction terms? In this example, the true model is given by Eq. 6.6. The matrices needed in evaluating the bias are

$$X_1 = \begin{bmatrix} 1 & -1 & -1 & -1 \\ 1 & 1 & 1 & -1 \\ 1 & -1 & 1 & 1 \\ 1 & 1 & -1 & 1 \end{bmatrix} \quad X_2 = \begin{bmatrix} 1 & 1 & 1 \\ 1 & -1 & -1 \\ -1 & -1 & 1 \\ -1 & 1 & -1 \end{bmatrix}$$

with columns labeled x_1, x_2, x_3 for X_1 and x_1x_2, x_1x_3, x_2x_3 for X_2.

$$\beta_2 = \begin{bmatrix} \beta_{12} \\ \beta_{13} \\ \beta_{23} \end{bmatrix}$$

Since the design is orthogonal, $(X_1'X_1)^{-1} = (1/4)I_4$; the matrix $X_1'X_2$ is given by

$$X_1'X_2 = \begin{bmatrix} 0 & 0 & 0 \\ 0 & 0 & -4 \\ 0 & -4 & 0 \\ -4 & 0 & 0 \end{bmatrix}.$$

The alias matrix is

$$A = (1/4)X_1'X_2 = \begin{bmatrix} 0 & 0 & 0 \\ 0 & 0 & -1 \\ 0 & -1 & 0 \\ -1 & 0 & 0 \end{bmatrix}.$$

When the experimenter fits a first order model in the presence of the second order interaction terms, with the treatment combinations given by this example, the biases are given by the following:

$$E(b_0) = \beta_0 \qquad E(b_1) = \beta_1 - \beta_{23}$$
$$E(b_2) = \beta_2 - \beta_{13} \qquad E(b_3) = \beta_3 - \beta_{12}.$$

It is easily observed that the biasing which occurs is a direct result of a fraction of the total factorial design being used. For a given main effect, the terms which occur in the bias are those representing the interactions that are aliased with that main effect. If the complete factorial were used to fit a first order function, the coefficients $b_0, b_1, b_2, \ldots$ would *not* be biased by the interaction coefficients $\beta_{12}, \beta_{13}, \ldots$, since in this case the columns of X_1, representing the factor levels in the complete design, are orthogonal to the columns of X_2, implying a zero alias matrix. For example, if a 2^2 factorial is used to fit the model

$$y = \beta_0 + \beta_1 x_1 + \beta_2 x_2 + \varepsilon,$$

and if one is concerned about the bias of the coefficients b_0, b_1, and b_2 in the presence of the interaction term $x_1 x_2$,

$$X_1 = \begin{matrix} & x_1 & x_2 & \\ \begin{bmatrix} 1 & -1 & 1 \\ 1 & -1 & -1 \\ 1 & 1 & 1 \\ 1 & 1 & -1 \end{bmatrix} \end{matrix} \qquad X_2 = \begin{matrix} x_1 x_2 \\ \begin{bmatrix} -1 \\ 1 \\ 1 \\ -1 \end{bmatrix} \end{matrix}.$$

Since $X_1'X_2 = 0$, b_0, b_1, and b_2 are not biased. That is,

$$Eb_0 = \beta_0$$
$$Eb_1 = \beta_1$$
$$Eb_2 = \beta_2.$$

An experimenter need not worry about biasing or aliasing in his first order coefficients if the true model is, in fact, first order. However, quite often this might not be known or a first order model may be merely a *postulated* representation. For this reason (1) biasing due to higher order terms should be considered, and (2) a first order design should nearly always be constructed so that the experimenter can measure lack-of-fit of the postulated model and be able to compare this contribution with mere chance variation or pure experimental error.

At this stage it may be interesting to consider the biasing that occurs in the first order coefficients when one fits a first order model with a 2^k factorial design in the presence of an existing *complete* second order response function. Suppose the design used is a 2^2 factorial and the *true* response function is described by

$$y = \beta_0 + \beta_1 x_1 + \beta_2 x_2 + \beta_{12} x_1 x_2 + \beta_{11} x_1^2 + \beta_{22} x_2^2 + \varepsilon.$$

The matrices which are needed in computing the biases are given by

$$
X_1 = \begin{matrix} x_1 x_2 \\ \begin{bmatrix} 1 & -1 & 1 \\ 1 & -1 & -1 \\ 1 & 1 & 1 \\ 1 & 1 & -1 \end{bmatrix} \end{matrix}
\qquad
X_2 = \begin{matrix} x_1 x_2 x_1^2 x_2^2 \\ \begin{bmatrix} -1 & 1 & 1 \\ 1 & 1 & 1 \\ 1 & 1 & 1 \\ -1 & 1 & 1 \end{bmatrix} \end{matrix}.
$$

The alias matrix is given by

$$
A = \begin{bmatrix} 1/4 & 0 & 0 \\ 0 & 1/4 & 0 \\ 0 & 0 & 1/4 \end{bmatrix} \begin{bmatrix} 0 & 4 & 4 \\ 0 & 0 & 0 \\ 0 & 0 & 0 \end{bmatrix} = \begin{bmatrix} 0 & 1 & 1 \\ 0 & 0 & 0 \\ 0 & 0 & 0 \end{bmatrix}.
$$

Thus

$$
E \begin{bmatrix} b_0 \\ b_1 \\ b_2 \end{bmatrix} = \begin{bmatrix} \beta_0 \\ \beta_1 \\ \beta_2 \end{bmatrix} + \begin{bmatrix} 0 & 1 & 1 \\ 0 & 0 & 0 \\ 0 & 0 & 0 \end{bmatrix} \begin{bmatrix} \beta_{12} \\ \beta_{11} \\ \beta_{22} \end{bmatrix} = \begin{bmatrix} \beta_0 + \beta_{11} + \beta_{22} \\ \beta_1 \\ \beta_2 \end{bmatrix}.
$$

Therefore, b_0 is biased by $\beta_{11} + \beta_{22}$, while b_1 and b_2 remain unbiased. Quite generally, if a full 2^k factorial is used to fit a first order model in the presence of a second order system, b_0 is biased by $\sum_{i=1}^{k} \beta_{ii}$ and $b_1, b_2, \ldots, b_k$ remain unbiased.

6.2 | addition of points in the center of the 2^k factorial design

The advantages of a 2^k factorial and fractional factorial design should, by now, be apparent. One *disadvantage* is that, as the design has been defined, the 2^k design points (or 2^{k-p} where $p < k$) do not afford an estimate of the experimental error variance. In fact, the reader may recall from Chapter 3 that when one fits a first order model with the ordinary 2^k or fractional 2^k, the residual or error sum of squares contains variation due to experimental error *plus* the lack-of-fit of the first order equation. In practice, it is often very helpful to have a value which represents an estimate of the experimental error variance, the latter being independent of model selection. This, then, can be used to make a significance test on the lack-of-fit contribution. In certain circumstances, this estimate of "pure error" can be obtained from a previous experiment. The estimate may also be gotten by replicating the design points, but this procedure is not always desirable due to the amount of experimentation involved. This consideration of economics is particularly pertinent where fractional factorials are used, since the sole purpose of the design is to reduce experimentation.

A procedure which can be used to obtain an estimate of the experimental error variance free from lack-of-fit is to augment the basic design with experimental runs in the *center* of the design, the center being taken as the design point for which $(x_1, x_2, \ldots, x_k) = (0, 0, \ldots, 0)$ in coded units, that is, the *origin* of the design. This is illustrated in Fig. 6.1 for a two-dimensional factorial design. Suppose the coded units are

$$x_1 = \frac{\text{time (hr)} - 1.5}{0.5}$$

$$x_2 = \frac{\text{temp. (°C)} - 175}{25}.$$

Here, the design origin ($x_1 = 0, x_2 = 0$) corresponds to a time of 1.5 hours and a temperature of 175°C.

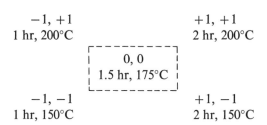

Fig. 6.1. 2^2 Factorial design with a center point.

If the origin of the 2^k factorial design is replicated, for instance n_2 times, the result is (1) the attainment of $n_2 - 1$ degrees of freedom for pure error to use in testing for the significance of the variation encountered due to lack-of-fit, and (2) a single degree of freedom to obtain certain information concerning the existence of pure quadratic terms in the actual response surface. In fact, this additional degree of freedom, which represents a portion of lack-of-fit, has as its contrast the variation that accounts for the coefficients $\beta_{11}, \beta_{22}, \ldots, \beta_{kk}$. If we call $\bar{y}_1$ the *average* of the n_1 observations on the 2^k design, and $\bar{y}_2$ the average of the n_2 observations taken at the design origin, and if the actual surface is quadratic, the statistic $\bar{y}_1 - \bar{y}_2$ has as its expected value

$$E(\bar{y}_1 - \bar{y}_2) = \sum_i \beta_{ii}. \tag{6.12}$$

Actually, Eq. 6.12 holds not only for a 2^k factorial but also for a 2^k fractional factorial in which no two first order coefficients are aliased with one another.

As one example, let us consider the design given in Fig. 6.1. If the actual model is second order,

$$E(\bar{y}_1) = \frac{4\beta_0 + 4\beta_{11} + 4\beta_{22}}{4}$$

$$E(\bar{y}_2) = \frac{n_2\beta_0}{n_2} = \beta_0.$$

Therefore,

$$E(\bar{y}_1 - \bar{y}_2) = \beta_{11} + \beta_{22}.$$

Actually, then, a statistic can be developed for testing

$$H_0: \sum_{i=1}^{k} \beta_{ii} = 0$$

$$H_1: \sum_{i=1}^{k} \beta_{ii} \neq 0.$$

The single degree of freedom sum of squares which is used for this purpose is given by

$$\frac{n_1 n_2 (\bar{y}_1 - \bar{y}_2)^2}{n_1 + n_2}. \tag{6.13}$$

In order to illustrate the partitioning of the degrees of freedom for a first order design augmented by center points, let us consider a 1/2 fraction of a 2^4 factorial design with factors A, B, C, and D corresponding, respectively, to the independent variables x_1, x_2, x_3, and x_4. Suppose we use as the defining contrast

$$ABCD = I,$$

with the design augmented by four center points. The design points are symbolically illustrated by

$$[(1), ab, ac, ad, bc, bd, cd, abcd, 0_1, 0_2, 0_3, 0_4]$$

where the last four points represent replications at the center of the design. The partitioning of the degrees of freedom is given in Table 6.1. Regarding the estimation of the first order coefficients in the response model, b_1, b_2, b_3, and b_4 are found by the usual contrasts (ignoring the center points). For example,

$$b_1 = \frac{ab + ac + ad + abcd - (1) - bc - bd - cd}{8}.$$

The term b_0 is now the average over the entire experiment. This can be easily verified by utilizing the normal estimating equations.

Table 6.1. Partitioning of the Degrees of Freedom for a 1/2 Fraction of a 2^4 Design Augmented by Four Center Points[a]

Source	Degrees of Freedom	
β_0	1	
β_1	1	
β_2	1	
β_3	1	
β_4	1	
lack-of-fit	4	
cross product		3
pure quadratic		1
error	3	
total	12	

[a]Defining contrast is $ABCD$.

The three degrees of freedom for cross product terms represent, in this case, the variation due to two factor interactions. There are six such terms that are aliased in pairs in this design, with the alias structure being given by

$$\beta_{12} \equiv \beta_{34}$$
$$\beta_{13} \equiv \beta_{24}$$
$$\beta_{23} \equiv \beta_{14}.$$

The pure error sum of squares is found by computing the sum of squares between the observations at the center of the design. That is,

$$SS_E = (0_1^2 + 0_2^2 + 0_3^2 + 0_4^2) - \frac{(0_1 + 0_2 + 0_3 + 0_4)^2}{4}.$$

The single degree of freedom sum of squares for pure quadratic contribution is computed using Eq. 6.13 for $n_1 = 8$ and $n_2 = 4$.

6.3 | simplex designs for fitting first order models

The *simplex* design is another in the class of orthogonal designs, useful for fitting first order models. The main feature of this experimental design is that it requires exactly $N = k + 1$ observations, that is, one more than the number of variables in the response model. Geometrically, the design *points* represent the vertices of a k-dimensional regular-sided figure or simplex. That is, the design points, given by the rows of the design matrix,

$$D = \begin{bmatrix} x_{11} & x_{21} & \cdots & x_{k1} \\ x_{12} & x_{22} & \cdots & x_{k2} \\ \cdots & \cdots & \cdots & \cdots \\ x_{1N} & x_{2N} & \cdots & x_{kN} \end{bmatrix}$$

are points in k dimensions such that the angle that *any two* points make with the origin is θ, where

$$\cos(\theta) = -1/(N - 1) = -1/k. \tag{6.14}$$

For $k = 2$, $N = 3$, $\cos(\theta) = -1/2$ and therefore $\theta = 120°$. Thus, for this case, the points are coordinates of an *equilateral triangle*. For $k = 3$ and $N = 4$, the design points are the vertices of a *tetrahedron*. Figure 6.2 shows the coordinates of the simplex for two variables.

The design matrix for the simplex in Fig. 6.2 is given by

$$D = \begin{bmatrix} \sqrt{3/2} & -1/\sqrt{2} \\ -\sqrt{3/2} & -1/\sqrt{2} \\ 0 & 2/\sqrt{2} \end{bmatrix} \begin{matrix} \text{(point 1)} \\ \text{(point 2)} \\ \text{(point 3)} \end{matrix} \tag{6.15}$$

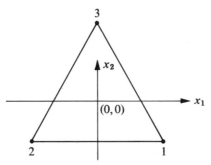

Fig. 6.2. Design points for the simplex in two variables.

The rows of the design matrix correspond to the coordinates in the two-dimensional figure. The X matrix is D augmented by a column of 1's that is,

$$X = \begin{bmatrix} 1 & \sqrt{3/2} & -1/\sqrt{2} \\ 1 & -\sqrt{3/2} & -1/\sqrt{2} \\ 1 & 0 & 2/\sqrt{2} \end{bmatrix}. \qquad (6.16)$$

The $X'X$ matrix is easily seen to be

$$X'X = \begin{bmatrix} 3 & 0 & 0 \\ 0 & 3 & 0 \\ 0 & 0 & 3 \end{bmatrix}.$$

In general, the X matrix for a k-dimensional simplex can be constructed very simply. One starts with an orthogonal matrix O of order $N \times N$, the elements in the first column being equal. The X matrix is then

$$X = (O)(N)^{1/2}, \qquad (6.17)$$

and it is easily seen that

$$X'X = N(O'O) = NI_N.$$

The design for the $k = 2$ simplex with the X matrix given by Eq. 6.16, may be constructed from the orthogonal matrix

$$O = \begin{bmatrix} 1 & 1 & -1 \\ 1 & -1 & -1 \\ 1 & 0 & 2 \end{bmatrix}.$$
$$\quad 1/\sqrt{3} \quad 1/\sqrt{2} \quad 1/\sqrt{6}$$

The values at the bottom of each column are to be multiplied by each element in the column. Multiplying O by $\sqrt{3}$ yields the X matrix given by Eq. 6.16.

Consider as a second example, a situation where one wishes to fit a $k = 3$ first order model with a simplex. An appropriate design can be constructed by starting with the orthogonal matrix

$$O = \begin{bmatrix} 1 & 1 & -1 & -1 \\ 1 & -1 & 1 & -1 \\ 1 & -1 & -1 & 1 \\ 1 & 1 & 1 & 1 \end{bmatrix}. \qquad (6.18)$$
$$\quad 1/2 \quad 1/2 \quad 1/2 \quad 1/2$$

The X matrix for the simplex can then be formed by multiplying O by $\sqrt{N} = 2$. The resulting experimental design is represented by the design matrix

$$
\begin{array}{ccc}
x_1 & x_2 & x_3
\end{array}
$$

$$
D = \begin{bmatrix} 1 & -1 & -1 \\ -1 & 1 & -1 \\ -1 & -1 & 1 \\ 1 & 1 & 1 \end{bmatrix}. \tag{6.19}
$$

Note that the four design points form an orthogonal design; $X'X = 4I_4$. A close look at the simplex given by Eq. 6.19 reveals that in this special case the design is actually a 1/2 fraction of a 2^3 factorial.

Simplex designs for $k = 4, 5, 6, \ldots$ can be constructed by the procedures mentioned in the preceding paragraphs. At this stage, it should be obvious to the reader that the simplex designs illustrated by Eqs. 6.15 and 6.19 are *not* unique for $k = 2$ and $k = 3$, respectively, and that, in general, one can construct different simplex designs by merely varying the choice of the orthogonal matrix O. For example, for $k = 2$ a second simplex can be constructed by changing the orientation of the equilateral triangle. For $k = 3$, a second simplex can be constructed by starting with the matrix

$$
O = \begin{bmatrix} 1 & 0 & 1 & -1 \\ 1 & -1 & 0 & 1 \\ 1 & 0 & -1 & -1 \\ 1 & 1 & 0 & 1 \end{bmatrix},
$$

$$
1/2 \quad \sqrt{2}/2 \quad \sqrt{2}/2 \quad 1/2
$$

the design matrix then being written

$$
D = \begin{bmatrix} 0 & \sqrt{2} & -1 \\ -\sqrt{2} & 0 & 1 \\ 0 & -\sqrt{2} & -1 \\ \sqrt{2} & 0 & 1 \end{bmatrix}. \tag{6.20}
$$

further remarks concerning simplex design

With only $N = k + 1$ observations at the experimenter's disposal, the simplex does not afford any degrees of freedom for lack-of-fit. Indeed, its real utility is that it enables one to estimate the coefficients in a first order response model with an orthogonal design containing the *minimum* of information. As a result, if the true response surface were of the second order, it would not be detected in any analysis conducted on the observations.

As was stated in the previous section, various simplexes can be constructed for a specific value of k. They represent different orientations of the regular-sided geometric figure. The $X'X$ matrix is diagonal for each and every simplex, and thus they are all orthogonal. However, the biases of the regression coefficients in the presence of a quadratic response surface are definitely dependent on which simplex (which orientation) is used. This can be illustrated by comparing the biases of b_0, b_1, b_2, and b_3 for the simplexes given by Eq. 6.19 (simplex a) and Eq. 6.20 (simplex b) if the true response surface were second order. For the simplex in Eq. 6.19 the biases are

$$
\begin{aligned}
E(b_0) &= \beta_0 + \beta_{11} + \beta_{22} + \beta_{33} \\
E(b_1) &= \beta_1 + \beta_{23} \\
E(b_2) &= \beta_2 + \beta_{13} \\
E(b_3) &= \beta_3 + \beta_{12}.
\end{aligned}
\tag{6.21}
$$

For the simplex given by Eq. 6.20 the biases are

$$
\begin{aligned}
E(b_0) &= \beta_0 + \beta_{11} + \beta_{22} + \beta_{33} \\
E(b_1) &= \beta_1 + \beta_{13} \\
E(b_2) &= \beta_2 - \beta_{23} \\
E(b_3) &= \beta_3 + \beta_{11} - \beta_{22}.
\end{aligned}
\tag{6.22}
$$

Equations 6.21 and 6.22 are obtained by computing bias structures as indicated on page 112. For example, in simplex b if we express the second order surface in the form of Eq. 6.9, we have

$$
X_2 = \begin{array}{c c c c c c c}
& \beta_{11} & \beta_{22} & \beta_{33} & \beta_{12} & \beta_{13} & \beta_{23} \\
& \begin{bmatrix}
0 & 2 & 1 & 0 & 0 & -\sqrt{2} \\
2 & 0 & 1 & 0 & -\sqrt{2} & 0 \\
0 & 2 & 1 & 0 & 0 & \sqrt{2} \\
2 & 0 & 1 & 0 & \sqrt{2} & 0
\end{bmatrix}
\end{array}.
$$

The alias matrix is given by

$$
A = (X_1'X_1)^{-1}X_1'X_2 = \begin{array}{c c c c c c c}
& \beta_{11} & \beta_{22} & \beta_{33} & \beta_{12} & \beta_{13} & \beta_{23} \\
& \begin{bmatrix}
1 & 1 & 1 & 0 & 0 & 0 \\
0 & 0 & 0 & 0 & 1 & 0 \\
0 & 0 & 0 & 0 & 0 & -1 \\
1 & -1 & 0 & 0 & 0 & 0
\end{bmatrix}
\end{array}
$$

and the biases are those in Eq. 6.22.

Example. A simplex design is used in a laboratory experiment designed to fit a first order model relating the growth (y) of a particular organism to the percentage of glucose (x_1), concentration of yeast extract (x_2), and the time in hours (x_3) allowed for organism growth. Other variables are held constant. The variables in coded form are

$$x_1 = \frac{\% \text{ glucose} - 3.0}{1.0}$$

$$x_2 = \frac{\% \text{ yeast} - 0.50}{0.10}$$

$$x_3 = \frac{\text{hr} - 45}{15}.$$

Table 6.2 gives the design in terms of the original and coded variables, and indicates the observed response.

Table 6.2. Experimental Observations for Organism Growth Experiment Using Simplex Design

Run	% Glucose (x_1)		% Yeast (x_2)		Time, hr (x_3)		Growth, g/liter
	a	b	a	b	a	b	
1	3.0	0	0.641	$\sqrt{2}$	30	-1	8.52
2	1.586	$-\sqrt{2}$	0.500	0	60	1	9.76
3	3.0	0	0.359	$-\sqrt{2}$	30	-1	7.38
4	4.414	$\sqrt{2}$	0.500	0	60	1	12.50

^{a}Uncoded. ^{b}Coded.

The least squares estimators are given by

$$
\begin{bmatrix} b_0 \\ b_1 \\ b_2 \\ b_3 \end{bmatrix} =
\begin{bmatrix} 1/4 & 0 & 0 & 0 \\ 0 & 1/4 & 0 & 0 \\ 0 & 0 & 1/4 & 0 \\ 0 & 0 & 0 & 1/4 \end{bmatrix}
\begin{bmatrix} 8.52 + 9.76 + 7.38 + 12.50 \\ -\sqrt{2}(9.76) + \sqrt{2}(12.50) \\ (8.52)\sqrt{2} - (7.38)\sqrt{2} \\ -8.52 + 9.76 - 7.38 + 12.50 \end{bmatrix}
$$

$$
= 1/4 \begin{bmatrix} 38.16 \\ 3.87 \\ 1.61 \\ 6.36 \end{bmatrix}
$$

$$
= \begin{bmatrix} 9.54 \\ 0.97 \\ 0.40 \\ 1.59 \end{bmatrix}.
$$

6.4 | further remarks concerning adequacy of fitted response models

Much emphasis has been placed on the detection of lack-of-fit, that is, making a comparison, in terms of an F-ratio, between the lack-of-fit mean square, and the experimental error mean square. The following ratio is formed:

$$F = \frac{\text{mean square for lack-of-fit}}{\text{mean square for experimental error}},$$

and if it is not significant, the conclusion is made that the errors about the fitted model (lack-of-fit) are on the same order of magnitude as those accounted for by error of observation (experimental error). The pure experimental error mean square is computed by considering variation between observations at the same experimental conditions run in random sequence. The conclusion is then that the model *is an adequate representation* of the data.

If the F-ratio is significant, the implication is that the numerator mean square is estimating something which is in excess of σ^2, the experimental error variance. This excess variation is due to higher order terms, those beyond the postulated model. Thus one concludes that the model *does not* adequately represent the data. The higher order terms that are accounted for in the aggregate we refer to as lack-of-fit depend on the experimental design used. Essentially, they represent terms that the experimenter could have included in the model but didn't. For example, for a 2^2 factorial design used to fit a model of order one, there will be 1 degree of freedom for lack-of-fit, that which accounts for the x_1x_2 interaction term. Lack-of-fit, will not include the curvature coefficients β_{11} and β_{22}. One should augment in the design center to include these terms. Therefore, it is possible for the lack-of-fit to show no significance, indicating an adequate representation, but giving poor prediction on the response in later confirmatory trials. One should not only be aware of the existence of lack-of-fit variation provided by the design but also what this variation is accounting for.

The experimenter should also remember that the first and second order models applied in RSM are used because they adequately represent many scientific phenomena *and* because they are simple to work with. A fitted first or second order function is, however, not the only model that can be shown to be adequate for a set of experimental data. In fact, the model fitting aspect of RSM only represents empirical devices and when it is determined that a model is adequate by our criterion, it means that the existence of such a model was not contradicted by the evidence, namely, the data. The scientist should constantly be in search of the *true structure* of the system so that eventually he may not have to resort to empirical devices.

exercises

6.1. In the example on page 112, the biases were given for the first order coefficients for the case of a first order model in three variables fit in the presence of two factor interactions. The design used was the 1/2 fraction determined by the defining contrast $ABC = -I$. Write out the biases for the case of a design given by the defining contrast $ABC = +I$.

6.2. For the above case, how is the alias matrix altered by the addition of n center points to the design?

6.3. Write out the alias matrix and the resulting bias structure of the coefficients in the fitted model

$$\hat{y} = b_0 + \sum_{i=1}^{5} b_i x_i$$

when the true model also contains second order interaction terms. The design used is a 1/4 fraction of a 2^5 factorial with the defining contrasts being

$$ABC = I,$$
$$CDE = I.$$

6.4. Construct an orthogonal first order design containing six experimental points for a model involving five variables.

6.5. Name several characteristics that one should attempt to attain in constructing a first order design.

6.6. Suppose a 2^2 factorial design is used to fit a planar response function. The design matrix and vector of responses are given by

$$
X = \begin{array}{c} \begin{array}{cc} x_1 & x_2 \end{array} \\ \begin{bmatrix} -1 & -1 \\ -1 & -1 \\ 1 & -1 \\ 1 & -1 \\ -1 & 1 \\ -1 & 1 \\ 1 & 1 \\ 1 & 1 \\ 0 & 0 \\ 0 & 0 \\ 0 & 0 \\ 0 & 0 \end{bmatrix} \end{array}
\qquad
y = \begin{bmatrix} 55.8 \\ 54.4 \\ 60.3 \\ 60.9 \\ 63.9 \\ 64.4 \\ 67.9 \\ 68.5 \\ 61.5 \\ 62.0 \\ 61.9 \\ 62.4 \end{bmatrix}.
$$

Notice that there are four observations at the center of the design and every other design point is replicated.

a) Estimate the first order response function and plot lines of constant response in the $x_1 x_2$ plane.

b) Provide an analysis of variance table showing significance tests on each coefficient. Also show the experimental error mean square and make a significance test for lack-of-fit. Partition the lack-of-fit into two components—that attributed to the interaction and that due to pure quadratic contribution.

references

Box, G. E. P.: "Multi-factor Designs of First Order," *Biometrika* **39,** 49 (1952).

———: "The Exploration and Exploitation of Response Surfaces," *Biometrics* **10,** 16 (1954).

Box, G. E. P. and J. S. Hunter: "The 2^{k-p} Fractional Factorial Designs," *Technometrics, Part I* **3** (3), 333 (1961a).

———: "The 2^{k-p} Fractional Factorial Designs," *Technometrics, Part II* **3** (4), 449 (1961b).

7 | designs for fitting second order models

Experimental designs for fitting a second order response surface must involve at least three levels of each variable so that the coefficients in the model can be estimated. The experimental design should be chosen on the basis of (1) relative precision in estimating the coefficients and (2) the amount of experimental effort; that is, the number of observations required. Obviously, the design that is automatically suggested by the model requirement is the 3^k factorial, a factorial experiment with each factor at three levels. For small values of k, e.g. 2 or even 3, this design is well suited. However, when a large quantity of variables are under study, the number of observations required are excessive. For example, for $k = 4$, not an unreasonable situation from a practical point of view, eighty-one design points are required to estimate only fifteen coefficients, β_0, four first order coefficients, four pure quadratic coefficients, and six that account for mixed quadratic terms.

Box and Wison have devised a workable alternative to the 3^k factorial system through the development of the class of *composite designs*, a special type of which is called the *central composite design*. This design, which is greatly used by workers applying second order response surface techniques, is discussed in Section 7.1.

It will be assumed that three evenly spaced levels of the controlled or independent variables can be coded to $-1, 0, 1$. For example, if ξ_1 is temperature, and the levels of interest are 100°C, 150°C, and 200°C, then the coded design variable is

$$x_1 = \frac{\xi_1 - 150}{50}.$$

For the case of a 3^2 factorial design, if the observed response is given by the usual second order relationship

$$y_u = \beta_0 + \beta_1 x_{1u} + \beta_2 x_{2u} + \beta_{11} x_{1u}^2 + \beta_{22} x_{2u}^2 + \beta_{12} x_{1u} x_{2u} + \varepsilon_u,$$

the X matrix is written as in Eq. 3.32. The coefficients are then estimated using techniques described in Chapter 3. The calculations can be simplified by transforming to the variables $x_1^2 - \overline{x_1^2}$ and $x_2^2 - \overline{x_2^2}$, resulting in a diagonal $X'X$. Essentially, this results in defining a new intercept or constant term whose estimate is orthogonal to the estimates of β_{11} and β_{22}. The model can now be written

$$y_u = \beta_0' + \beta_1 x_{1u} + \beta_2 x_{2u} + \beta_{11}(x_{1u}^2 - 2/3)$$
$$+ \beta_{22}(x_{2u}^2 - 2/3) + \beta_{12} x_{1u} x_{2u} + \varepsilon_u, \qquad (7.1)$$

and the $X'X$ matrix is given in Eq. 3.34. It should be emphasized that it is the orthogonal nature of the 3^k factorial design which allows the construction of an $X'X$ which is diagonal.

When fitting a first order model, the property of orthogonality has definite advantages, other than computational convenience, as was indicated in Chapter 6. For the second order case, the situation is not so "clear." As a result, we shall present in later material other design properties, with the overall goal being that of giving the experimenter pertinent facts and illustrations so that he can decide what constitutes the best experimental layout for his particular second order response surface problem. With regard to the 3^k factorial design, although certain advantages and disadvantages have been pointed out here, further discussion which is pertinent to this design will be given in succeeding sections.

7.1 | central composite design

The composite designs are first order factorial designs augmented by additional points to allow estimation of the coefficients of a second order surface. The central composite design is the 2^k factorial or fractional factorial (the two levels of each variable coded to the usual $-1, +1$) augmented by the following:

$$
\begin{array}{ccccc}
x_1 & x_2 & x_3 & \cdots & x_k \\
\left[\begin{array}{ccccc}
0 & 0 & 0 & \cdots & 0 \\
-\alpha & 0 & 0 & \cdots & 0 \\
\alpha & 0 & 0 & \cdots & 0 \\
0 & -\alpha & 0 & \cdots & 0 \\
0 & \alpha & 0 & \cdots & 0 \\
0 & 0 & -\alpha & \cdots & 0 \\
0 & 0 & \alpha & \cdots & 0 \\
\cdots & \cdots & \cdots & \cdots & \cdots \\
0 & 0 & 0 & \cdots & -\alpha \\
0 & 0 & 0 & \cdots & \alpha
\end{array}\right]
\end{array}.
$$

The value of α is selected by the experimenter. Various criteria can be used in making the choice. For a case of three independent variables the design matrix is given by

$$
D = \begin{array}{c}
\begin{array}{ccc} x_1 & x_2 & x_3 \end{array} \\
\left[
\begin{array}{ccc}
-1 & -1 & -1 \\
-1 & -1 & 1 \\
-1 & 1 & -1 \\
-1 & 1 & 1 \\
1 & -1 & -1 \\
1 & -1 & 1 \\
1 & 1 & -1 \\
1 & 1 & 1 \\
\hline
0 & 0 & 0 \\
-\alpha & 0 & 0 \\
\alpha & 0 & 0 \\
0 & -\alpha & 0 \\
0 & \alpha & 0 \\
0 & 0 & -\alpha \\
0 & 0 & \alpha
\end{array}
\right].
\end{array}
\qquad (7.2)
$$

It often becomes desirable for the experimenter to invest in more than one center point in order to attain certain design properties. Unless specified, we shall assume in what follows that there are $n_2 \geq 1$ observations at $(0, 0, \ldots, 0)$.

The first eight points in Eq. 7.2 are the usual factorial points for fitting a first order model. The ninth point is the center point of the design, and the

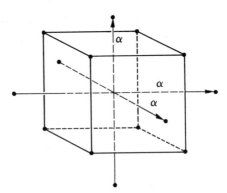

Fig. 7.1. Central composite design for $k = 3$.

six remaining points are the *axial points* of the cube. Figure 7.1 gives a geometric illustration of the three variable central composite design (ccd).

Notice that if $\alpha \neq 1$, each variable is actually measured at five levels. Also, it should be observed that the number of experimental points needed are sufficient for fitting a second order surface. For $k > 2$ they are considerably less than the number required by a 3^k factorial design. The ccd lends itself to sequential experimentation extremely well. For example, suppose that the experimenter begins a response surface study with a 2^k factorial experiment, such as in a steepest ascent program, and discovers the significance of the lack-of-fit in the analysis of variance, indicating inadequacy of the first order model. One needs only to add to the 2^k observations the additional $2k + n_2$ experimental runs at the treatment combinations representing the axial points and the design center, thus allowing the estimation of a second order response surface. There are other less obvious advantages to the ccd which will be discussed in succeeding sections.

In order that a comparison can be made between the ccd and the 3^k factorial (or any other design for fitting second order models), attention will be given to the X and $X'X$ matrix for the general ccd. An example for the case of $k = 3$ and the results for the general case follow.

Suppose we call F the number of factorial points ($F = 2^k$ if a *complete* factorial is used) and $T = 2k + n_2$ the number of additional points in the ccd (axial points plus center point). For $k = 3$ and $n_2 = 1$ the **y** vector and X matrix are given by

$$
\mathbf{y} = \begin{bmatrix}
(1) \\
c \\
b \\
bc \\
a \\
ac \\
ab \\
abc \\
\hdashline
0, 0, 0 \\
-\alpha, 0, 0 \\
\alpha, 0, 0 \\
0, -\alpha, 0 \\
0, \alpha, 0 \\
0, 0, -\alpha \\
0, 0, \alpha
\end{bmatrix}
$$

$$X = \begin{array}{c}
\begin{array}{cccccccccc}
\beta_0 & \beta_1 & \beta_2 & \beta_3 & \beta_{11} & \beta_{22} & \beta_{33} & \beta_{12} & \beta_{13} & \beta_{23}
\end{array} \\
\left[\begin{array}{cccccccccc}
1 & -1 & -1 & -1 & 1-c & 1-c & 1-c & 1 & 1 & 1 \\
1 & -1 & -1 & 1 & 1-c & 1-c & 1-c & 1 & -1 & -1 \\
1 & -1 & 1 & -1 & 1-c & 1-c & 1-c & -1 & 1 & -1 \\
1 & -1 & 1 & 1 & 1-c & 1-c & 1-c & -1 & -1 & 1 \\
1 & 1 & -1 & -1 & 1-c & 1-c & 1-c & -1 & -1 & 1 \\
1 & 1 & -1 & 1 & 1-c & 1-c & 1-c & -1 & 1 & -1 \\
1 & 1 & 1 & -1 & 1-c & 1-c & 1-c & 1 & -1 & -1 \\
1 & 1 & 1 & 1 & 1-c & 1-c & 1-c & 1 & 1 & 1 \\
\hline
1 & 0 & 0 & 0 & -c & -c & -c & 0 & 0 & 0 \\
1 & -\alpha & 0 & 0 & \alpha^2-c & -c & -c & 0 & 0 & 0 \\
1 & \alpha & 0 & 0 & \alpha^2-c & -c & -c & \cdots & \cdots & \cdots \\
1 & 0 & -\alpha & 0 & -c & \alpha^2-c & -c & \cdots & \cdots & \cdots \\
1 & 0 & \alpha & 0 & -c & \alpha^2-c & -c & \cdots & \cdots & \cdots \\
1 & 0 & 0 & -\alpha & -c & -c & \alpha^2-c & \cdots & \cdots & \cdots \\
1 & 0 & 0 & \alpha & -c & -c & \alpha^2-c & 0 & 0 & 0
\end{array}\right]
\end{array}$$

where $c = (F + 2\alpha^2)/(F + T)$. Here, we are considering the model with the pure quadratic terms corrected for their mean, that is,

$$y_u = \beta_0' + \sum_{j=1}^{3} \beta_j x_{ju} + \sum_{j=1}^{3} \beta_{jj}(x_{ju}^2 - \overline{x_j^2})$$
$$+ \sum_{j<p}\sum \beta_{jp} x_{ju} x_{pu} + \varepsilon_u \qquad (u = 1, 2, \ldots, N).$$

The $X'X$ matrix is written as

$$X'X = \begin{array}{c}
\begin{array}{cccccccccc}
\beta_0 & \beta_1 & \beta_2 & \beta_3 & \beta_{11} & \beta_{22} & \beta_{33} & \beta_{12} & \beta_{13} & \beta_{23}
\end{array} \\
\left[\begin{array}{cccccccccc}
15 & 0 & 0 & 0 & 0 & 0 & 0 & 0 & 0 & 0 \\
 & 8+2\alpha^2 & 0 & 0 & 0 & 0 & 0 & 0 & 0 & 0 \\
 & & 8+2\alpha^2 & 0 & 0 & 0 & 0 & 0 & 0 & 0 \\
 & & & 8+2\alpha^2 & 0 & 0 & 0 & 0 & 0 & 0 \\
 & & & & p & q & q & 0 & 0 & 0 \\
 & & & & & p & q & 0 & 0 & 0 \\
 & & & & & & p & 0 & 0 & 0 \\
 & & & & & & & 8 & 0 & 0 \\
 & & & & & & & & 8 & 0 \\
\text{sym} & & & & & & & & & 8
\end{array}\right]
\end{array}.$$

$$(7.3)$$

In general $X'X$ will take the form of Eq. 7.3, with the (1, 1) element being $N = F + T$ and the diagonal elements, which correspond to the first order coefficients, being $F + 2\alpha^2$. The diagonal elements corresponding to the mixed quadratic coefficients are, in general, all equal to F. The $k \times k$ symmetric matrix corresponding to the pure quadratic coefficients will generally have diagonal elements

$$p = \frac{FT - 4F\alpha^2 - 4\alpha^4 + 2(F + T)\alpha^4}{F + T}.$$ (7.4)

All off-diagonal elements are given by

$$q = \frac{FT - 4F\alpha^2 - 4\alpha^4}{F + T}.$$ (7.5)

The off-diagonal elements of the corresponding $(X'X)^{-1}$ will, in general, be zero except those corresponding to the *pure quadratic* coefficients. The latter can be made diagonal for a particular choice of α, resulting in a design which is orthogonal. The inverse of the matrix

$$\begin{bmatrix} p & q & q & \cdots & q \\ & p & q & \cdots & q \\ & & & \cdots & \cdots \\ & & & & p \end{bmatrix}$$

can be shown to be

$$\begin{bmatrix} e & f & f & \cdots & f \\ & e & f & \cdots & f \\ & & & \cdots & \cdots \\ & & & & e \end{bmatrix}$$

where

$$e = [p + (k - 2)q]/[(p - q)(p + kq - q)]$$

$$f = \frac{q}{[q - p][p + (k - 1)q]}.$$

The elements of $(X'X)^{-1}$ and thus the variances and covariances of the coefficients in the second order response model when a central composite design is used can now be noted.

$$\text{var } b' = \sigma^2/N$$ (7.6)

$$\text{var } (b_i) = \sigma^2/[F + 2\alpha^2] \quad (i = 1, 2, \ldots, k)$$ (7.7)

$$\text{var } (b_{ij}) = \sigma^2/F \quad (i = j)$$ (7.8)

$$\text{var } (b_{ii}) = \sigma^2 e$$ (7.9)

$$\text{cov } (b_{ii}, b_{jj}) = \sigma^2 f \quad (i = j)$$ (7.10)

where $F + T = N$. All other covariances are zero. Since the constant α appears in Eqs. 7.7, 7.9, and 7.10, it becomes apparent that the choice of α, which governs the location of the axial points, is very important.

Examples. Two examples of the use of a central composite design are given on page 78. In the first example, a second order model was fitted with $k = 3$. The design matrix is given in Eq. 5.14 with $\alpha = 1.682$ and multiple center points. For the second example, the design matrix is given by Eq. 5.17 and $\alpha = 1.4$.

As a third example, data are presented from an experiment designed for estimating optimum conditions for storing bovine semen to retain maximum survival. The variables under study are the % sodium citrate (ξ_1), % glycerol (ξ_2), and the equilibration time in hours (ξ_3). The important response measured was % survival of motile spermatozoa (y). Table 7.1 gives the experimental data for a three-dimensional central composite design with $\alpha = 2.0$.

Table 7.1. Treatment Combinations and % Survival[a]

Treatment Combination	% Sodium Citrate	% Glycerol	Equilibration Time, hr	% Survival
1	-1	-1	-1	57
2	1	-1	-1	40
3	-1	1	-1	19
4	1	1	-1	40
5	-1	-1	1	54
6	1	-1	1	41
7	-1	1	1	21
8	1	1	1	43
9	0	0	0	63
10	-2	0	0	28
11	2	0	0	11
12	0	-2	0	2
13	0	2	0	18
14	0	0	-2	56
15	0	0	2	46

[a]Responses are averages of eight measurements.

SOURCE: R. G. Cragle, R. M. Myers, R. K. Waugh, J. S. Hunter, and R. L. Anderson, "The Effects of Various Levels of Sodium Citrate, Glycerol, and Equilibrium Time on Survival of Bovine Spermatozoa after Storage at —79°C," *J. Dairy Sci.* **38** (5), 508 (1955).

The coded factor levels are given by

	−2	−1	0	1	2
ξ_1	1.6	2.3	3.0	3.7	4.4
ξ_2	2.0	5.0	8.0	11.0	14.0
ξ_3	4.0	10.0	16.0	22.0	28.0

The response function was estimated by the usual techniques and found to be

$$\hat{y} = 66.3889 - 1.4400x_1 - 2.2812x_2 - 1.0950x_3 - 11.3561x_1^2$$
$$- 13.6798x_2^2 - 3.4972x_3^2 + 9.1000x_1x_2 + 0.6075x_1x_3 + 0.8125x_2x_3$$

in terms of the coded independent variables. The stationary point was found by the techniques outlined in Chapter 5. The result is given by

$$x_{1,0} = -0.1198; \quad x_{2,0} = -0.1286; \quad x_{3,0} = -0.1819.$$

These values correspond to the uncoded x levels of 2.9% sodium citrate, 7.6% glycerol, and 14.9 hours equilibration time. The estimated response at the stationary point is $\hat{y}_0 = 66.72\%$ survival. The response surface was reduced to canonical form in order that the nature of the stationary point could be determined. As before, methods outlined in Chapter 5 apply. The λ values for the canonical form are

$$\lambda_1 = -3.4414; \quad \lambda_2 = -7.8765; \quad \lambda_3 = -17.2153,$$

indicating that the stationary point represents an estimate of the factor combinations where maximum % survival, the conditions sought by the experimenter, is obtained. The transformation indicating the relationship between the x's and the canonical variables, the w's, is given by

$$\begin{bmatrix} w_1 \\ w_2 \\ w_3 \end{bmatrix} = \begin{bmatrix} 0.81678 & 0.07572 & 0.99378 \\ 0.78586 & 0.60839 & -0.11084 \\ 0.61298 & -0.79003 & 0.01006 \end{bmatrix} \begin{bmatrix} x_1 + 0.1198 \\ x_2 + 0.1286 \\ x_3 + 0.1819 \end{bmatrix}.$$

orthogonal central composite design

The central composite design, in affording a rival for the 3^k-factorial, provides a certain flexibility for the experimenter. He has various possibilities for the choice of α, depending on what property he desires and can obtain in the design. The first choice to be discussed and illustrated here is that for which the design is orthogonal. The orthogonal ccd will, of course, have an $X'X$ which is diagonal, providing an ease in computations and uncorrelated estimates of the response model coefficients. In order to find the appropriate value of α, q in Eq. 7.5 must be made zero. The solution to

$$q = FT - 4F\alpha^2 - 4\alpha^4 = 0$$

is given by

$$\alpha = \left(\frac{QF}{4}\right)^{1/4} \tag{7.11}$$

where

$$Q = [(F + T)^{1/2} - F^{1/2}]^2. \tag{7.12}$$

Thus by using values of α given by Eq. 7.11, the ccd can be made to be orthogonal. Table 7.2 shows the values of α for various k which makes the ccd orthogonal, if a full 2^k factorial is used with a *single center point*.

Table 7.2. Values of α for an Orthogonal Central Composite Design

k	α
2	1.000
3	1.216
4	1.414
5	1.596
6	1.761
7	1.910
8	2.045

Note that for $k = 2$, $\alpha = 1$ and thus the orthogonal ccd is the 3^2 factorial design.

As we implied previously in this section, there are important choices of α to consider, other than the value which makes the design orthogonal. In many cases, these other choices are more desirable than the orthogonal ccd. In the following sections of this chapter, other important properties for second order designs will be discussed, with the central composite design continually being projected into the development.

7.2 | methods of comparing second order designs

The central composite design can be systematically compared with the 3^k factorial design (or any other design for fitting a second order surface) on the basis of *efficiency*, that is, efficiency in estimating particular coefficients in the response model. The efficiency criterion was developed to simultaneously take into consideration the precision with which the coefficient is estimated and the number of experimental trials required; for example, suppose it is of interest to consider a comparison between design 1 and design 2 with respect to estimating the mixed quadratic coefficient b_{ij}. Call N_1 the number of observations required for design 1 and N_2 for design 2. Then the efficiency of design 1 with respect to design 2 is given by

$$E = \frac{(\text{var } b_{ij} \text{ for design 2})N_2}{(\text{var } b_{ij} \text{ for design 1})N_1} . \tag{7.13}$$

The ratio N_2/N_1 is inserted to account for the relative cost in conducting the experiment. We shall discuss for purposes of illustration a comparison of the orthogonal ccd with, for example, the 3^k factorial design. Suppose we write the design matrix as

$$D = \begin{bmatrix} x_{11} & x_{21} & \cdots & x_{k1} \\ x_{12} & x_{22} & \cdots & x_{k2} \\ \cdots & \cdots & \cdots & \cdots \\ x_{1,N} & x_{2,N} & \cdots & x_{k,N} \end{bmatrix} . \tag{7.14}$$

For the 3^k factorial, using the usual $-1, 0, +1$ coding scheme,

$$\sum_{u=1}^{N} x_{iu} = 0, \quad \sum_{u=1}^{N} x_{iu}^2/N = 2/3 \quad (i = 1, 2, \ldots, k). \tag{7.15}$$

For the orthogonal ccd,

$$\sum_{u=1}^{N} x_{iu} = 0, \quad \sum_{u=1}^{N} x_{iu}^2/N = [F/(F + T)]^{1/2} \quad (i = 1, 2, \ldots, k). \tag{7.16}$$

Equation 7.16 can be easily verified by substituting the value of α of Eq. 7.11 into the equation

$$\sum_{u=1}^{N} x_{iu}^2/N = (F + 2\alpha^2)/(F + T),$$

which is an expression that holds for the general ccd.

In order that the two designs can be compared on the basis of efficiency, or any criterion involving the precision of the estimates of the model coefficients, the designs must be scaled so that the spread in the two designs are equal, the measure of spread being $\sum_u x_{iu}^2/N$, the *pure second moment* of the design. Otherwise, a fair comparison cannot be made. Ordinarily, for convenience in presenting theoretical aspects of these response surface designs, we use the scaling convention given by Eq. 6.2. This convention will be used throughout the balance of the material in this chapter. Suppose now one wishes to compare the 3^3 factorial design with the orthogonal $k = 3$ ccd, with respect to the mixed quadratic coefficient b_{ij} $(i \neq j)$. Prior to applying the scaling convention, var $(b_{ij}) = \sigma^2/12$ for the 3^3 design and var $(b_{ij}) = \sigma^2/8$ for the orthogonal ccd. Scaling to the convention essentially involves multiplying each column in the design matrix of the 3^3 by $(3/2)^{1/2}$ and each column in the design matrix of the orthogonal ccd by $[(F + T)/F]^{1/4}$. Therefore, the variances *after scaling* become

$$(\sigma^2/12)(4/9) = \sigma^2/27$$

for the 3^3 design, and

$$(\sigma^2/8)(F/(F + T)) = (\sigma^2/8)(8/15)$$
$$= \sigma^2/15$$

for the orthogonal ccd. The efficiency of the orthogonal ccd with respect to the 3^3 is given by

$$E = \left(\frac{\sigma^2/27}{\sigma^2/15}\right)\left(\frac{27}{15}\right)$$

$$= 1.00,$$

implying that the orthogonal ccd is *as efficient* as the 3^3 factorial for estimating the mixed quadratic coefficients. Table 7.3 gives the efficiencies for estimating the mixed and pure quadratic coefficients for the orthogonal ccd with respect to the 3^k factorial for various k. The $k = 5$ and $k = 6$ values are for a central composite design in which the factorial portion is a 1/2 fraction of a 2^k. That is, for $k = 5$, $F = 16$ points are used as the factorial and the usual eleven axial points are applied. For $k = 6$, $F = 32$ and $T = 13$.

The results in Table 7.3 indicate that *on a per observation* basis, the orthogonal ccd is certainly no worse than the 3^k factorial from the efficiency standpoint. The reader should keep in mind that this displays a comparison

Table 7.3. Efficiencies of Orthogonal ccd With Respect to 3^k Factorial

	$k = 2$	$k = 3$	$k = 4$	$k = 5^a$	$k = 6^a$
b_{st}	1.00	1.00	1.00	1.00	1.00
b_{ss}	1.00	1.07	1.00	1.43	1.1062

[a]Denotes ccd containing 1/2 fraction of a 2^k plus appropriate axial points and center point.

between the 3^k and *only one type* of ccd—namely, the orthogonal ccd. The ccd will not always be as efficient for estimating particular coefficients. For example, suppose we consider Tables 7.4 and 7.5 which show the efficiencies of a ccd with respect to a 3^k with $\alpha = 1.5$ and 2.0, respectively.

Table 7.4. Efficiencies of ccd for $\alpha = 1.5$ With Respect to 3^k Factorial

	$k = 2$	$k = 3$	$k = 4$	$k = 5^a$
b_{st}	0.4983	0.7680	0.9518	1.028
b_{ss}	0.8561	1.0561	1.077	1.3483

^{a}1/2 fraction of 2^k plus axial points and center point make up the ccd.

Table 7.5. Efficiencies of ccd for $\alpha = 2.0$ With Respect to 3^k Factorial

	$k = 2$	$k = 3$	$k = 4$	$k = 5^a$
b_{st}	0.25	0.4688	0.6944	0.75
b_{ss}	1.60	1.2980	0.9800	1.50

^{a}1/2 fraction of 2^k plus axial points and center point.

Notice that in some cases the 3^k factorial clearly is more efficient for the estimation of mixed quadratic coefficients.

We have introduced in this section the concept of *design moments*. The second design moment, $\sum_{u=1}^{N} x_{iu}^2/N$, plays a very important role in regard to certain design properties that are discussed in later sections. As these properties are introduced, it will become apparent that design moments are instrumental in assessing the worth of a design.

The second criterion to be considered for comparing two designs for fitting second order models is the bias of the model coefficients in the presence of higher order terms, such as *cubic* terms. We shall use the comparison between the orthogonal ccd and the 3^k for purposes of illustration. For example, for $k = 2$, the two designs are equivalent, and the bias structure is found by using Eq. 6.10 with

$$\boldsymbol{\beta}_2 = \begin{bmatrix} \beta_{111} \\ \beta_{222} \\ \beta_{122} \\ \beta_{112} \end{bmatrix}$$

where β_{111} is the coefficient of x_1^3, β_{222} is the coefficient of x_2^3, β_{122} the coefficient of $x_1 x_2^2$, etc. The matrix X_1 is given by Eq. 3.32 and

$$
X_2 = \begin{array}{c}
\begin{array}{cccc}
\beta_{111} & \beta_{222} & \beta_{122} & \beta_{112}
\end{array} \\
\left[\begin{array}{cccc}
-1 & -1 & -1 & -1 \\
-1 & 0 & 0 & 0 \\
-1 & 1 & -1 & 1 \\
0 & -1 & 0 & 0 \\
0 & 0 & 0 & 0 \\
0 & 1 & 0 & 0 \\
1 & -1 & 1 & -1 \\
1 & 0 & 0 & 0 \\
1 & 1 & 1 & 1
\end{array}\right]
\end{array}.
$$

Here, we are considering the model with the constant term β_0, that is with the x_i^2 ($i = 1, 2$) *not* corrected for their mean.

$$
(X_1'X_1)^{-1} = \begin{bmatrix}
9 & 0 & 0 & 6 & 6 & 0 \\
 & 6 & 0 & 0 & 0 & 0 \\
 & & 6 & 0 & 0 & 0 \\
 & & & 6 & 4 & 0 \\
 & & & & 6 & 0 \\
 & & & & & 4
\end{bmatrix}^{-1}
$$

$$
= \begin{bmatrix}
5/9 & 0 & 0 & -1/3 & -1/3 & 0 \\
 & 1/6 & 0 & 0 & 0 & 0 \\
 & & 1/6 & 0 & 0 & 0 \\
 & & & 1/2 & 0 & 0 \\
 & & & & 1/2 & 0 \\
 & & & & & 1/4
\end{bmatrix}
$$

After constructing the alias matrix $A = (X_1'X_1)^{-1}X_1'X_2$, we find that

$$
\begin{aligned}
E(b_0) &= \beta_0 \\
E(b_1) &= \beta_1 + \beta_{111} + (2/3)\beta_{122} \\
E(b_2) &= \beta_2 + \beta_{222} + (2/3)\beta_{112} \\
E(b_{11}) &= \beta_{11} \\
E(b_{22}) &= \beta_{22} \\
E(b_{12}) &= \beta_{12}
\end{aligned}
$$

The first order coefficients are biased by certain cubic coefficients, but the constant term b_0 and the quadratic coefficients are unbiased.

Suppose now we compare the 3^3 factorial with the $k = 3$ orthogonal ccd ($\alpha = 1.215$), from the standpoint of bias in the presence of third order coefficients. As in the case of the comparison using the efficiency criterion, the designs must be scaled in order that the second moments are equal. The biases are then computed in the usual way, with the X_2 matrix containing elements which account for the terms x_i^3, $x_i^2 \cdot x_j$ $(i \neq j)$, and $x_i x_j x_k$ $(i \neq j \neq k)$. The results obtained from this computation, for the orthogonal ccd, are given by

$$E(b_0) = \beta_0$$
$$E(b_i) = \beta_i + 1.03\beta_{iii} + 2/3 \sum_{j \neq i} \beta_{ijj} \qquad (i = 1, 2, 3),$$

with the second order coefficients being unbiased. For the 3^3 factorial

$$E(b_0) = \beta_0$$
$$E(b_i) = \beta_i + \beta_{iii} + 2/3 \sum_{j \neq i} \beta_{ijj} \qquad (i = 1, 2, 3),$$

with the second order coefficients being unbiased. As one can see, for this case, there is very little difference between the designs as far as bias is concerned. These results should not be taken as an indication of any general comparison between the 3^k and the ccd; rather they illustrate only a comparison between the 3^3 and the *orthogonal* $k = 3$ ccd.

7.3 | rotatable second order experimental designs

An interesting and important property in the study of response surface designs is that of *rotatability*. The concept of rotatability is not restricted to second order designs, but much of the work pertaining to the subject has emphasized the fitting of the second order model. A design is said to be rotatable when the variance of the estimated response—that is, the variance of $\hat{y}$, which of course depends on a point of interest $x_1, x_2, \ldots, x_k$—is a function only of the *distance* from the center of the design and *not* on the direction. In other words, a rotatable design is one for which the quality of the estimator $\hat{y}$ is the same for two points that are the same distance from the design center. As an illustration, suppose one fits a second order model in two independent variables, where the x's are coded as usual so that the design center is at the point $(0, 0)$. (See Fig. 7.2.)

Suppose we consider in the figure the points labeled 1 and 2, which are equidistant from the design center. Of course, the experimenter does not know, before the experiment is run, where the center of the contour system will be or what will be the orientation of the system. Thus, it would be

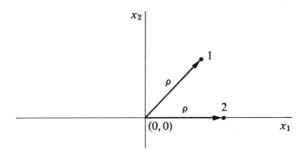

Fig. 7.2. Two-dimensional system with design center at (0, 0).

presumed that, as far as the response estimate is concerned, the two points are equally important. However, if there is a considerable difference between the two points as far as precision of $\hat{y}$ is concerned, a certain "imbalance" exists in the use of the surface for estimating the response. For a response function fit by a rotatable design, var $\hat{y}$ will be the same for any two points $(x_1, x_2, \ldots, x_k)_1$ and $(x_1, x_2, \ldots, x_k)_2$ which are the same distance from the design center.

In order that the reader be able to recognize or develop rotatable designs, it becomes necessary to make certain fundamental definitions. These definitions, given in the following section, apply quite generally—for response surface designs of any order. However, in succeeding sections, this basic material is used to establish more specifically the class of rotatable designs of second order.

moment matrix and precision matrix

There are certain parameters that aid in establishing the properties of a response surface experimental design. Among these are the design moments. The matrix which contains the design moments is called the *moment matrix* of the design and is given by $N^{-1}X'X$, where N is the total number of runs specified by the design. For example, for a response model of *first order*, it can easily be seen that

$$
N^{-1}X'X = \begin{bmatrix}
1 & [1] & [2] & [3] & \cdots & [k] \\
  & [11] & [12] & [13] & \cdots & [1k] \\
  &   & [22] & [23] & \cdots & [2k] \\
  &   &   &   & \cdots & \cdots \\
\text{sym} & & & & & [kk]
\end{bmatrix}
\begin{matrix} x_1 & x_2 & x_3 & \cdots & x_k \end{matrix}
$$

where

$$[ij] = \frac{1}{N} \sum_{u=1}^{N} x_{iu} x_{ju}$$

$$[i] = \frac{1}{N} \sum_{u=1}^{N} x_{iu}.$$

The elements in the above matrix are easily verified by observing the sums of squares and products in the $X'X$ matrix for a first order design. It is important that the reader clearly understand the square bracket notation. Moments of the form $[i]$ are called moments of first order, or merely *first moments*; $[ii]$ and $[ij]$ are called *second moments*. If one uses the usual scaling convention on the independent variables, namely that $\sum_{u=1}^{N} x_{iu} = 0$ and $\sum_{u=1}^{N} x_{iu}^2 = N$, the moment matrix in Eq. 7.17 is given by

$$N^{-1}X'X = \begin{array}{cccccc} & x_1 & x_2 & \cdots & x_k & \\ \begin{bmatrix} 1 & 0 & 0 & \cdots & 0 \\ & 1 & [12] & \cdots & [1k] \\ & & 1 & \cdots & [2k] \\ & & & \cdots & \\ & & & & [k-1,k] \\ & & & & 1 \end{bmatrix} \end{array}. \qquad (7.18)$$

Of course, the spacing of the design points governs the magnitude of these moments.

In the case of the second order model, the matrix $N^{-1}X'X$ will contain moments through order *four*. Using the scaling convention, we write for purposes of illustration the moment matrix for two variables:

$$N^{-1}X'X = \begin{array}{ccccccc} & x_1 & x_2 & x_1^2 & x_2^2 & x_1 x_2 \\ \begin{bmatrix} 1 & 0 & 0 & 1 & 1 & [12] \\ & 1 & [12] & [111] & [122] & [112] \\ & & 1 & [112] & [222] & [122] \\ & & & [1111] & [1122] & [1112] \\ & & & & [2222] & [1222] \\ & & & & & [1122] \end{bmatrix} \end{array}. \qquad (7.19)$$

For example,

$$[1111] = \frac{1}{N} \sum_{u=1}^{N} x_{1u}^4, \quad [1122] = \frac{1}{N} \sum_{u=1}^{N} x_{1u}^2 x_{2u}^2,$$

$$[1112] = \frac{1}{N} \sum_{u=1}^{N} x_{1u}^3 x_{2u}, \text{ etc.}$$

The *inverse* $N(X'X)^{-1}$ of the moment matrix contains elements which are related to the variances and the covariances of the model coefficients and is called the *precision matrix* of the design. For example, for the moment matrix of Eq. 7.19, the diagonal elements of the precision matrix are (in order) $N \operatorname{var} b_0/\sigma^2$, $N \operatorname{var} b_1/\sigma^2$, $N \operatorname{var} b_2/\sigma^2$, $N \operatorname{var} b_{11}/\sigma^2$, $N \operatorname{var} b_{22}/\sigma^2$, and $N \operatorname{var} b_{12}/\sigma^2$. In fact, these diagonal elements of the precision matrix are the quantities used to measure design efficiencies, discussed in Section 7.2. The elements off the diagonal in the precision matrix are covariances, weighted by N/σ^2.

general form of moment matrix for rotatable designs

In the case of an experimental design for fitting a response surface of order d in k variables, the design moment of order δ is to be referred to in the following way:

$$\frac{1}{N} \sum_{u=1}^{N} x_{1u}^{\delta_1} x_{2u}^{\delta_2}, \dots, x_{ku}^{\delta_k}$$

where $\delta_1 + \delta_2 + \dots + \delta_k = \delta$. For example, for $k = 3$, the fourth moment $[1233] = N^{-1} \sum_{u=1}^{N} x_{1u} x_{2u} x_{3u}^2$ would have $\delta_1 = 1$, $\delta_2 = 1$, and $\delta_3 = 2$. Whether or not a design is rotatable is determined by the form of the moments of order through $2d$. In fact, a necessary and sufficient condition that a design be rotatable is that the moment of order δ ($\delta = 1, \dots, 2d$) be of the form

$$N^{-1} \sum_{u=1}^{N} x_{1u}^{\delta_1} x_{2u}^{\delta_2}, \dots, x_{ku}^{\delta_k} = \frac{\lambda_\delta \prod_{i=1}^{k} (\delta_i)!}{2^{\delta/2} \prod_{i=1}^{k} (\delta_i/2)!} \tag{7.20}$$

for all δ_i even, and

$$N^{-1} \sum_{u=1}^{N} x_{1u}^{\delta_1} x_{2u}^{\delta_2}, \dots, x_{ku}^{\delta_k} = 0 \tag{7.21}$$

if any δ_i is odd. Here λ_δ is some quantity which is a function of δ, and $\prod_{i=1}^{k}$ represents product notation. The derivation of the expressions in Eqs. 7.20 and 7.21 is quite lengthy and is shown in Appendix A.

Suppose we consider now, the form that the moments take for a rotatable design in the case of the simplest type of response surface, namely the first order model. The moment matrix is given in Eq. 7.18. All off-diagonal elements of this matrix will be of the form $[i]$ or $[ij]$ with $i \neq j$ and thus the δ_i are either zero or unity. Therefore, from Eq. 7.21 for the design to be rotatable, the moments on the off-diagonal are zero; in other words the moment matrix is *diagonal*. For the diagonal elements $[11]$, $[22]$, etc., using Eq. 7.20, $[ii] = \lambda_2$. When we apply the usual scaling convention that $\sum_{u=1}^{N} x_{iu}^2 = N$, these pure second moments $\sum_{u=1}^{N} x_{iu}^2/N$ are automatically unity. So for a first order model, a rotatable design is one for which

$$N^{-1}X'X = \begin{bmatrix} 1 & 0 & 0 & \cdots & 0 \\ & 1 & 0 & \cdots & 0 \\ & & 1 & \cdots & 0 \\ & & & \cdots & \cdots \\ & & & & 1 \end{bmatrix}. \qquad (7.22)$$

The reader will recognize Eq. 7.22 as the moment matrix for an *orthogonal* first order design. In other words an orthogonal design, such as a 2^k factorial design, certain fractions of 2^k factorial, or simplex is likewise a *rotatable* design. It must be emphasized that the synonymity between the orthogonal design and the rotatable design applies for the first order response model but *not in general*. It is quite easy to show in another fashion that a first order orthogonal design is rotatable; for suppose one writes

$$\text{var } \hat{y} = \text{var } [b_0 + b_1x_1 + \cdots + b_kx_k], \qquad (7.23)$$

where $(x_1, x_2, \ldots, x_k)$ is a point of interest in the region of the factors. If the design is orthogonal, Eq. 7.23 can be written

$$\text{var } \hat{y} = \frac{\sigma^2}{N}[1 + x_1^2 + x_2^2 + \cdots + x_k^2],$$

since an orthogonal design implies that the covariances among the model coefficient estimates are zero, and of course,

$$\text{var } b_0 = \text{var } (b_i) = \sigma^2/N.$$

Thus

$$\text{var } \hat{y} = \sigma^2[1 + \rho^2]/N \qquad (7.24)$$

where $\rho = (\sum_{i=1}^{k} x_i^2)^{1/2}$ is the distance from the design center $(0, 0, \ldots, 0)$ to the point of interest $(x_1, x_2, \ldots, x_k)$. The variance of the response estimate is directly a function of ρ, and thus $\hat{y}$ will be estimated with equal precision at two points which are the same distance from the center, the variance of the predictor $\hat{y}$ being independent of direction. Figure 7.3 shows the plot of *concentric circles* of constant $N \text{ var } \hat{y}/\sigma^2$ in the space of x_1, x_2 for a first order orthogonal (and thus rotatable) design. Notice that the *precision is greatest at* $(0, 0)$ and becomes smaller as one considers points further away from the center.

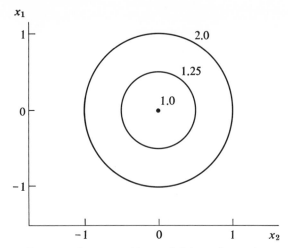

Fig. 7.3. Contour of constant N var $\hat{y}/\sigma^2$ for a first order rotatable design for $k = 2$.

form of moment matrix for second order rotatable design

By making use of Eqs. 7.20 and 7.21, we can write the form of the moments for a second order rotatable design as follows:

$$
N^{-1}X'X =
\begin{array}{c}
\\
x_1 \\
x_2 \\
\cdots \\
x_k \\
\\
x_1^2 \\
x_2^2 \\
\cdots \\
x_{k-1}^2 \\
x_k^2 \\
\\
x_1 x_2 \\
x_1 x_3 \\
\cdots \\
x_{k-1} x_k
\end{array}
\left[
\begin{array}{c|c|c}
 & \begin{array}{ccccc} 1 & 1 & \cdots & 1 & 1 \\ 0 & 0 & \cdots & 0 & 0 \\ 0 & 0 & \cdots & 0 & 0 \\ \cdots & \cdots & \cdots & \cdots & \cdots \\ 0 & 0 & \cdots & 0 & 0 \end{array} & \\
I_{k+1} & & 0 \\
\hline
\begin{array}{ccccc} 1 & 0 & 0 & \cdots & 0 \\ 1 & 0 & 0 & \cdots & 0 \\ \cdots & \cdots & \cdots & \cdots & \cdots \\ 1 & 0 & 0 & \cdots & 0 \\ 1 & 0 & 0 & \cdots & 0 \end{array} & G & 0 \\
\hline
0 & 0 & \lambda_4 I_{\binom{k}{2}}
\end{array}
\right]
$$

$$x_1, x_2, \ldots, x_k \qquad x_1^2\, x_2^2, \ldots, x_{k-1}^2\, x_k^2 \qquad x_1 x_2, x_1 x_3, \ldots, x_{k-1} x_k$$

(7.25)

where the G matrix, containing the moments $[iiii]$ and $[iijj]$ for $i \neq j$ has the value $3\lambda_4$ for all diagonal elements and λ_4 for all off-diagonal elements. The pure second moments are once again unity by the scaling convention. It is important to note the following from Eq. 7.25:

1. All moments that have at least one δ_i odd are zero
2. Pure fourth moments—$[iiii]$—are *three times* the mixed fourth moments.

$$\sum_{u=1}^{N} x_{iu}^4 = 3 \sum_{u=1}^{N} x_{iu}^2 x_{ju}^2 . \qquad (7.26)$$

Therefore, a second order design with moments which have the conditions given by (1) and (2) is a rotatable design.

. As an example of a design which meets the moment conditions for rotatability, consider a central composite design in two variables with $\alpha = \sqrt{2}$.

$$D = \begin{bmatrix} x_1 & x_2 \\ -1 & -1 \\ -1 & +1 \\ +1 & -1 \\ +1 & +1 \\ 0 & 0 \\ \sqrt{2} & 0 \\ -\sqrt{2} & 0 \\ 0 & \sqrt{2} \\ 0 & -\sqrt{2} \end{bmatrix}.$$

Note that the moments $[i]$, $[ij]$, $[iij]$, $[iii]$, and $[iiij]$ are all zero. In the order that the moment matrix take on the form of Eq. 7.25, the design must be scaled to the usual convention. However, rotatability is insured with the verification of conditions (1) and (2) above. Condition (1) obviously holds; note that $\sum x_{iu}^4 = 12$ and $\sum x_{iu}^2 x_{ju}^2 = 4$ and thus condition (2) also holds.

From Eq. 7.25 one can see a certain amount of flexibility in the choosing of rotatable designs for use. That is, there remains the freedom of choosing λ_4. This means that we can choose from a *class* of rotatable designs, one with a desirable λ_4 parameter, depending on some other criterion. In succeeding sections, various second order rotatable designs will be constructed and illustrated including the rotatable central composite design. However, one should first obtain some insight on how changes in the value of λ_4, the mixed fourth moment $[iijj]$, affects the properties of the fitted response surface for a rotatable design.

Suppose we consider the precision of $\hat{y}$, or more specifically $N \operatorname{var} \hat{y}/\sigma^2$, a quantity that will be constant on spheres of radius $\rho = (\sum_{i=1}^{k} x_i^2)^{\frac{1}{2}}$. We can write

$$N \operatorname{var} \hat{y}/\sigma^2 = \frac{N}{\sigma^2} \left[\operatorname{var} \left(b_0 + \sum_i b_i x_i + \sum_i b_{ii} x_i^2 + \sum_i \sum_j b_{ij} x_i x_j \right) \right] \quad (7.27)$$
$$\phantom{N \operatorname{var} \hat{y}/\sigma^2 = \frac{N}{\sigma^2} [} {}_{i<j}$$

where $x_1, x_2, \ldots, x_k$ is the point of interest. Equation 7.27 can be seen to be equivalent to

$$N \operatorname{var} \hat{y}/\sigma^2 = \frac{N}{\sigma^2} \left[\operatorname{var} b_0 + \sum_i x_i^2 \operatorname{var} b_i + \sum_i x_i^4 \operatorname{var} b_{ii} \right.$$

$$+ \sum_i \sum_{\substack{j \\ i<j}} x_i^2 x_j^2 \operatorname{var} b_{ij} + 2 \sum_i x_i^2 \operatorname{cov}(b_0, b_{ii})$$

$$\left. + 2 \sum_i \sum_{\substack{j \\ i<j}} x_i^2 x_j^2 \operatorname{cov}(b_{ii}, b_{jj}) \right]. \quad (7.28)$$

Before the expression in Eq. 7.28 can be written as a function of λ_4, expressions for the variances and covariances of the coefficients need to be developed. If one inverts the moment matrix given in Eq. 7.25, the following elements of the precision matrix $N(X'X)^{-1}$ are obtained:

$$N \operatorname{var} b_0/\sigma^2 = 2\lambda_4^2(k+2)A \quad (7.29)$$

where $A = \{2\lambda_4[(k+2)\lambda_4 - k]\}^{-1}$

$$N \operatorname{var}(b_i)/\sigma^2 = 1 \quad (7.30)$$

$$N \operatorname{var} b_{ii}/\sigma^2 = [(k+1)\lambda_4 - (k-1)] \cdot A \quad (7.31)$$

$$N \operatorname{var} b_{ij}/\sigma^2 = 1/\lambda_4 \quad (i \neq j) \quad (7.32)$$

$$N \operatorname{cov}(b_0, b_{ii})/\sigma^2 = 2\lambda_4 \cdot A \quad (7.33)$$

$$N \operatorname{cov}(b_{ii}, b_{jj})/\sigma^2 = (1 - \lambda_4) \cdot A \quad (i \neq j). \quad (7.34)$$

All of the other elements of the inverse matrix are zero. A very important point to note here is that, if the quantity $2\lambda_4[(k+2)\lambda_4 - k]$ is zero, then certain of the variances and covariances are infinite. This can be attributed to the determinant of $X'X$ being zero, thus yielding a useless experimental design. This will occur when $\lambda_4 = k/(k+2)$.

The results of Eqs. 7.29 through 7.34 can be used to relate N var $\hat{y}/\sigma^2$ to λ_4. Equation 7.28 can now be written

$$N \text{ var } \hat{y}/\sigma^2 = A[2\lambda_4^2(k+2) + \rho^2(1/A) + 2\rho^2(-2\lambda_4)]$$
$$+ \frac{N}{\sigma^2}\left[\sum_i x_i^4 \text{ var } (b_{ii}) + \sum_i \sum_{\substack{j \\ i<j}} x_i^2 x_j^2 \text{ var } (b_{ij})\right.$$
$$\left. + 2 \sum_i \sum_{\substack{j \\ i<j}} x_i^2 x_j^2 \text{ cov } (b_{ii}, b_{jj})\right]. \qquad (7.35)$$

From Eqs. 7.31, 7.32, and 7.34, we can write

$$\frac{N}{\sigma^2} \text{ cov } (b_{ii}, b_{jj}) + N/(2\sigma^2) \text{ var } (b_{ij}) = \frac{N}{\sigma^2} \text{ var } (b_{ii}). \qquad (7.36)$$

Equation 7.35 can be written

$$N \text{ var } \hat{y}/\sigma^2 = A\{2\lambda_4^2(k+2) + 2\rho^2\lambda_4(\lambda_4 - 1)(k+2)\}$$
$$+ \frac{N}{\sigma^2}\left[\sum_i x_i^4 \text{ var } (b_{ii}) + 2\sum_i \sum_{\substack{j \\ i<j}} x_i^2 x_j^2\right.$$
$$\left. \times \left[\text{cov } (b_{ii}, b_{jj}) + \tfrac{1}{2} \text{ var } b_{ij}\right]\right].$$

Since

$$\rho^4 = \sum_i x_i^4 + 2\sum_i \sum_{\substack{j \\ i<j}} x_i^2 x_j^2,$$

we have from Eq. 7.36

$$N \text{ var } \hat{y}/\sigma^2 = A\{2\lambda_4^2(k+2) + 2\rho^2\lambda_4(\lambda_4 - 1)(k+2)$$
$$+ \rho^4[(k+1)\lambda_4 - (k-1)]\} \qquad (7.37)$$

Therefore, for a design which is second order rotatable, it can be seen from Eq. 7.37 that the variance of an estimated response at some point $(x_1, x_2, \ldots, x_k)$ is a function only of ρ, the distance from the point to the center, k, and λ_4, the mixed fourth moment. It would seem reasonable, then, that one should be able to make use of this expression to select from the class of rotatable second order designs those that give desirable values of λ_4.

choice of λ_4 for second order rotatable designs

For purposes of graphical illustration, we have constructed Figs. 7.4 and 7.5 to show the role that λ_4 plays in connection with the quantity N var $\hat{y}/\sigma^2$.

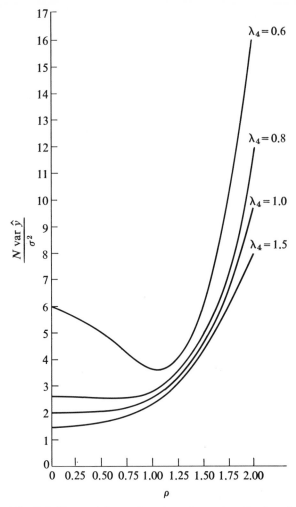

Fig. 7.4. N var $\hat{y}/\sigma^2$ as a function of ρ and λ_4 for $k = 2$.

It is indicated by these illustrations that larger values of λ_4 lead to good precision in the center of the design, whereas the precision drops off rapidly for $\rho > 1$. Before drawing any conclusions concerning "optimum choice" of λ_4, one should consider how this parameter effects the bias in the model coefficients in the presence of third order terms, that is, how coefficients of terms such as x_i^3, $x_i^2 x_j$ for $i \neq j$, etc. bias the coefficients in the fitted response surface in the case of a second order rotatable design. These biases are given, without derivation, in Appendix a (Section a.2). The bias expressions indicate that the first order coefficients may be heavily biased for large values of λ_4.

Box and Hunter have suggested as a possible choice of λ_4 that value for which the precision on $\hat{y}$, i.e. N var $\hat{y}/\sigma^2$, at the design center is equal to the precision at $\rho = 1$, resulting in a design which will be called a *uniform precision design*. The uniform precision design is based on the philosophy that in the region for which $\rho < 1$, there should be uniform importance as far as estimation of response is concerned, as opposed to, for example, a situation in which the variance is low in the center of the design but increases drastically as one moves away from the design center. Table 7.6 gives the value of λ_4 for various k which result in a uniform precision design.

Table 7.6 will be of value in constructing and discussing actual rotatable second order designs which are useful in practice, and in particular, certain

Table 7.6. Values of λ_4 for Second Order Rotatable Design Which Result in Uniform Precision

k	2	3	4	5	6	7	8	9
λ_4	0.7844	0.8385	0.8704	0.8918	0.9070	0.9184	0.9274	0.9346

SOURCE: G. E. P. Box and J. S. Hunter, "Multifactor Experimental Designs for Exploring Response Surfaces," *Ann. Math. Stat.* **28** (1), 195 (1957).

useful rotatable central composite designs which are discussed in the next section. It should be noted that the property of uniform precision is merely one choice of a second order rotatable design; certainly, there is no implication here that it would always be the best choice in all cases.

The reader might speculate at this stage about whether or not the experimenter can conveniently alter the parameter λ_4 for a second order rotatable design. For the designs that are used in practice, this can be done by beginning with the basic rotatable design and simply using additional experimental runs at the center of the design, the number of points added being dependent on the value of λ_4 which the experimenter desires. In general, by using these additional center points, the experimenter cannot expect to attain exactly the value of λ_4 needed for, e.g. a uniform precision design. A design which is near-uniform precision can be obtained by adding the number of center points which result in a λ_4 close to the appropriate value given in Table 7.6. Another interesting point regarding the choice of λ_4 is that by making $\lambda_4 = 1$, cov $(b_{ii}, b_{jj}) = 0$ (see Eq. 7.34) and thus the resulting design is orthogonal. It is possible in certain cases to construct designs for the second order response model which are both rotatable *and* orthogonal.

rotatable central composite designs

The second order rotatable response surface designs which find the most use in practical situations are the rotatable central composite designs. One can construct the rotatable central composite design by merely choosing the appropriate value for α, the quantity which specifies the axial points.

Consider now a portion of the X matrix for the ccd, namely, that portion containing $x_1^2, x_2^2, \ldots, x_k^2$.

$$
\begin{array}{cccccc}
 & x_1^2 & x_2^2 & x_3^2 & \cdots & x_k^2 \\
\text{factorial} & \left(\begin{array}{c} 1 \\ 1 \\ \cdots \\ 1 \end{array} \right. & \begin{array}{c} 1 \\ 1 \\ \cdots \\ 1 \end{array} & \begin{array}{c} 1 \\ 1 \\ \cdots \\ 1 \end{array} & \begin{array}{c} \cdots \\ \cdots \\ \cdots \\ \cdots \end{array} & \left. \begin{array}{c} 1 \\ 1 \\ \cdots \\ 1 \end{array} \right) \\
\text{portion} & & & & & \\
\end{array}
$$

$$
\begin{array}{cccccc}
\text{axial portion} & \left(\begin{array}{c} 0 \\ \alpha^2 \\ \alpha^2 \\ 0 \\ 0 \\ \cdots \\ 0 \\ 0 \end{array} \right. & \begin{array}{c} 0 \\ 0 \\ 0 \\ \alpha^2 \\ \alpha^2 \\ \cdots \\ 0 \\ 0 \end{array} & \begin{array}{c} 0 \\ 0 \\ 0 \\ 0 \\ 0 \\ \cdots \\ \cdots \\ \cdots \end{array} & \begin{array}{c} \cdots \\ \cdots \\ \cdots \\ \cdots \\ \cdots \\ \cdots \\ \cdots \\ \cdots \end{array} & \left. \begin{array}{c} 0 \\ 0 \\ 0 \\ 0 \\ 0 \\ \cdots \\ \alpha^2 \\ \alpha^2 \end{array} \right) \\
\end{array}
$$

It is easily seen that

$$
\sum_{u=1}^{N} x_{iu}^4 = F + 2\alpha^4
$$
$$(i = 1, 2, \ldots, k). \tag{7.38}$$
$$
\sum_{u=1}^{N} x_{iu}^2 x_{ju}^2 = F
$$

Of the two conditions given on page 145, which must be met in order that a second order design be rotatable, the first is automatically met, for it can be verified by merely observing the entire X matrix of the central composite design that

$$[ij] = 0 \quad (i \neq j)$$
$$[iii] = 0$$
$$[iij] = 0 \quad (i \neq j)$$
$$[ijk] = 0 \quad (i < j < k)$$
$$[iiij] = 0 \quad (i \neq j)$$
$$[iijk] = 0 \quad (i < j < k).$$

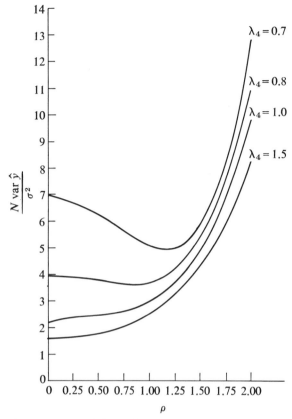

Fig. 7.5. N var $\hat{y}/\sigma^2$ as a function of ρ and λ_4 for $k = 3$.

Thus it only remains to find the value of α for which the second condition holds. From Eq. 7.38 and by equating $\sum_u x_{iu}^4$ to $3 \sum_u x_{iu}^2 x_{ju}^2$, we have

$$F + 2\alpha^4 = 3F.$$

So in order for a ccd to be rotatable

$$\alpha = (F)^{1/4}. \tag{7.39}$$

Table 7.7 gives the value for α for various k for the rotatable central composite design. Note that for $k = 5, 6, 7$, and 8, a central composite design is suggested in which a fractional factorial is used instead of a complete factorial. Also tabulated are F and T.

The designs that are considered in the table contain a single center point. This by no means implies that one would always use *only* one center point.

Table 7.7. Values of α for Rotatable Central Composite Design

k	F	T^a	N	α
2	4	5	9	1.414
3	8	7	15	1.682
4	16	9	25	2.000
5	32	11	43	2.378
5 ($\frac{1}{2}$ rep)	16	11	27	2.000
6	64	13	77	2.828
6 ($\frac{1}{2}$ rep)	32	13	45	2.378
7	128	15	143	3.364
7 ($\frac{1}{2}$ rep)	64	15	79	2.828
8	256	17	273	4.000
8 ($\frac{1}{2}$ rep)	128	17	145	3.364

^{a}Implies ccd with single center point; $T = 2k + 1$.

In fact, the parameter λ_4 for the rotatable ccd is conveniently altered to obtain uniform precision or near-uniform precision conditions by adding center points to the *basic rotatable ccd* given in the table. It becomes necessary, then, that a relationship be developed for the rotatable ccd which expresses λ_4 as a function of N, the total sample size, and F, the number of points in the factorial portion of the design. The λ_4 values in Table 7.6 depend on the scaling convention, therefore in determining λ_4 for the rotatable ccd one must consider the scaled design. Before scaling, $\sum_u x_{iu}^2 = F + 2\alpha^2$. Thus the design is scaled by the factor

$$g = \sqrt{\frac{N}{F + 2\alpha^2}}, \tag{7.40}$$

where, from Eq. 7.39, $\alpha = (F)^{\frac{1}{4}}$. The moment $[iiii]$ can now be written

$$[iiii] = (Fg^4 + 2\alpha^4 g^4)/N$$
$$= g^4(F + 2\alpha^4)/N$$
$$= g^4(3F)/N.$$

Substituting g from Eq. 7.40

$$[iiii] = 3NF/(F + 2\alpha^2)^2$$
$$= 3N/(F + 4F^{\frac{1}{2}} + 4)$$

For the design to be rotatable, $[iijj] = \lambda_4 = 1/3[iiii]$, then

$$\lambda_4 = N/(F + 4F^{\frac{1}{2}} + 4). \tag{7.41}$$

It can readily be seen that the addition of center points, while not affecting rotatability [conditions (1) and (2) on page 145 are not changed], increases the value of λ_4. For example, for $k = 2$, *no* center points yield a $\lambda_4 = 1/2$

which is equivalent to $k/(k + 2)$, resulting in a singular $X'X$. However, a total of five center points yields

$$\lambda_4 = 13/(4 + 8 + 4)$$
$$= 0.81$$

which is a near-uniform precision design. For the same case, a total of eight center points yields a λ_4 of 1.0, resulting in an orthogonal design. Table 7.8 outlines some useful rotatable central composite designs which are a result of using Eq. 7.41 to determine the number of center points necessary for an orthogonal design and uniform precision design. In some cases the condition is an approximate one—designs are given which are near-uniform precision or near-orthogonal. The value of λ_4 and the number of center points needed is given for each case. The notation n_2 stands for the number of center points and n_a the number of axial points. The value $T = n_a + n_2$.

Table 7.8. Uniform Precision and Orthogonal Rotatable Central Composite Designs

k	2	3	4	5	5 $\frac{1}{2}$ rep	6	6 $\frac{1}{2}$ rep	7 $\frac{1}{2}$ rep	8 $\frac{1}{2}$ rep
F	4	8	16	32	16	64	32	64	128
n_a	4	6	8	10	10	12	12	14	16
n_2 (up)	5	6	7	10	6	15	9	14	20
n_2 (orth)	8	9	12	17	10	24	15	22	33
N (up)	13	20	31	52	32	91	53	92	164
N (orth)	16	23	36	59	36	100	59	100	177
α	1.414	1.682	2.000	2.378	2.000	2.828	2.378	2.828	3.364
λ_4 (up)	0.81	0.86	0.86	0.89	0.89	0.91	0.90	0.92	0.93
λ_4 (orth)	1.00	0.99	1.00	1.01	1.00	1.00	1.01	1.00	0.998

SOURCE: G. E. P. Box and J. S. Hunter, "Multifactor Experimental Designs for Exploring Response Surfaces," *Ann. Math. Stat.* **28** (1), 195 (1957).

Example. In Chapter 5, page 78, an example was given of an extensive response surface analysis in which it was noted that the experimental design used was a central composite design. Notice that, in the example, $\alpha = 1.682$ and six center points were used, resulting in a near-uniform precision rotatable central composite design.

other types of rotatable second order designs

In this section, additional rotatable designs are considered. Although it is true that the rotatable central composite is probably the most often used of the class of rotatable designs, there are others which can be useful, particularly for cases where k is small.

EQUIRADIAL DESIGNS IN TWO VARIABLES

For the case of two independent variables, it is quite simple to construct useful designs, other than the ccd, which have the property of rotatability. Consider the situation where the experimenter places $n_1 \geq 5$ *equally spaced* points on a *circle* of radius ρ, augmented by n_2 center points. If the first design point makes an angle θ with the real axis, then the portion of the design matrix involving the points on a circle can be written

$$\overset{x_1}{\{\rho \cos [\theta + (2\pi u)/n_1],} \quad \overset{x_2}{\rho \sin [\theta + (2\pi u)/n_1]\}} \quad (u = 0, 1, 2, \ldots, n_1 - 1).$$

For example, consider an experimental design which consists of six equally spaced points on a circle—a *hexagon*, plus $n_2 = 2$ center points. The design matrix can be written

$$D = \begin{bmatrix} \rho \cos \theta & \rho \sin \theta \\ \rho \cos (\theta + \pi/3) & \rho \sin (\theta + \pi/3) \\ \rho \cos (\theta + 2\pi/3) & \rho \sin (\theta + 2\pi/3) \\ \rho \cos (\theta + \pi) & \rho \sin (\theta + \pi) \\ \rho \cos (\theta + 4\pi/3) & \rho \sin (\theta + 4\pi/3) \\ \rho \cos (\theta + 5\pi/3) & \rho \sin (\theta + 5\pi/3) \\ 0 & 0 \\ 0 & 0 \end{bmatrix}. \tag{7.42}$$

It is of interest now to investigate the elements of the moment matrix for such designs. The elements of $X'X$ are derived in Appendix a (Section a.3) and the results are as follows:

$$\sum_{u=0}^{n_1-1} x_{1u} = \sum_{u=0}^{n_1-1} x_{2u} = 0 \tag{7.43}$$

$$\sum_u x_{1u}x_{2u} = 0 \tag{7.44}$$

$$\sum_u x_{1u}^2 x_{2u} = \sum_u x_{1u} x_{2u}^2 = 0 \tag{7.45}$$

$$\sum_u x_{1u}^3 = \sum_u x_{2u}^3 = 0 \tag{7.46}$$

$$\sum_u x_{1u}^2 = \sum_u x_{2u}^2 = \rho^2 n_1/2 \tag{7.47}$$

$$\sum_u x_{1u}^4 = \sum_u x_{2u}^4 = 3\rho^4 n_1/8 \tag{7.48}$$

$$\sum_u x_{1u}^2 x_{2u}^2 = \rho^4 n_1/8 \tag{7.49}$$

$$\sum_u x_{1u}^3 x_{2u} = \sum_u x_{1u} x_{2u}^3 = 0. \tag{7.50}$$

From Eqs. 7.43 through 7.50, it can be observed that, in fact, conditions (1) and (2) on page 145 hold and thus the design is rotatable. It should be noted that at least five design points are needed on the circle of radius ρ, and *at least one* center point is needed. While the first requirement should be obvious to the reader at this point, perhaps the second should be clarified. Consider the key equations, Eqs. 7.47 through 7.49, in the case of a design *without* center points. In order that the moment matrix be consistent with the usual scaling convention, each design point must be multiplied by

$$g = \sqrt{2}/\rho.$$

This amounts to multiplying (before scaling) the term $\sum x_{1u}^2 x_{2u}^2 = \rho^4 n_1/8$ by $g^4 = 4/\rho^4$. Therefore,

$$\lambda_4 = [1122] = \sum x_{1u}^2 x_{2u}^2 / n_1$$
$$= 1/2$$

which results in a *singular* $X'X$. Adding center points will of course increase λ_4. In general, the value of λ_4 for the equiradial design is given by

$$\lambda_4 = \frac{n_2 + n_1}{2n_1}. \tag{7.51}$$

This can easily be derived by expressing $[1122]$ as a function of n_1 and n_2, after applying the appropriate scale factor. Equation 7.51 can be used to construct rotatable experimental designs for two variables that are, in fact, uniform precision designs or orthogonal designs; one starts with a set of $n_1 \geq 5$ equally spaced points and augments with n_2 center points, where n_2 is the value that makes λ_4 in Eq. 7.51 attain a value of 1.0 for the case of an orthogonal design and a value near 0.78 (Table 7.6) for a uniform precision design. For example, in the case of a hexagonal design, that is, $n_1 = 6$ points equally spaced on a circle, $n_2 = 6$ center points gives $\lambda_4 = 1.0$, resulting in a design which is both rotatable and orthogonal. Table 7.9 gives a guide to constructing equiradial designs for various values of n_1.

Table 7.9. Values of n_2 for Orthogonality and Uniform Precision for Equiradial Designs in Two Variables

n_1	5	6	7	8	9	10
n_2 (orth)	5	6	7	8	9	10
n_2 (up)	3	3	4	4	5	6
λ_4 (orth)	1.0	1.0	1.0	1.0	1.0	1.0
λ_4 (up)	0.8	0.75	0.786	0.75	0.778	0.80

As an example, consider the situation in which $n_1 = 6$. The near-uniform precision design consists of six equally spaced points on a circle with three points in the center of the circle. Figure 7.6 shows the geometric configuration when $\theta = 0$.

The design matrix for this experimental plan is given by

$$
D = \begin{array}{c c}
 & \begin{array}{c c} x_1 & x_2 \end{array} \\
\left[\begin{array}{c c}
1 & 0 \\
0.5 & \sqrt{0.75} \\
-0.5 & \sqrt{0.75} \\
-1 & 0 \\
-0.5 & -\sqrt{0.75} \\
0.5 & -\sqrt{0.75} \\
0 & 0 \\
0 & 0 \\
0 & 0
\end{array}\right] & \begin{array}{l}
\text{point 1} \\
\text{,,}\quad 2 \\
\text{,,}\quad 3 \\
\text{,,}\quad 4 \\
\text{,,}\quad 5. \\
\text{,,}\quad 6 \\
\text{,,}\quad 7 \\
\text{,,}\quad 8 \\
\text{,,}\quad 9
\end{array}
\end{array}
$$

The X matrix is given by

$$
X = \begin{array}{c}
\begin{array}{c c c c c} x_1 & x_2 & x_1^2 & x_2^2 & x_1 x_2 \end{array} \\
\left[\begin{array}{c c c c c c}
1 & 1 & 0 & 1 & 0 & 0 \\
1 & 0.5 & \sqrt{0.75} & 0.25 & 0.75 & \sqrt{0.75}/2 \\
1 & -0.5 & \sqrt{0.75} & 0.25 & 0.75 & -\sqrt{0.75}/2 \\
1 & -1 & 0 & 1 & 0 & 0 \\
1 & -0.5 & -\sqrt{0.75} & 0.25 & 0.75 & \sqrt{0.75}/2 \\
1 & 0.5 & -\sqrt{0.75} & 0.25 & 0.75 & -\sqrt{0.75}/2 \\
1 & 0 & 0 & 0 & 0 & 0 \\
1 & 0 & 0 & 0 & 0 & 0 \\
1 & 0 & 0 & 0 & 0 & 0
\end{array}\right]
\end{array}
$$

with $N^{-1}X'X$ given by

$$
\begin{array}{c}
\begin{array}{c c c c c} x_1 & x_2 & x_1^2 & x_2^2 & x_1 x_2 \end{array} \\
\left[\begin{array}{c c c c c c}
1 & 0 & 0 & 1/3 & 1/3 & 0 \\
 & 1/3 & 0 & 0 & 0 & 0 \\
 & & 1/3 & 0 & 0 & 0 \\
 & & & 1/4 & 1/12 & 0 \\
 & & & & 1/4 & 0 \\
 & & & & & 1/12
\end{array}\right]
\end{array}.
$$

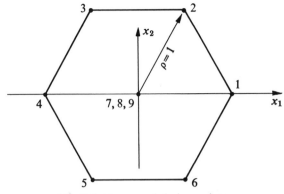

Fig. 7.6. Hexagonal design points.

It is clear that conditions (1) and (2) on page 145 hold, and thus the design is rotatable. In order to determine λ_4, the design must be scaled to the convention and the resulting mixed fourth moment computed. In order that $\sum_u x_{iu}^2 = 9$, each column of the design matrix must be multiplied by $\sqrt{3}$.

Table 7.10. Tabulation of Twelve Experimental Runs on Synthesis of Mercaptobenzothiazole[a]

| Run | Design Levels | | Controlled Levels | | Response, % MBT |
	x_1	x_2	hr	°C	
1	-1	0	4	250	83.8
2	1	0	20	250	81.7
3	0	0	12	250	82.4
4	0	0	12	250	82.9
5	0	-1	12	220	84.7
6	0	1	12	280	57.9
7	0	0	12	250	81.2
8	$-\sqrt{2}/2$	$-\sqrt{2}/2$	6.3	229	81.3
9	$-\sqrt{2}/2$	$\sqrt{2}/2$	6.3	271	83.1
10	$\sqrt{2}/2$	$-\sqrt{2}/2$	17.7	229	85.3
11	$\sqrt{2}/2$	$\sqrt{2}/2$	17.7	271	72.7
12[a]	-1	0	4	250	82.0

[a]Run 12 was not originally requested, but was used in the calculations.
SOURCE: S. A. Frankel, "Statistical Design of Experiments for Process Development of MBT," *Rubber Age* **89**, 453 (1961).

This results in the x_1x_2 column being multiplied by 3 and the mixed fourth moment multiplied by 9. Thus $\lambda_4 = 3/4$, as indicated in Table 7.9.

Example. In an experiment [Frankel] that was conducted to explore the synthesis of mercaptobenzothiazole (MBT), the variables

$$x_1 = \frac{\text{time (hr)} - 12}{8}$$

$$x_2 = \frac{\text{temp. (°C)} - 250}{30}$$

were varied in an octogonal arrangement with three center points. Table 7.10 gives the design levels in both coded and uncoded units. Also given is the value of the response. Notice that *two* observations were taken at the point $(-1, 0)$.

The second order model, estimated by least squares, turned out to be

$$\hat{y} = 82.17 - 1.01x_1 - 8.61x_2 + 1.40x_1^2 - 8.76x_2^2 - 7.20x_1x_2 .$$

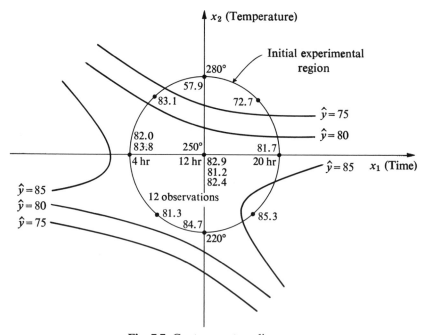

Fig. 7.7. Contour system diagram.

Although no canonical analysis was reported, the contour system could be easily interpreted graphically, in this case, since there are only two variables. The response function is illustrated in Fig. 7.7.

The results of the initial study indicated that high yield would result from (1) high temperature and low reaction time, and (2) low temperature and high reaction time. Notice that the system in Fig. 7.7 is a *saddle* contour system. In light of this, it was decided that further experimental runs should be made, with conditions being somewhat more extreme than those in the initial experimental region. The levels of x_1 and x_2, and the response for the additional runs follow:

Run	x_1	x_2	Time, hr	Temp., °C	% MBT
13	-1	1	4	280	82.1
14	1	-1	20	220	88.5

For further examination in the area of low reaction time and high temperature, three confirmatory runs were made. The results are

Run	x_1	x_2	Time, hr	Temp., °C	y
15	-1	1.3	4	289	84.4
16	-1.25	0.5	2	265	85.2
17	-1.25	1	2	280	83.2

The conclusions essentially are the following:

1. Low temperatures (approximately 220°C) and high reaction times result in high yields.

2. It is possible that medium to high temperatures (250–280°C) and low reaction times (3.5 hr) generate high yields.

COMBINATIONS OF EQUIRADIAL DESIGNS

Another class of rotatable designs for two independent variables involves combining two or more of the regular polygons discussed in the previous section to form configurations on concentric circles. In general, s sets of equiradial points, the wth containing n_w points ($n_w \geq 5$) and having radius ρ_w, will form a rotatable design. In fact, each set by itself is rotatable, but as we have seen, results in a singular $X'X$ and thus requires additional runs. The combination is rotatable (see Box and Hunter) with

$$\lambda_4 = \frac{N \cdot \sum\limits_{w=1}^{s} n_w \rho_w^4}{2 \left(\sum\limits_{w=1}^{s} n_w \rho_w^2 \right)^2}. \tag{7.52}$$

This key expression can be used to develop rotatable designs involving combinations of equiradial sets which are uniform precision or orthogonal designs. As can be seen by observation of Eq. 7.52, for the special case of a combination of *two* sets, the first set containing, e.g. n_1 points and the second containing n_2 points, the ratio ρ_2/ρ_1 of the design radii is vital in determining λ_4. For example, consider a design consisting of a combination of a hexagon (inside) and a pentagon, with the design radius of the former being 0.204 of the latter. We can rewrite Eq. 7.52 for the case of $s = 2$,

$$\lambda_4 = \left(\frac{N}{2} \right) \left[\frac{n_1 \rho_1^4 + n_2 \rho_2^4}{n_1^2 \rho_1^4 + n_2^2 \rho_2^4 + 2 n_1 n_2 \rho_1^2 \rho_2^2} \right]$$

$$= \left(\frac{N}{2} \right) \left(\frac{\rho_1}{\rho_2} \right)^4 \left[\frac{n_1 + n_2 (\rho_2/\rho_1)^4}{n_1^2 (\rho_1/\rho_2)^4 + n_2^2 + 2 n_1 n_2 (\rho_1/\rho_2)^2} \right]. \tag{7.53}$$

Substituting $n_1 = 5$, $n_2 = 6$, and $\rho_2/\rho_1 = 0.204$ into Eq. 7.53 gives $\lambda_4 = 1.0$, so the design is orthogonal.

Table 7.11. Rotatable Designs Involving Two Equiradial Sets (Concentric Circles)

n_1	5	5	5	6	6	7
n_2	6	7	8	7	8	8
ρ_2/ρ_1 (up)	0.414	0.438	0.454	0.407	0.430	0.404
ρ_2/ρ_1 (orth)	0.204	0.267	0.304	0.189	0.250	0.176

SOURCE: G. E. P. Box and J. S. Hunter, "Multifactor Experimental Designs for Exploring Response Surfaces," *Ann. Math. Stat.* **28** (1), 195 (1957).

Table 7.11 shows specifications for rotatable designs involving combinations of two equiradial sets. Included are values of ρ_2/ρ_1 for both uniform precision and orthogonal designs.

OTHER ROTATABLE DESIGNS FOR MORE THAN TWO INDEPENDENT VARIABLES

The most useful class of rotatable designs for $k > 2$ is the class of rotatable central composite designs. There are, however, other arrangements which conveniently afford rotatable designs. An example, for $k = 3$ is the twelve point-configuration given by the design matrix

$$
D = \begin{bmatrix}
0 & a_1 & a_2 \\
0 & a_1 & -a_2 \\
0 & -a_1 & a_2 \\
0 & -a_1 & -a_2 \\
a_2 & 0 & a_1 \\
-a_2 & 0 & a_1 \\
-a_2 & 0 & -a_1 \\
a_2 & 0 & -a_1 \\
a_1 & a_2 & 0 \\
a_1 & -a_2 & 0 \\
-a_1 & a_2 & 0 \\
-a_1 & -a_2 & 0
\end{bmatrix}
\tag{7.54}
$$

where a_1 and a_2 are such that

$$
a_1/a_2 = 1.617.
\tag{7.55}
$$

This design configuration is called an *icosahedron*.

It should be noted that if one computes the design moments for the configuration given in Eq. 7.54, the rotatability conditions given on page 145 will hold. However, when the design is scaled to the convention, $a_1 = 1.473$ and $a_2 = 0.911$. These are found by merely equating the moment $[ii] = 4(a_1^2 + a_2^2)/12$ to unity with the constraint given in Eq. 7.55. Then, upon computing the fourth moment, one obtains $[iiii] = 1.8$, and $[iijj] = 0.6$, the latter being equal to $k/(k + 2)$ for three independent variables. This configuration, of course, results in a singular $X'X$. As a result, points must be added to ensure estimation of the parameters in the model. In fact, $n_2 = 5$ center points gives a uniform precision design and $n_2 = 8$ gives an orthogonal design. For the icosahedron, one fits a second order model, estimating ten coefficients with $(n_2 + 12)$ observations, giving 3 degrees of freedom for lack-of-fit and $(n_2 - 1)$ for pure error.

Another experimental design which results in a rotatable configuration is that which consists of the twenty points which form a *dodecahedron*. The design matrix is given by

$$D = \begin{array}{c} \begin{array}{ccc} x_1 & x_2 & x_3 \end{array} \\ \left[\begin{array}{ccc} 0 & 1/c & c \\ 0 & -1/c & c \\ 0 & 1/c & -c \\ 0 & -1/c & -c \\ c & 0 & 1/c \\ -c & 0 & -1/c \\ -c & 0 & 1/c \\ c & 0 & -1/c \\ 1/c & c & 0 \\ -1/c & -c & 0 \\ -1/c & c & 0 \\ 1/c & -c & 0 \\ -1 & -1 & -1 \\ 1 & -1 & -1 \\ -1 & 1 & -1 \\ -1 & -1 & 1 \\ 1 & 1 & -1 \\ 1 & -1 & 1 \\ -1 & 1 & 1 \\ 1 & 1 & 1 \end{array} \right] \end{array} \qquad (7.56)$$

where $c = 1.618$. Once again it is simple to verify that the rotatability conditions hold. However, as in the case of the icosahedron, $[iijj] = 0.6$ and thus the $X'X$ matrix is singular and the design must be augmented, center points once again being the likely choice.

It turns out that one cannot attain an orthogonal dodecahedron, but $n_2 = 8$ center points results in a dodechahedron which is a uniform precision design.

general comments concerning center points for rotatable design with k variables

In many instances, we have recommended augmenting a rotatable design with center points in order to attain a certain value of λ_4, the mixed fourth moment $[iijj]$. It has been pointed out that particular values of this parameter, if attained, can actually produce a design having such properties as orthogonality or uniform precision. However, before an attempt is made to embark on a new topic, some effort will be made to clarify the question regarding what general conditions dictate the need of center points (or other points) in order that singularity be avoided but rotatability be preserved.

It was seen on page 155 that rotatable designs for two factors on a circle of radius ρ, e.g. the pentagon, hexagon, etc., (without center points) are singular designs. The same is true for the dodecahedron and icosahedron for fitting a response surface in three variables. Consider as another example the $k = 4$ rotatable central composite design ($\alpha = 2.0$) *without* center points. The design matrix, written in abbreviated form is given by

$$
D =
\begin{array}{cccc}
x_1 & x_2 & x_3 & x_4 \\
\left[\begin{array}{cccc}
\pm 1 & \pm 1 & \pm 1 & \pm 1 \\
-2 & 0 & 0 & 0 \\
2 & 0 & 0 & 0 \\
0 & -2 & 0 & 0 \\
0 & 2 & 0 & 0 \\
0 & 0 & -2 & 0 \\
0 & 0 & 2 & 0 \\
0 & 0 & 0 & -2 \\
0 & 0 & 0 & 2
\end{array}\right]
\end{array}.
$$

The ± 1 notation refers to a vector of $+1$'s and -1's, making up the factorial portion of the design. The design is scaled to the convention, i.e. $\sum_{u=1}^{24} x_{iu}^2 = 24$, therefore, no correction factor is needed in computing λ_4 ; thus we have

$$
\lambda_4 = \frac{\sum\limits_u x_{iu}^2 x_{ju}^2}{24}
$$

$$
= 2/3
$$

which is the singular value $k/(k + 2)$ for $k = 4$, indicating that center points are needed for this design too. The interesting question which should be asked at this point is "what general class of rotatable designs require additional points to avoid singularity?"

A close inspection of the design matrices for the examples mentioned in this section reveals that they all consist of design points which are equidistant from the design center. In the case of the pentagon, hexagon, etc., the points lie on a circle, whereas in the case of the icosahedron and dodecahedron, the points lie on a sphere. For example, in the case of the dodecahedron, the radius of the sphere is given by

$$
e = \sqrt{c^2 + 1/c^2} = 3
$$

In general, *rotatable designs which consist of points that are equidistant from the design origin will have a singular X'X and should be augmented by center points.* (It should be noted that all rotatable designs do *not* fall into this category. A case in point is the rotatable ccd, for three variables. The points in this design are not equidistant from the center.) The following paragraph outlines a proof of the result quoted here.

Consider a design matrix given by

$$D = [\mathbf{x}_1, \mathbf{x}_2, \ldots, \mathbf{x}_k]$$

where each vector $\mathbf{x}_i$ of D represents a column of the design matrix. That is,

$$\mathbf{x}_i = [x_{i1} x_{i2}, \ldots, x_{iN}].$$

Assuming that the design is scaled to the convention, then

$$N^{-1} \sum_{u=1}^{N} \sum_{i=1}^{k} x_{iu}^2 = \sum_{i=1}^{k} [ii] \tag{7.57}$$
$$= k.$$

At this stage, assume that the design has all points on a sphere of radius ρ. From Eq. 7.57, since

$$\sum_{i=1}^{k} x_{iu}^2 = \rho^2 \qquad (u = 1, 2, \ldots, N),$$
$$\rho^2 = k. \tag{7.58}$$

Now consider the quantity

$$\rho^4 = N^{-1} \sum_{u=1}^{N} \left\{ \sum_{i=1}^{k} x_{iu}^2 \right\}^2$$

$$= N^{-1} \sum_{u=1}^{N} \left\{ \sum_{i=1}^{k} x_{iu}^4 + \sum_{\substack{i=1 \\ i \neq j}}^{k} \sum_{j=1}^{k} x_{iu}^2 x_{ju}^2 \right\}$$

$$= \sum_{i=1}^{k} \left\{ N^{-1} \sum_{u} x_{iu}^4 \right\} + \sum_{\substack{i \\ i \neq j}} \sum_{j} \left\{ N^{-1} \sum_{u=1} x_{iu}^2 x_{ju}^2 \right\}$$

$$= k[iiii] + k(k-1)[iijj].$$

Now, if the design is rotatable, $[iiii] = 3[iijj]$, and

$$\rho^4 = k(3\lambda_4) + k(k-1)\lambda_4.$$

But from Eq. 7.58, $\rho^4 = k^2$, and thus

$$k^2 = k(3\lambda_4) + (k^2 - k)\lambda_4. \tag{7.59}$$

Solving Eq. 7.59 for λ_4,

$$\lambda_4 = k/(k + 2),$$

which indicates that a rotatable design for which all points are the same distance ρ from the center is, in fact, a singular design.

7.4 | summary remarks concerning designs for fitting second order response models

Before an attempt is made to summarize the high spots of this chapter, it should be mentioned that the discussion concerning designs for fitting the second order response surface has not been finished at this stage. Indeed, other topics are covered in succeeding chapters which rely heavily on information regarding *both* first and second order designs.

In summarizing the material in this chapter, it should first be mentioned that probably the most useful and versatile class of experimental designs for fitting second order models is the central composite design. This design serves as a natural alternative to the 3^k factorial design due to its requirement of fewer experimental observations and its flexibility.

An experimental design is said to be *rotatable* if the variance of the estimated response $\hat{y}$ at some point $(x_1, x_2, \ldots, x_k)$ depends on the distance from the point to the design center and not on the direction. In other words, as far as the design is concerned, points in the factor space which are the same distance from the origin are treated as being *equally important*. The conditions that must hold in order that an experimental design be rotatable are essentially requirements on the design moments, and are given in Eqs. 7.20 and 7.21. More importantly, the conditions are given for special cases; for the first order case, the requirement is that the design be orthogonal; the conditions for a second order rotatable design are given on page 145. Table 7.7 gives the value of α (specifying the location of the axial points) in order that a central composite design be rotatable. The parameter $\lambda_4 = [iijj]$ can be conveniently altered, without loss of rotatability, by adding center points to the basic design configuration. Often one strives to attain a rotatable design which is either an orthogonal design or a uniform precision design, the latter having the properties that the variance of an estimated response is essentially uniform on the unit sphere in the factor space. Table 7.8 contains information specifying various rotatable central composite designs which are useful in practice.

For two independent variables, designs involving five or more equally spaced points on a circle form a useful rotatable configuration if augmented by center points. The unaugmented design is useless due to the fact that the experimenter encounters a singular $X'X$ in attempting to estimate the model coefficients. More generally, $X'X$ will be singular for any rotatable design in which $\lambda_4 = k/(k + 2)$. This will *always* occur if the rotatable design consists of points which are all on a sphere of radius ρ. The condition can, however, be alleviated with the addition of center points.

7.5 | coding of the independent variables

In the development given to this point, it has been assumed that the experimenter has assigned a "coding" to the variables, i.e., one has been able to redefine units in the basic measured variables in terms of new units. For example, suppose one of the variables in a response surface study is temperature, T, controlled at three levels, 100°C, 150°C, and 200°C. If the variable used in the model is

$$x = \frac{T - 150}{50},$$

then essentially one has assigned as *one unit* for the variable in the response function, the equivalent of *50°C* in the measured variable. It is true that the actual experimental design levels and certain properties of the design depend heavily on what coding system is used. For example in the temperature illustration, the x levels are $-1, 0, +1$, and the levels of the corresponding measured variables depend on the coding system. If it is decided, after the experiment has been designed, that the coding should be changed to one which equates one unit to 25°C, then the levels are changed to $-2, 0, +2$.

Considering the use of rotatable response surface designs, the property of rotatability is very much dependent on the coding system used. By its very nature the rotatable experimental plan is designed to give equal variance of $\hat{y}$ for all points which are the same *distance* from the design center, distance in the factor space being a function of the coding system used on all of the variables. Strictly speaking, a rotatable design has this property for a particular assignment of basic response surface units. If the coding is changed, then it is likely that a design which was rotatable under the original coding system will not be rotatable in the new variables. It is often argued that an engineer, biologist, etc. should know what is the appropriate coding in going from the "natural" variables to the standardized ones. If this is true, and if the other assumptions indicated in Chapter 4 hold, there should be no great problem in expressing the response function in terms of the redefined units. The selection of experimental region and proper units are certainly reasons enough for the need of close cooperation between physical scientist and statistician. The fact is, however, that the scientist does not always know what the best coordinate system is. In fact, if the phenomenon that he is studying is relatively new to him, he may have little or no information on which to base his decision. All scientific investigations should, however, yield information which is used to improve future experiments. As a result, these basic response surface units may be modified from study to study, depending on the intuition of the scientist and the basic nature of the results found in intermediate work. In fact, one may find that a change in going from one coding system to the other may result in a much more simple geometrical representation of the response system in future work.

Multiple Response Example. All of the examples given to this point represent attempts to illustrate the procedures outlined and discussed in the text. Some of the examples represent actual industrial experiences and some are artificial. All, however, illustrate situations in which only *one* response was measured by the experimenter.

In many (and perhaps most) modern technological situations more than one response variables is pertinent to the success of an industrial process or system. For example, an industrial engineer in a tool-life experiment may be interested in how the cutting speed (x_1) and depth of cut (x_2) influence the life of the tool (η_1). The study could conceivably involve an attempt to determine the optimum settings on the independent variable in order that maximum life be obtained. In addition, a secondary response, rate of metal removed (η_2), may also be of importance in the study. In all probability the experimenter might find it necessary to arrive at some satisfactory setting of x_1 and x_2 which represents a compromise as far as the two responses are concerned. A chemical engineer, in attempting to maximize a yield response (η_1) may be simultaneously attempting to minimize a second response, concentration (η_2) of an undesirable impurity.

The main features of response surface methods lend themselves well to the study of multiple response situations. Diagrams showing the fitted surface in the form of contours of constant response often indicate more than one region where the predicted response is at a level which is considered to be satisfactory. The experimenter can then use this information, in addition to similar contours for a second response, to arrive at a setting $(x_1, x_2, \ldots, x_k)$ that represents approximately the "best" operating conditions. In the chemical example, the point at which the maximum yield is expected may very well be a point for which the concentration of the undesirable impurity is at a critical level. Thus the situation may dictate that the experimenter move away from the stationary point on yield to a region where, according to the contour diagrams, the yield is merely *close to the maximum* but, in addition, the concentration of the impurity is sufficiently low. The study of multiple response surfaces is often effectively carried out by *superimposing* contour diagrams corresponding to the various responses in order to visually determine the most fruitful operating conditions. As one would expect, studies of this type become more difficult to accomplish as the number of independent variables becomes larger. One example of a multiple response study will be given presently.

In a process designed to purify an antibiotic product (Lind, Goldin, and Hickman), it was decided that a response surface study should be employed in the *solvent extraction* operation in the process. The yield of the product at this stage of the process and the cost of the operation represent very critical

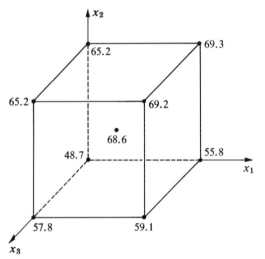

Fig. 7.8. Results of 2^3 factorial experiment.

responses. The operation involved extracting the antibiotic into an organic solvent. Certain chemicals, called reagents *A* and *B*, were added to form material which is soluble in the solvent.

Concentration of the two reagents and the pH in the extraction environment were chosen as the independent variables to be studied. In the past, it had been the policy to use excessive amounts of the reagents to produce high yield. However, it was decided that *cost of operation* should be included as well as yield in the study.

Initially, a simple 2^3 factorial experiment was planned in order that yield and cost could be studied. The ranges on the independent variables were determined from previous experience on the same process. The ranges were such that the experimenter was reasonably certain that the true maximum yield would be included within the limits of experimentation. Units were chosen for the variables, and it was decided that the fitted equation would contain

$$x_1 = \frac{\%A - 0.5}{0.5} \; ; \qquad x_2 = \frac{\%B - 0.5}{0.5} \; ; \qquad x_3 = \frac{pH - 5.0}{0.5} \; .$$

The graphical illustration of the first phase of the study, namely, the 2^3 factorial experiment is shown in Fig. 7.8. Two observations were taken at each of the eight basic treatment combinations and four observations were taken at the origin of the design.

The numbers on the cube indicate averages of the observations taken in the first phase. Table 7.12 shows the analysis of variance conducted on the complete set of yield data.

Table 7.12. Analysis of Variance on Yield Data Using 2^3
Factorial Experiment Indicated in Fig. 7.8

Source of Variation	Sum of Squares	Degrees of Freedom	Mean Square	F
first order terms				
(x_1, x_2, x_3)	668.05	3	222.68	sig.
lack-of-fit	226.69	5		
interactions	56.22	4	14.06	
pure quadratic terms	170.47	1	170.47	sig.
error	293.53	11	26.69	

The first order response function is given by

$$\hat{y}_1 = 62.7 + 4.11x_1 + 11.86x_2 + 30.63x_3 .$$

The subscript "1" on the response indicates the yield response. The results in Table 7.12 indicate a strong possibility of contribution from second order terms, particularly the pure quadratic terms.

Phase II of the study involved augmenting the factorial experiment illustrated by Fig. 7.9 with additional points in order to allow the fitting of a second order surface. One observation was added to each of the two already recorded for the factorial treatment combinations. In addition, three observations were taken at each of six axial treatment combinations, and five center points were added. The resulting configuration formed a central composite design, with a total of fifty-one observations. The value of the parameter α was chosen to be 1.0. The geometric layout showing the average of the experimental runs at each treatment combination is given by Fig. 7.9.

Numbers for factorial and axial treatment combinations are the average of three. Number at midpoint is an average of nine.

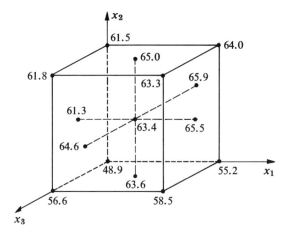

Fig. 7.9. Layout of experimental design for phase II of yield response study.

The estimated response function found by using these data is given by

$$\hat{y}_1 = 65.05 + 1.63x_1 + 3.28x_2 + 0.93x_3 - 2.93x_1^2 - 2.02x_2^2$$
$$- 1.07x_3^2 - 0.53x_1x_2 - 0.68x_1x_3 - 1.44x_2x_3. \qquad (7.60)$$

The stationary point was found to be $x_{1,0} = 0.2256$; $x_{2,0} = 0.8589$; $x_{3,0} = -0.2150$, the coordinates of which correspond to $\%A = 0.6128$, $\%B = 0.9294$, and pH = 4.8925. The estimated yield at this point is given by $\hat{y}_{1,0} = 66.542$. The λ values in the canonical form of the response function of Eq. 7.60 are found as the characteristic roots of the matrix

$$B = \begin{bmatrix} -2.93 & -0.265 & -0.34 \\ & -2.02 & -0.72 \\ & & -1.07 \end{bmatrix}.$$

The roots are given as solutions to the equation

$$\lambda^3 + 6.02\lambda^2 + 10.5109\lambda + 4.6352 = 0,$$

which yields

$$\lambda = -0.6687, \quad \lambda_2 = -3.1515, \quad \lambda_3 = -2.1999.$$

Thus the stationary point gives maximum yield. Figure 7.10 gives a set of three yield contours, corresponding to fixed levels of the variable x_3. Notice that the middle figure, although not displaying exactly the optimum yield, does indicate an estimated yield which is close to the maximum.

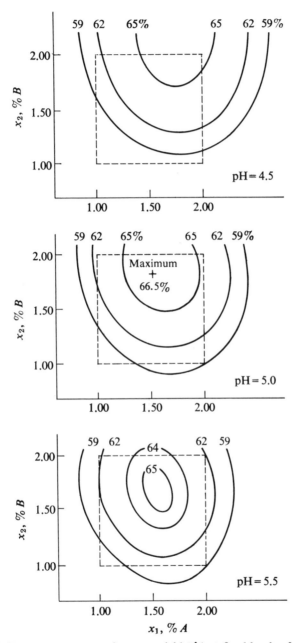

Fig. 7.10. Response contours of percent yield ($\hat{y}_1$) at fixed levels of pH (x_3).

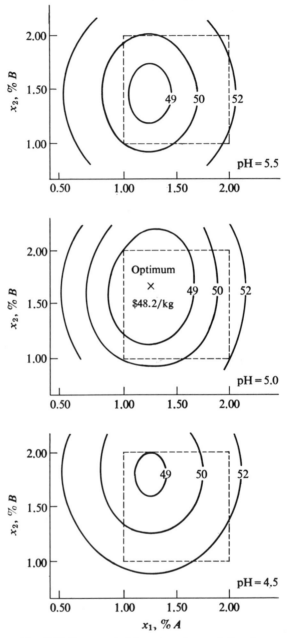

Fig. 7.11. Raw material cost contours, dollars/kg.

It can be seen that in the vicinity of the optimum there appears to be a great deal of flexibility as far as yield is concerned. Yield does *not* decrease rapidly, as changes in the variables are made in this region. On the other hand, if the concentrations of the reagents are excessive, that is, in the region of 2.0% (or higher) on each reagent, estimated yield is not only lower but there seems to be much less flexibility. Strangely enough, this very region had been the standard operating region before this study was undertaken.

The two reagents represent critical industrial costs. So it was felt that further evidence could be produced to support the hypothesis that reduced levels of the reagents represent a more economic approach than the standard plant operating levels. The plan was to illustrate this evidence by displaying response surfaces showing *cost* (η_2) as a second response. This was accomplished by merely transforming the experimental data given in phase II on yield and material usage, the latter a function of the concentrations of A and B to cost; the basic unit on this response was dollars cost per kilogram of product. A second order response surface analysis of the type

$$\eta_2 = f(x_1, x_2, x_3)$$

was performed. Examples of some two-dimensional cost diagrams are shown in Fig. 7.11.

Note that the middle set of contours indicate the point of optimum as far as cost is concerned. Figure 7.12 shows an another view of this set, with

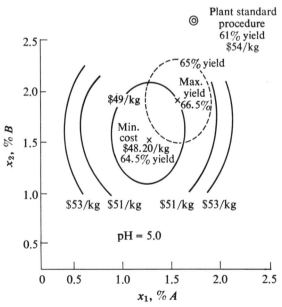

Fig. 7.12. Contours of cost and yield.

the corresponding set of yield contours, displaying the optimum yield, superimposed. Notice that the point representing the standard operating conditions, formerly accepted as optimum, is indicated on the figure.

In summary, it was learned from this response surface study, that the operating conditions should be altered from the standard plant conditions. In fact, the study indicated that the original opinion that it is best to add both reagents in excess, in order to improve yield, is faulty. In fact, lowering the amounts of reagents A and B to the region of the maximum yield point will result in an estimated increase in yield of approximately 5% and an estimated reduction in cost of approximately \$5.00/kg of product.

exercises

7.1. Verify the efficiency figures given in Table 7.5.

7.2. Compare the following two designs from the standpoint of efficiency for estimating pure quadratic coefficients. Also compare the designs from the standpoint of bias in the pure quadratic coefficients in the presence of a third order model.

Design 1		Design 2	
x_1	x_2	x_1	x_2
-1	-1	-1	-1
-1	1	0	-1
1	-1	1	-1
1	1	-1	0
0	-2	0	0
0	2	1	0
-2	0	-1	1
2	0	0	1
0	0	1	1
0	0		
0	0		
0	0		

7.3. Write out the design matrix for a two variable experimental layout which displays seven points equally spaced on a circle and contains a sufficient number of center points to be approximately a uniform precision design. Write out the moment matrix for this design.

7.4. Compare, in terms of efficiency of estimating pure quadratic coefficients, a uniform precision icosahedron design with a uniform precision dodecahedron.

7.5. What is the hazard of comparing response surface designs purely on the basis of the efficiency criterion?

7.6. The following represents the design matrix and the vector of observations in which a simplex design in two variables was used to measure the effect of the variables on a single response.

$$
\begin{array}{ccc}
x_1 & x_2 & y \\
\end{array}
\left[
\begin{array}{ccc}
1.0 & 0 & 95.6 \\
0.5 & 0.866 & 77.9 \\
-0.5 & 0.866 & 76.2 \\
-1.0 & 0 & 54.5 \\
-0.5 & -0.866 & 63.9 \\
0.5 & -0.866 & 79.1 \\
0 & 0 & 96.8 \\
0 & 0 & 94.8 \\
0 & 0 & 94.4 \\
\end{array}
\right]
$$

a) Estimate the response function and determine the stationary point.

b) Determine the nature of the stationary point and plot contours of constant response in two dimensions.

c) Conduct an analysis of variance including the sources of variation due to:
linear terms;
quadratic terms;
lack-of-fit.

references

Box, G. E. P. and J. S. Hunter: "Multifactor Experimental Designs for Exploring Response Surfaces," *Ann. Math. Stat.* **28** (1), 195 (1957).

Box, G. E. P. and K. B. Wilson: "On the Experimental Attainment of Optimum Conditions," *J. Roy. Statist. Soc.*, B **13**, 1 (1951).

Cragle, R. G., R. M. Myers, R. K. Waugh, J. S. Hunter, and R. L. Anderson: "The Effects of Various Levels of Sodium Citrate, Glycerol, and Equilibration Time on Survival of Bovine Spermatozoa after Storage at $-79°C$," *J. Dairy Sci.* **38** (5), 508 (1955).

Frankel, S. A.; "Statistical Design of Experiments for Process Development of MBT," *Rubber Age* **1961**, 453.

Lind, E. E., J. Goldin, and J. B. Hickman: "Fitting Yield and Cost Response Surfaces," *Chem. Eng. Prog.* **56**, 62 (1960).

8 | response surface analysis and design for experiments in blocks

Very often, due to physical limitations, it is necessary when fitting a response surface to conduct the experiment in "blocks." Blocking becomes an essential part of the experimental procedure when all of the experimental runs required by the design cannot be made under homogeneous conditions. For example, a chemist may find that he lacks sufficient uniform raw material to be used in a complete study of a particular chemical reaction. As a result, two or more batches of material *must* be used in the experiment. If, in fact, it is assumed that the influence of the batch or *block* is represented by an additive effect—that is, the effect of a change from one batch to another results in the addition of a constant to the response, despite the levels of the independent variables—then one can often fit the response function, *free from the disturbing influence* of the blocks. Blocking can often be used to eliminate a portion of time trends which often inflate the experimental error in statistical analysis. In this chapter, blocking in the first and second order cases are treated. As far as design is concerned, one seeks designs for which the block effects, which now must be inserted into the response model, are orthogonal to the coefficients. Such designs are said to *block orthogonally*. In the section that follows, steps are outlined for constructing designs that admit to orthogonal blocking for first order models.

8.1 | blocking in the case of the first order model

For the first order model, appropriate experimental plans are very simple to construct. In fact, a very useful set of designs are the 2^k factorial arrange-

176

ments, divided into 2^p blocks ($p < k$). The use of these configurations is taught in most elementary experimental design courses, the concepts which apply in the construction of these designs being identical to those used in constructing 2^k fractional factorial designs.

For a 2^k factorial design in 2^p blocks, one chooses p defining contrasts. It is convenient once again to use the upper case letters $A, B, C, \ldots$, to denote the variables and the lower case notation $(1), a, b, \ldots, ab, \ldots$, to denote the treatment combinations as outlined in Chapter 3. Thus, for the case in which two blocks are required, $p = 1$ defining contrast is chosen, the single contrast being of the form

$$A^{\gamma_1} B^{\gamma_2} \cdots$$

where the γ_i are either zero or unity. The defining equation

$$L = \gamma_1 z_1 + \gamma_2 z_2 + \cdots$$

modulo 2 is evaluated for each treatment combination. The z values are either 0 or 1, depending on whether or not the corresponding lower case letter appears in the treatment combination. Half of the treatment combinations yield $L = 0$ and half yield $L = 1$. The assignment to blocks then becomes as follows:

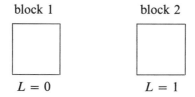

with the assignment to experimental units being random within blocks. In performing the experiment in this fashion, one has *confounded* with blocks the effect represented by the defining contrast, that is, the influence of the blocks and the effect due to the defining contrast are not separable in this experiment. Of course, if the defining contrast is an interaction, then it does not occur in the response model and the confounding represents no real problem. When a large number of blocks are needed, obviously more effects are confounded with blocks.

For the case where *four blocks* are needed, $p = 2$ defining contrasts are selected and the two defining equations L_1 and L_2 modulo 2 are evaluated for each treatment combination, the procedure being identical to that used in the construction of the 1/4 fraction of the 2^k factorial. The assignment to blocks is then

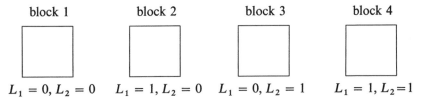

block 1   block 2   block 3   block 4

$L_1 = 0, L_2 = 0$ $L_1 = 1, L_2 = 0$ $L_1 = 0, L_2 = 1$ $L_1 = 1, L_2 = 1$

with the treatment combinations being divided equally among the blocks. It is important to note that in the case of four blocks, although two defining contrasts are selected by the experimenter and are thus used to construct the design, a *third effect* is automatically confounded with blocks, making a total of three, corresponding to the 3 degrees of freedom for blocks. The third effect is found by multiplying the two initial defining contrasts, and reducing the exponents modulo 2. For example, if the two initially chosen defining contrasts are $ABCD$ and CD, then

$$(ABCD)(CD) = ABC^2D^2 = AB$$

is also confounded with blocks in the resulting experiment.

For the case in which eight blocks are necessary, the same general procedure applies, namely, three defining contrasts are selected and four additional effects are confounded with blocks making a total of seven. The assignment of the treatment combinations to blocks is given by

block

1	2	3	4	5	6	7	8
$L_1 = 0$	$L_1 = 1$	$L_1 = 1$	$L_1 = 1$	$L_1 = 1$	$L_1 = 0$	$L_1 = 0$	$L_1 = 0$
$L_2 = 0$	$L_2 = 0$	$L_2 = 1$	$L_2 = 1$	$L_2 = 0$	$L_2 = 0$	$L_2 = 1$	$L_2 = 1$
$L_3 = 0$	$L_3 = 0$	$L_3 = 0$	$L_3 = 1$	$L_3 = 1$	$L_3 = 1$	$L_3 = 1$	$L_3 = 0$

In general, for the case of 2^p blocks, p defining contrasts are chosen by the experimenter, while $2^p - p - 1$ additional effects are confounded, making a total of $2^p - 1$.

Examples of 2^k Factorial Designs In Blocks. The actual procedure of constructing the blocks is considerably more simple to illustrate than it is to describe. "Shortcut" methods can be used which will become evident as examples are given. Suppose it is desired to use four factors at two levels with the requirement that the experimental runs must be made in four blocks with, of course, four runs per block. The defining contrasts chosen are the interactions ACD and BCD. As a result,

$$(ACD)(BCD) = AB$$

is also confounded with blocks. If the design is constructed properly, all of the effects which appear in the first order response model will be orthogonal to blocks.

The defining equations are written as

$$L_1 = z_1 + z_3 + z_4 \quad (ACD)$$
$$L_2 = z_2 + z_3 + z_4 \quad (BCD).$$

The $L_1 = L_2 = 0$ block, called the *principal block*, contains the treatment combinations

$$\{(1),\ cd,\ abd,\ abc\}.$$

In general, the principal block has the interesting property that the treatment combinations in it form a *group* with respect to multiplication, with the exponents reduced to the modulo 2 base. In other words, any treatment combination in the block can be generated as a product of two others. The remaining three blocks are now very easily constructed by (1) picking a treatment combination that has not been accounted for, and (2) generating the block containing that treatment combination by multiplying it by those in the principal block, modulo 2. If one selects the treatment combination ab, the block having $L_1 = 1$ and $L_2 = 1$ given by

$$ab,\ abcd,\ d,\ c$$

is constructed. In a similar manner, the two remaining blocks are found to be

$$\{b,\ bcd,\ ad,\ ac\} \quad (L_1 = 0, L_2 = 1)$$
$$\{a,\ acd,\ bd,\ bc\} \quad (L_1 = 1, L_2 = 0).$$

As a second example, suppose the experimenter wishes to design an experiment involving five factors (A, B, C, D, and E) at two levels but he is forced to design in eight blocks, the block size being four. This necessitates choosing $p = 3$ defining contrasts. The choices are, say ABC, $BCDE$, and ABE. The four additional effects that are confounded with blocks are

$$(ABC)(BCDE) = ADE$$
$$(ABC)(ABE) = CE$$
$$(BCDE)(ABE) = ACD$$
$$(ADE)(ABE) = BD$$

resulting in 7 single degree of freedom effects that are essentially sacrificed in the experiment. The principal block is constructed by finding the treatment combinations that yield zero values for the three defining equations

$$L_1 = z_1 + z_2 + z_3$$
$$L_2 = z_2 + z_3 + z_4 + z_5$$
$$L_3 = z_1 + z_2 + z_5.$$

The treatment combinations in the principal block are given by

$$\{(1),\ abd,\ bcde,\ ace\}.$$

The remaining seven blocks are constructed by using the methods described earlier. The final design is given by the following assignment to the eight blocks:

(1)	a	b	c	d	e	de	be
abd	bd	ad	abcd	ab	abde	abe	ade
bcde	abcde	cde	bde	bce	bcd	bc	cd
ace	ce	abce	ae	acde	ac	acd	abc

Notice, for example, that the second block is easily constructed by multiplication, modulo 2, of, say, the treatment combination a with the treatment combinations in the principal block.

Since the method of constructing the 2^k factorial designs in blocks is relatively simple and well known, no attempt will be made in this text to tabulate these designs. It is felt that the user can apply the mechanics described here to construct an appropriate design for his particular situation.

use of 2^k factorials in p blocks for fitting first order response surfaces

Experimental designs of the type described in the preceding examples are useful for fitting first order models simply because the block effects are orthogonal to the estimates of the first order coefficients. Since the first order response function normally contains terms which correspond only to the contribution of main effects, it is important that *no main effect be confounded with blocks*. Orthogonality with blocks is best illustrated with a simple example. If a response surface is to be estimated for the case of three independent variables, and the conditions necessitate designing in two blocks of size four, one possible design is the following:

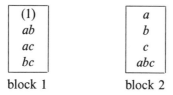

block 1		block 2
(1)		a
ab		b
ac		c
bc		abc

The reader can easily verify that the defining contrast is ABC. One can systematically construct a model to account for the two block effects, the observation on the uth response being given by

$$y_u = \beta_0 + \beta_1 x_{1u} + \beta_2 x_{2u} + \beta_3 x_{3u} + \delta_1 z_{1u} + \delta_2 z_{2u} + \varepsilon_u$$
$$(u = 1, 2, \ldots, 8). \qquad (8.1)$$

Here, δ_1 and δ_2 are the effects of the first and second block, respectively, and the z_{ju} take on a value of either 0 or 1, the latter if the uth observation is in the jth block. It is convenient for our illustration to redefine the model in Eq. 8.1 as

$$y_u = \beta_0' + \beta_1 x_{1u} + \beta_2 x_{2u} + \beta_3 x_{3u} + \delta_1(z_{1u} - \bar{z}_1) + \delta_2(z_{2u} - \bar{z}_2) + \varepsilon_u$$
$$(u = 1, 2, \ldots, 8). \qquad (8.2)$$

The structure can now be put into the usual form of the general linear model as follows:

$$
\mathbf{y} =
\begin{bmatrix}
(1) \\
ab \\
ac \\
bc \\
--- \\
a \\
b \\
c \\
abc
\end{bmatrix}
\begin{array}{l}
\left.\rule{0pt}{2.2em}\right\} \text{block 1} \\
\\
\left.\rule{0pt}{2.2em}\right\} \text{block 2}
\end{array}
\qquad
X =
\begin{array}{cccccc}
\beta_0' & \beta_1 & \beta_2 & \beta_3 & \delta_1 & \delta_2 \\
\begin{bmatrix}
1 & -1 & -1 & -1 & 1/2 & -1/2 \\
1 & 1 & 1 & -1 & 1/2 & -1/2 \\
1 & 1 & -1 & 1 & 1/2 & -1/2 \\
1 & -1 & 1 & 1 & 1/2 & -1/2 \\
\hline
1 & 1 & -1 & -1 & -1/2 & 1/2 \\
1 & -1 & 1 & -1 & -1/2 & 1/2 \\
1 & -1 & -1 & 1 & -1/2 & 1/2 \\
1 & 1 & 1 & 1 & -1/2 & 1/2
\end{bmatrix}
\end{array}.
$$

Notice that the δ columns, which are the columns that account for the block effects, are orthogonal to the other columns of the X matrix. This, of course, implies that the coefficients b_0', b_1, b_2, and b_3 of the model of Eq. 8.2 are estimated *in the usual fashion*, free from block effects. That is, we can write down the least squares estimators as

$$b_0' = \sum y_i/8$$

$$b_1 = \left[\frac{a + ab + ac + abc - (1) - b - c - bc}{8}\right]$$

$$b_2 = \left[\frac{b + ab + bc + abc - (1) - a - c - ac}{8}\right]$$

$$b_3 = \left[\frac{c + ac + bc + abc - (1) - a - b - ab}{8}\right].$$

As the reader should readily observe, all effects except the defining contrasts (in this case a *single* defining contrast) will be orthogonal to blocks. The outline of degrees of freedom for the analysis of variance for this example is given in Table 8.1. In general, of course, there will be $2^p - 1$ degrees of freedom associated with blocks. The block sum of squares is equivalent to the sum of squares for the effect with which it is confounded, namely, the three factor interaction ABC. The sum of squares associated with the individual main effects are computed in the usual way, ignoring blocks.

Table 8.1. Outline of Degrees of Freedom for 2^3 Factorial in Two Blocks With ABC As Defining Contrast

mean	1
blocks	1
factor A (x_1)	1
factor B (x_2)	1
factor C (x_3)	1
lack-of-fit	3
total	8

The 2^k factorial design in blocks can also very conveniently accommodate the addition of center points. For example, in the 2^3 illustration mentioned earlier in this chapter, if the experimenter decides to use three center points in each block in order to obtain degrees of freedom for error, the coefficients of the first order model will still be orthogonal to the block effect. In fact, the orthogonality is preserved even if the number of center points in each block is not the same. The *pure error* sum of squares is found by pooling the sum of squares between center points in the same block. In our example if there were three center points in each block, there would be 4 degrees of freedom for error.

8.2 | blocking in the case of the second order model

There are several classes of second order designs that admit to orthogonal blocking. Whether or not an appropriate design can be found for a given situation depends on the number of factors and the number of blocks dictated by the experimental situation. The experimental plans that are used in practice are actually the designs which were presented in Chapter 7. It remains, however, to establish some method for determining what are the proper assignments of experimental runs to blocks, so that the block effects will be orthogonal to the model coefficients. It will be demonstrated here that the central composite design is very important when one is attempting to find an experimental plan which blocks orthogonally.

Suppose the experiment is run in b blocks. Then the second order model for this situation is as follows:

$$y_u = \beta'_0 + \sum_{i=1}^{k} \beta_i x_{iu} + \sum_{i=1}^{k} \beta_{ii} x_{iu}^2 + \sum_{i}\sum_{j \atop i<j} \beta_{ij} x_{iu} x_{ju}$$

$$+ \sum_{m=1}^{b} \delta_m(z_{mu} - \bar{z}_m) + \varepsilon_u \qquad (u = 1, 2, \ldots, N). \qquad (8.3)$$

Here, as in the case of the specific first order model of Eq. 8.3, z_{mu} is unity if the uth observation arises from an experimental run in the mth block; otherwise, it is zero.

conditions for orthogonal blocking for designs used for fitting second order response surfaces

One can see at the outset that the conditions for orthogonal blocking, that is, the block effects being orthogonal to b'_0, b_i, b_{ii}, and b_{ij}, can be written initially as

$$\sum_{u=1}^{N} x_{iu}(z_{mu} - \bar{z}_m) = 0 \qquad (i = 1, 2, \ldots, k) \tag{8.4}$$

$$\sum_{u=1}^{N} x_{iu}^2(z_{mu} - \bar{z}_m) = 0 \qquad (i = 1, 2, \ldots, k) \tag{8.5}$$

$$\sum_{u=1}^{N} x_{iu}x_{ju}(z_{mu} - \bar{z}_m) = 0 \qquad (i, j = 1, 2, \ldots, k; i \neq j). \tag{8.6}$$

In what follows, the discussion is restricted to designs for which the first moment and the second mixed moments are zero, namely

$$\sum_{u=1}^{N} x_{iu} = 0 \qquad (i = 1, 2, \ldots, k) \tag{8.7}$$

$$\sum_{u=1}^{N} x_{iu}x_{ju} = 0 \qquad (i, j = 1, 2, \ldots, k; i \neq j). \tag{8.8}$$

If we consider Eqs. 8.7 and 8.8, together with Eqs. 8.4 and 8.6, the first condition for orthogonal blocking becomes that

$$\sum_{b1.m} x_{iu} = 0 \qquad \begin{array}{l} (m = 1, 2, \ldots, b) \\ (i, j = 1, 2, \ldots, k; i \neq j) \end{array} \tag{8.9}$$

$$\sum_{b1.m} x_{iu}x_{ju} = 0 \qquad (m = 1, 2, \ldots, b). \tag{8.10}$$

The $b1.m$ notation implies that the sum is being taken over the observations in the mth block. Considering each block separately, Eqs. 8.9 and 8.10 actually stipulate that each block must itself contain experimental runs which simulate a *first order orthogonal* experimental design. The second condition for orthogonal blocking is developed by beginning with Eq. 8.5. By definition, $\bar{z}_m$ is merely the fraction of the total observations that are assigned to block m. Thus, for orthogonal blocking,

$$\sum_{u=1}^{N} x_{iu}^2 z_{mu} = \sum_{u} x_{iu}^2 \bar{z}_m \qquad \begin{array}{l} (m = 1, 2, \ldots, b) \\ (i = 1, 2, \ldots, k) \end{array}$$

which essentially specifies that the contribution *in a particular block* to the total sum of squares of the variable x_i—the contribution to $\sum_{u=1}^{N} x_{iu}^2$, is proportional to the number of runs in the block.

The two conditions given here for orthogonal blocking in the case of a second order model are very simple to illustrate with an example. Consider the design matrix

$$D = \begin{array}{ccc} x_1 & x_2 & x_3 \end{array}$$

$$D = \left[\begin{array}{rrr}
1 & 1 & 1 \\
1 & -1 & -1 \\
-1 & 1 & -1 \\
-1 & -1 & 1 \\
0 & 0 & 0 \\
0 & 0 & 0 \\
\hline
1 & 1 & -1 \\
1 & -1 & 1 \\
-1 & 1 & 1 \\
-1 & -1 & -1 \\
0 & 0 & 0 \\
0 & 0 & 0 \\
\hline
-1.633 & 0 & 0 \\
1.633 & 0 & 0 \\
0 & -1.633 & 0 \\
0 & 1.633 & 0 \\
0 & 0 & -1.633 \\
0 & 0 & 1.633 \\
0 & 0 & 0 \\
0 & 0 & 0
\end{array}\right] \begin{array}{l} \left.\vphantom{\begin{array}{c}1\\1\\1\\1\\1\\1\end{array}}\right\} \text{block 1} \\[2em] \left.\vphantom{\begin{array}{c}1\\1\\1\\1\\1\\1\end{array}}\right\} \text{block 2} \\[2.5em] \left.\vphantom{\begin{array}{c}1\\1\\1\\1\\1\\1\\1\\1\end{array}}\right\} \text{block 3} \end{array} \qquad (8.11)$$

Notice that the first two blocks each contain a 1/2 fraction of a 2^3 factorial design augmented by two center points, while the third block contains what is also a first order orthogonal design. In fact, the entire experimental setup is a central composite design, with the axial portion being in one block, and the factorial portion being divided into two blocks. The first condition for orthogonal blocking has already been verified. The second is verified by some very simple calculations.

$$\sum_u x_{iu}^2 = 40/3 \qquad (i = 1, 2, 3)$$

$$\sum_{b1.1} x_{iu}^2 = 4 \qquad \sum_{b1.2} x_{iu}^2 = 4,$$

while

$$\sum_{b1.3} x_{iu}^2 = 16/3.$$

The block sizes are 6, 6, and 8 respectively, while $N = 20$. Blocks 1 and 2 each account for 3/10 of the sum of squares for each variable and block 3 accounts for the remaining 4/10. Thus, it is verified that the contribution from each block *is* proportional to the block size, and as a result, the block effects are orthogonal to the estimates of the model coefficients. As in the case of the first order designs that were discussed in Section 8.1, the estimates of the parameter coefficients are computed in the usual fashion, disregarding blocks.

central composite design—use of two blocks

The central composite design lends itself well to practical blocking arrangements as was illustrated in the example presented in the preceding section. The ccd consists of two parts, the factorial and the axial portions, each of which is a first order orthogonal design. In fact, if k is large enough, the factorial portion can itself be usefully divided into two or more than two first order orthogonal designs, creating the possibility of a large number of blocks in the total configuration.

Consider the ccd partitioned into *two blocks*. Assign to block 1 the factorial portion of the design (F design points) and to block 2 the axial portion ($2k$ points). Also assign F_0 center points to block 1 and a_0 center points to block 2, a_0 not necessarily being equal to F_0. The first condition for orthogonal blocking will then hold despite the value of α in the ccd. For the second condition to hold,

$$\frac{\sum_{ax.b1.} x_{iu}^2}{\sum_{fac.b1.} x_{iu}^2} = \frac{2k + a_0}{F + F_0}. \tag{8.12}$$

The left-hand side of Eq. 8.12 is $2\alpha^2/F$, thus we can solve for α after this substitution and obtain

$$\alpha = \sqrt{\frac{F(2k + a_0)}{2(F + F_0)}}. \tag{8.13}$$

Therefore, if the experimenter requires two blocks, the value of α given by Eq. 8.13, applying the preselected values for F_0 and a_0, gives a ccd which blocks orthogonally.

rotatable central composite design—two blocks

The value of α given in Eq. 8.13 will not, in general, be that which makes the design rotatable, or even near rotatable. If the design is to be rotatable, $\alpha = (F)^{1/4}$, which requires that

$$(F)^{1/2} = \frac{F(2k + a_0)}{2(F + F_0)}. \tag{8.14}$$

One cannot always find, for any k, a design which satisfies Eq. 8.14. For $k = 3$, Eq. 8.14 cannot be satisfied, while for $k = 4$, a rotatable central composite design blocks orthogonally when $F_0 = 4$ and $a_0 = 2$. For $k = 5$, a rotatable central composite design with the factorial portion being a 1/2 fraction of a 2^5 blocks orthogonally. In this case $\alpha = 2.0$, and in order for Eq. 8.14 to be satisfied, $F_0 = 6$ center points are added to the factorial portion and $a_0 = 1$ center point is added to the axial portion. This topic is discussed in more detail in the section beginning on page 188.

central composite design—more than two blocks

Often experimental situations dictate the need for more than two blocks in a second order response surface study. As before, the central composite design displays its versatility. The factorial portion can be subdivided into two orthogonal first order designs by considering appropriate fractions of the complete 2^k. The example given in the section on page 185 is a good illustration. Note that the 2^3 factorial is itself subdivided into two blocks with the interaction ABC being the defining contrast. The axial portion, then, forms the third block. In this case, with two center points being added to each block, the value of α which satisfies the second condition for orthogonal blocking is 1.633. The reader recalls that for $k = 3$, the rotatable ccd has $\alpha = 1.682$ (Table 7.7), and thus the design given in the example is near rotatable.

As a second example of a ccd in three blocks, consider a situation in which it is necessary that the experimenter use *four* center points in each of the three blocks of a $k = 3$ ccd. The design matrix is identical to that of Eq. 8.11, except for the difference in center points *and* the difference in the value of α. The contribution to the sum of squares of $x_i(i = 1, 2, 3)$ is the same for the first two blocks and the block sizes are also the same. To find the appropriate value of α, we have

$$\frac{2\alpha^2}{8 + 2\alpha^2} = \frac{10}{26}$$

and the solution is $\alpha = 1.581$. It can easily be seen, then, that many different arrangements using the ccd can be developed which block orthogonally in more than two blocks. One first needs to be sure that the factorial portion is divided into blocks which form orthogonal first order designs, this being accomplished by the use of techniques described in Section 8.1. Secondly, the value of α must be that which satisfies the *second* condition of orthogonal blocking.

Perhaps a bit more attention should be devoted to the first condition of orthogonal blocking, particularly where more than two blocks are involved. In subdividing the factorial portion into blocks, one must be sure that in considering the individual blocks as first order designs, no two main effects are aliased with each other. In the example given in the section on page 000, suppose that rather than using ABC as the defining contrast in forming blocks 1 and 2, AB had been chosen. The design matrix would then become, ignoring center points,

$$
D = \begin{array}{c}
\begin{array}{ccc} x_1 & x_2 & x_3 \end{array} \\
\left.\left[\begin{array}{ccc}
-1 & -1 & -1 \\
1 & 1 & -1 \\
-1 & -1 & 1 \\
1 & 1 & 1
\end{array}\right.\right\} \text{block 1} \\
\left.\begin{array}{ccc}
1 & -1 & -1 \\
-1 & 1 & -1 \\
1 & -1 & 1 \\
-1 & 1 & 1
\end{array}\right\} \text{block 2} \\
\left.\begin{array}{ccc}
-\alpha & 0 & 0 \\
\alpha & 0 & 0 \\
0 & -\alpha & 0 \\
0 & \alpha & 0 \\
0 & 0 & -\alpha \\
0 & 0 & \alpha
\end{array}\right] \right\} \text{block 3}
\end{array}
\qquad (8.15)
$$

Notice that blocks 1 and 2 are *not* first order orthogonal designs, a fact which is a result of choosing a defining contrast which caused aliasing among main effects in the configurations formed as blocks.

rotatable or near rotatable central composite design in more than two blocks

Isolated cases were given on page 187 of central composite designs in two blocks, in which the block effect is orthogonal to the model coefficients, and in addition, the design is rotatable. Table 8.1 shows several rotatable or near rotatable central composite designs with b, the number of blocks, ranging from 2 to 17. In each case, the design blocks orthogonally and the number of center points is indicated. The partitioning of the factorial portion into blocks must be done so that each block is an orthogonal first order design. Likewise, the number of center points added to each factorial block is the same. Notice that in three cases, $k = 5, k = 6$, and $k = 7$, the factorial portion is taken as a 1/2 fraction of a 2^k. For example, for $k = 6$, a 1/2 fraction of a 2^6, that is thirty-two observations, is divided into two blocks, each block being a set which is an orthogonal first order design. This is accomplished by assigning to each block an appropriate 1/4 fraction of a 2^6 factorial arrangement.

other designs which block orthogonally

There are designs other than the ccd which block orthogonally in the case of the second order model. Probably the most useful is the hexagonal design for $k = 2$. A second example for the case of two variables is the configuration called the nonagon (nine points equally spaced on a circle). Both, of course, are rotatable designs.

For the hexagon with design matrix given on p. 156, one can actually divide the design into two equilateral triangles, or two-dimensional simplexes, one for each of two blocks. Since the simplex is an orthogonal first order design, the first condition for orthogonal blocking holds. For an even number, n_2, of center points, the second condition for orthogonal blocking will hold if $n_2/2$ center points are assigned to each block. Figure 8.1 is given as an illustration, where $n_2 = 4$ center points are used, two allotted to each block.

The hexagonal design provides an alternative to the $k = 2$ rotatable central composite design for the situation where two blocks are required. As Table 8.2 indicates, fourteen design points are required for the ccd; one can "get by" with as few as eight points for the hexagon. In order to provide an estimate of the experimental error variance, however, at least four center points (two in each block) should be used with the hexagon.

The design matrix for the nonagon can be easily constructed, and the design itself can be subdivided into *three simplexes* in a fashion similar to the way the hexagon was divided into two. The conditions for orthogonal blocking are satisfied if n_2 is a multiple of three and $n_2/3$ center points are assigned to each of the three blocks.

Example. The data given in Figure 8.2 are from a hexagonal experimental design for two factors in two blocks. The asterisks denote observations in the same block.

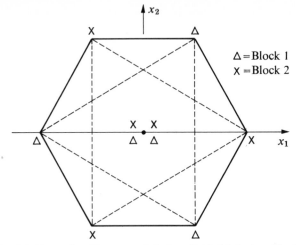

Fig. 8.1. Example of hexagonal design divided into two blocks.

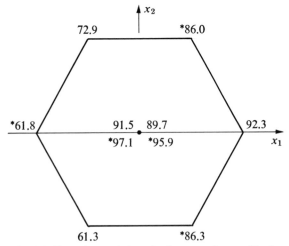

Fig. 8.2. Experimental data for hexagon in two blocks.

Table 8.2. Rotatable and Near-Rotatable Central Composite Designs Which Block Orthogonally

k	2	3	4	5	5 ($\frac{1}{2}$ rep)	6	6 ($\frac{1}{2}$ rep)	7	7 ($\frac{1}{2}$ rep)
Factorial block									
F: number of points in factorial portion	4	8	16	32	16	64	32	128	64
number of blocks in factorial portion	1	2	2	4	1	8	2	16	8
number of points in each block from factorial portion	4	4	8	8	16	8	16	8	8
number of added center points in each block	3	2	2	2	6	1	4	1	1
total number of points in each block	7	6	10	10	22	9	20	9	9
Axial block									
number of axial points	4	6	8	10	10	12	12	14	14
number of added center points	3	2	2	4	1	6	2	11	4
total number of points in block	7	8	10	14	11	18	14	25	18
grand total of points in the design	14	20	30	54	33	90	54	169	80
value of α for orthogonal blocking	1.4142	1.6330	2.0000	2.3664	2.0000	2.8284	2.3664	3.3636	2.8284
value of α for rotatability	1.4142	1.6818	2.0000	2.3784	2.0000	2.8284	2.3784	3.3333	2.8284

SOURCE: G. E. P. Box and J. S. Hunter, "Multifactor Designs for Exploring Response Surfaces," *Ann. Math. Stat.* **28** (1), 195 (1957).

Note that the experimental points (other than the center points) which are in the same block form a simplex. Two center points are used for each block. Using the model as described by Eq. 8.3 with $k = 2$, the X matrix is given by

$$X = \begin{array}{c} \quad\;\; x_1 \quad\;\; x_2 \quad\;\;\; x_1^2 \quad\;\; x_2^2 \quad\;\; x_1 x_2 \quad\;\; \delta_1 \quad\;\; \delta_2 \\ \left[\begin{array}{ccccccc} 1 & -1.0 & 0 & 1.0 & 0 & 0 & 1/2 & -1/2 \\ 1 & 0.5 & \sqrt{0.75} & 0.25 & 0.75 & \sqrt{3/16} & 1/2 & -1/2 \\ 1 & 0.5 & -\sqrt{0.75} & 0.25 & 0.75 & -\sqrt{3/16} & 1/2 & -1/2 \\ 1 & 0 & 0 & 0 & 0 & 0 & 1/2 & -1/2 \\ 1 & 0 & 0 & 0 & 0 & 0 & 1/2 & -1/2 \\ \hline 1 & -0.5 & \sqrt{0.75} & 0.25 & 0.75 & -\sqrt{3/16} & -1/2 & 1/2 \\ 1 & -0.5 & -\sqrt{0.75} & 0.25 & 0.75 & \sqrt{3/16} & -1/2 & 1/2 \\ 1 & 1.0 & 0 & 1.0 & 0 & 0 & -1/2 & 1/2 \\ 1 & 0 & 0 & 0 & 0 & 0 & -1/2 & 1/2 \\ 1 & 0 & 0 & 0 & 0 & 0 & -1/2 & 1/2 \end{array}\right] \begin{array}{l} \\ \left.\vphantom{\begin{array}{c}1\\1\\1\\1\\1\end{array}}\right\} \text{block 1} \\ \\ \\ \left.\vphantom{\begin{array}{c}1\\1\\1\\1\\1\end{array}}\right\} \text{block 2} \\ \\ \end{array}$$

and thus the $X'X$ matrix and the $X'\mathbf{y}$ vector are given by

$$X'X = \begin{bmatrix} 10 & 0 & 0 & 3 & 3 & 0 \\ & 3 & 0 & 0 & 0 & 0 \\ & & 3 & 0 & 0 & 0 \\ & & & 2.25 & 0.75 & 0 \\ & & & & 2.25 & 0 \\ & & & & & 0.75 \end{bmatrix} \qquad X'\mathbf{y} = \begin{bmatrix} 834.8 \\ 49.55 \\ 9.7858 \\ 230.725 \\ 229.875 \\ -5.1527 \end{bmatrix}.$$

Notice the "block contribution" in $X'X$ and $X'\mathbf{y}$ was ignored since the design blocks orthogonally. In fact, the coefficients are estimated as if no blocking were required.

Using the usual least squares techniques we arrive at the following estimates of the model coefficients

$$\begin{aligned} b_0' &= 93.55 \\ b_1 &= 16.515 \\ b_2 &= 3.2616 \\ b_{11} &= -16.5077 \\ b_{22} &= -17.0744 \\ b_{12} &= -6.8701. \end{aligned}$$

The stationary point is computed by the methods described in Chapter 5 and is found in this example to be

$$x_{1,0} = 0.5013 \qquad x_{2,0} = -0.0053.$$

The λ values in the canonical analysis are the characteristic roots of the matrix

$$B = \begin{bmatrix} -16.5077 & -3.4350 \\ & -17.0744 \end{bmatrix}$$

and are found to be

$$\lambda_1 = -13.3443 \qquad \lambda_2 = -20.2378,$$

indicating that the stationary point represents the location of maximum estimated response.

The analysis of variance is accomplished in the usual fashion. The following computations show the appropriate sums of squares for linear and quadratic regression:

$$\text{sum of squares for linear regression} = b_1(49.55) + b_2(9.7858)$$
$$= 850.24$$

$$\text{sum of squares for quadratic regression} = b_{11}(230.725)$$
$$+ b_{22}(229.875)$$
$$+ b_{12}(-5.1527)$$
$$+ b_0'(834.80)$$
$$- (834.8)^2/10$$
$$= 708.12.$$

The sum of squares for blocks (1 degree of freedom) is found in the usual fashion. Table 8.3 shows the analysis.

Table 8.3. Analysis of Variance for Hexagon Given in Fig. 8.2

Source	Sum of Squares	Degrees of Freedom	Mean Square	F
blocks	37.64	1	37.64	32.17
linear regression	850.24	2	425.12	363.35
quadratic regression	708.12	3	236.04	201.74
lack-of-fit	10.44	1	10.44	8.92
error	2.34	2	1.17	

exercises

8.1. Construct an experimental design in four blocks with four factors at two levels each. Use $ABCD$ and AD as the defining contrasts.

8.2. Show the construction of a design in eight blocks with six factors, A, B, C, D, E, and F. Be sure that no main effect is confounded with blocks.

8.3. The following design matrix describes a central composite design which is near rotatable. The design has been divided into three blocks. Show that the conditions for orthogonal blocking for second order designs do in fact hold.

	x_1	x_2	x_3	x_4	x_5	x_6	
	−1	−1	−1	−1	−1	−1	
	1	1	−1	−1	−1	−1	
	1	−1	1	−1	−1	−1	
	−1	1	1	−1	−1	−1	
	−1	−1	−1	1	1	−1	
	−1	−1	−1	1	−1	1	
	−1	−1	−1	−1	1	1	
	1	1	−1	1	1	−1	
	1	1	−1	1	−1	1	
	1	1	−1	−1	1	1	block 1
	1	−1	1	1	1	−1	
	1	−1	1	1	−1	1	
	1	−1	1	−1	1	1	
	−1	1	1	1	1	−1	
	−1	1	1	1	−1	1	
	−1	1	1	−1	1	1	
	0	0	0	0	0	0	
	0	0	0	0	0	0	
	0	0	0	0	0	0	
	0	0	0	0	0	0	
	1	−1	−1	−1	1	−1	
	−1	1	−1	−1	1	−1	
	−1	−1	1	−1	1	−1	
	1	1	1	−1	1	−1	
	1	−1	−1	1	−1	−1	
	1	−1	−1	1	1	1	
	1	−1	−1	−1	−1	1	
$D =$	−1	1	−1	1	−1	−1	
	−1	1	−1	1	1	1	
	−1	1	−1	−1	−1	1	
	−1	−1	1	1	−1	−1	block 2
	−1	−1	1	1	1	1	
	−1	−1	1	−1	−1	1	
	1	1	1	1	−1	−1	
	1	1	1	1	1	1	
	1	1	1	−1	−1	1	
	0	0	0	0	0	0	
	0	0	0	0	0	0	
	0	0	0	0	0	0	
	0	0	0	0	0	0	

$$D = \begin{bmatrix}
2.3664 & 0 & 0 & 0 & 0 & 0 \\
-2.3664 & 0 & 0 & 0 & 0 & 0 \\
0 & 2.3664 & 0 & 0 & 0 & 0 \\
0 & -2.3664 & 0 & 0 & 0 & 0 \\
0 & 0 & 2.3664 & 0 & 0 & 0 \\
0 & 0 & -2.3664 & 0 & 0 & 0 \\
0 & 0 & 0 & 2.3664 & 0 & 0 \\
0 & 0 & 0 & -2.3664 & 0 & 0 \\
0 & 0 & 0 & 0 & 2.3664 & 0 \\
0 & 0 & 0 & 0 & -2.3664 & 0 \\
0 & 0 & 0 & 0 & 0 & 2.3664 \\
0 & 0 & 0 & 0 & 0 & -2.3664 \\
0 & 0 & 0 & 0 & 0 & 0 \\
0 & 0 & 0 & 0 & 0 & 0
\end{bmatrix} \Bigg\} \text{block 3}$$

references

Box, G. E. P. and J. S. Hunter: "Multifactor Experimental Designs for Exploring Response Surfaces," *Ann. Math. Stat.* **28** (1), 195 (1957).

9 | other criteria for choosing response surface designs

In much of the development presented in the preceding chapters on experimental designs, the emphasis has been on the use of orthogonal and rotatable designs for fitting first and second order models. Inherent in the use of rotatable designs is the consideration of the variance of an estimated response $\hat{y}$, the latter being a function of the point $x_1, x_2, \ldots, x_k$ in some region of the independent variables. In many cases, equally important is the consideration of the *bias* of $\hat{y}$ due to the inadequacy of the polynomial of order d in representing the *true* response function. The concept of bias has not been totally disregarded in our previous development. In Chapter 6, the theory of aliasing was discussed and later applied to certain first and second order designs.

Here, certain additional criteria for choosing designs will be presented—criteria which consider bias and variance simultaneously. Consideration of bias seems particularly pertinent in cases in which a first order model is used; the question arises as to whether or not the choice of a response surface design can offer proper protection against the possibility of curvature in the response system in the region of interest of the variables. In the case of a second order design, one might be interested in a design which affords protection against the existence of cubic terms in the true response function.

9.1 | design criterion of average mean squared error

Several researchers have concentrated on experimental design criteria which included bias as a significant consideration. In fact, there is no shortage of design criteria in the statistics literature; many have been suggested and explored.

In general, we can formulate the problem by supposing that the experimenter fits a model $\hat{y}(x_1, x_2, \ldots, x_k)$ of order d_1 in a region R of the independent variables; the true model, however, is a polynomial $g(x_1, x_2, \ldots, x_k)$ of order d_2, where $d_2 > d_1$. Then, a reasonable design criterion is the minimization of

$$J = \left\{ [N/\sigma^2] \int_R E[\hat{y}(\mathbf{x}) - g(\mathbf{x})]^2 \, d\mathbf{x} \right\} \Big/ \int_R d\mathbf{x}. \qquad (9.1)$$

Here, the vector notation $\mathbf{x}$ has been chosen for convenience. The multiple integral in Eq. 9.1 actually represents the *average* of the expected squared deviations of the true response from the estimated response over the region R. The appeal of this criterion is twofold: (1) it provides a means of simultaneously considering both the bias and variance of $\hat{y}$; (2) it does not suffer from being restricted to considering only particular model coefficients, or the bias and variance at a single point $x_1, x_2, \ldots, x_k$; rather it takes into consideration the quality of $\hat{y}$ as an estimator in the entire region R. Writing the integral $\int_R d\mathbf{x} = 1/K$,

$$J = \frac{NK}{\sigma^2} \int_R E[\hat{y}(\mathbf{x}) - g(\mathbf{x})]^2 \, d\mathbf{x}$$

$$= \frac{NK}{\sigma^2} \int_R E[\hat{y} - E(\hat{y}) + E(\hat{y}) - g]^2 \, d\mathbf{x}$$

$$= \frac{NK}{\sigma^2} \left\{ \int_R E[\hat{y} - E(\hat{y})]^2 \, d\mathbf{x} + \int_R [E(\hat{y}) - g]^2 \, d\mathbf{x} \right\}. \qquad (9.2)$$

The first quantity in Eq. 9.2 is the variance of $\hat{y}$, integrated or, rather, averaged over the region R, whereas the second quantity is the square of the bias, similarly averaged. Thus J is naturally divided as follows:

$$J = V + B, \qquad (9.3)$$

where V is the average variance of $\hat{y}$, and B is the average squared bias of $\hat{y}$. It would seem, then, that a reasonable choice of design might be taken from the following:

1. The experimental design which minimizes V.
2. The experimental design which minimizes B.
3. The experimental design which minimizes $V + B$.

Although the minimization of $V + B$ has the most appeal, it is impossible to do in a practical situation, as will subsequently be shown. This then leads one to considering either Step (1) or (2).

9.2 | the first order response model

In the case of the first order model, these *average squared bias* and *average variance* quantities are easiest to illustrate for the case of a single independent variable, that is, when the fitted response surface takes the form of a simple straight line. The design criterion becomes simple to understand, and the algebra used in the development does not include the manipulation of complicated matrices that are involved in the more general case.

single independent variable

Suppose the experimenter decides to fit a straight line, and is confronted with the decision as to what experimental design to choose. The design problem in this case is one of deciding how to space the levels of the independent variable x in the experimental runs. Recall that x is a coded variable so that the region, or in this case the *interval R*, is scaled to $[-1, +1]$. The fitted equation, that is, the one that the experimenter feels is adequate, takes the form

$$\hat{y} = b_0 + b_1 x \tag{9.4}$$

and, e.g., the true condition is best described by

$$E(y) = \beta_0 + \beta_1 x + \beta_{11} x^2. \tag{9.5}$$

Suppose we consider Eq. 9.4 in deciding on a proper design. The design is specified by the matrix (in this simple case a column vector)

$$D = \begin{bmatrix} x_1 \\ x_2 \\ \cdots \\ x_N \end{bmatrix}.$$

It is assumed here that we are restricting ourselves to designs for which $\sum_{u=1}^{N} x_u = 0$. The integral J can then be expressed as

$$J = \frac{NK}{\sigma^2} \left\{ \int_{-1}^{1} [\text{var } b_0 + x^2 \text{ var } b_1] \, dx \right.$$
$$\left. + \int_{-1}^{1} [E\hat{y} - \beta_0 - \beta_1 x - \beta_{11} x^2]^2 \, dx \right\}. \tag{9.6}$$

In this case, $\int_{-1}^{1} dx = 2$. The variance portion of J is immediately evaluated since var $b_0 = \sigma^2/N$ and var $(b_1) = \sigma^2/N[11])$, where $[11]$ is the second moment of the design, that is, $[11] = \sum_{u=1}^{N} x_u^2/N$. Therefore,

$$V = \frac{1}{2} \int_{-1}^{1} \left(1 + \frac{x^2}{[11]}\right) dx$$

$$= 1 + \frac{1}{3[11]}. \qquad (9.7)$$

In order that the bias portion can be evaluated, the bias in the individual coefficients must first be determined. Using the techniques and notation described in Chapter 6, the alias structure can very simply be developed for this case. The matrices X_1 and X_2 are given by

$$X_1 = \begin{bmatrix} 1 & x_1 \\ 1 & x_2 \\ \cdots & \cdots \\ 1 & x_N \end{bmatrix} \qquad X_2 = \begin{bmatrix} x_1^2 \\ x_2^2 \\ \cdots \\ x_N^2 \end{bmatrix}.$$

The X_1 matrix indicates the fitted model, namely, first order, whereas X_2 contains a column giving the levels of the x^2 term. The alias matrix $A = (X_1'X_1)^{-1}X_1'X_2$, is given by

$$A = \begin{bmatrix} 1/N & 0 \\ 0 & 1/(N[11]) \end{bmatrix} \begin{bmatrix} N[11] \\ N[111] \end{bmatrix}$$

$$= \begin{bmatrix} [11] \\ [111]/[11] \end{bmatrix}.$$

Here, the usual vector $\boldsymbol{\beta}_2$ takes the form of the single element β_{11}. Thus, one can write

$$E(b_0) = \beta_0 + [11]\beta_{11} \qquad (9.8)$$

$$E(b_1) = \beta_1 + \{[111]/[11]\}\beta_{11}. \qquad (9.9)$$

Using Eqs. 9.8 and 9.9,

$$E(\hat{y}) = \beta_0 + \beta_1 x + \beta_{11}\{[11] + [111]x/[11]\},$$

and so from Eq. 9.6, the average squared bias can be written

$$B = \frac{N\beta_{11}^2}{2\sigma^2} \int_{-1}^{1} \{[11] + [111]x/[11] - x^2\}^2 \, dx$$

$$= \frac{N\beta_{11}^2}{\sigma^2} \{[11]^2 - (2/3)[11] + 1/5 + [111]^2/(3[11]^2)\}. \qquad (9.10)$$

Notice that, initially, despite the values of $[11]$, β_{11}, σ^2, and N, B *is minimized with respect to the third moment* $[111]$ *by making the latter zero.* Turning our attention to $J = V + B$, with $[111]$ set equal to zero,

$$J = \{1 + 1/(3[11])\} + \frac{N\beta_{11}^2}{\sigma^2}\{([11] - 1/3)^2 + 4/45\}. \quad (9.11)$$

The second moment occurs in both V and B. Unfortunately, the value of $[11]$ which minimizes J depends on the quadratic coefficient β_{11}. Therefore, one cannot realistically use the J criterion to find a design *without prior knowledge about* β_{11}.

In observing Eq. 9.11, the following conclusions become apparent:

1. If the bias in the straight line approximation is expected to be negligible in comparison to the error variance, resulting in a small value for $N\beta_{11}^2/\sigma^2$, one should minimize V, this being accomplished with $[11]$ *being as large as possible.*
2. In order to protect against a substantial bias in $\hat{y}$, B should be minimized, this being accomplished by a value of $[11] = 1/3$.

The conclusions that have been reached should not be surprising to the practitioner. That is, in order to minimize the average variance, the spread in the design points, reflected by the value of the second design moment, should be as large as possible. In order to guard against possibility of curvature in the response function, the spread should be made smaller; more specifically a value of $1/3$ should be used. In the case where the criterion is conclusion (1), care should be taken to avoid using design points outside the region where it is felt that the first order approximation is adequate. That is, when variance is the sole consideration, while the design which minimizes the average variance is one in which $[11] = \infty$, there is obviously some practical limit or bound on $[11]$ in nearly all problems of this nature.

Criteria (1) and (2) are used as the two extreme cases, bias being the heavy contributor to J on one hand, and variance on the other. Of course all problems do not fall into one of these two categories. However, there is considerable evidence which indicates that unless bias is very unlikely (that is, the fitted model is the true model), then choosing the experimental plan which protects against bias, the design called the *all-bias* design, seems to be the more fruitful approach. If, in fact, one knows the values of $N\beta_{11}/\sigma^2$ and could then find the best design, namely, that which minimizes J, the design would often be very close to the all-bias design; this argument obviously becomes less valid as the V contribution becomes greater compared to B. As an illustration, consider a value of $\sqrt{N}\beta_{11}/\sigma$ of 4.499. The optimum design is one in which $[11] = 0.3844$, which deviates little from the second moment for the all-bias design. This particular numerical example was selected because the resulting values of V and B are equal. As a second example, a situation is considered which is closer to the extreme of dominating variance, namely, when $\sqrt{N}\beta_{11}/\sigma = 1.822$. Here, the V contribution to J is four times the contribution of B, and the optimum design is one for which $[11] = 0.5184$. For this situation, the optimum design gives a J value of 2.052 while the J value for the all-bias design is 2.296. Thus, even though the variance contribution to J overwhelms the bias, one encounters very little increase in J over the minimum by using the design which minimizes B. Further illustration is given in Table 9.1. Several values of the parameter $\sqrt{N}\beta_{11}/\sigma$ are assumed and the optimum design is given. The J values are compared with the J that results when the all-bias design is chosen. Notice that the all-bias design is effective in a wide variety of situations. In fact, only when the variance contribution, V, is more than six times the bias, B, is there an apparent significant increase in J over the minimum value when one uses the all-bias design.

Table 9.1. Values of J for Optimum and All-Bias Design for a First Order Model With $k = 1$

$\sqrt{N}\beta_{11}/\sigma$	[11] (optimum)	J (optimum)	J (all-bias)
9.375 ($V = \frac{1}{4}B$)	0.349	9.777	9.800
6.540 ($V = \frac{1}{2}B$)	0.363	5.755	5.799
4.499 ($V = B$)	0.388	3.718	3.798
2.994 ($V = 2B$)	0.433	2.656	2.797
1.822 ($V = 4B$)	0.519	2.052	2.296
1.215 ($V = 6B$)	0.623	1.790	2.131
0.501 ($V = 10B$)	1.000	1.467	2.022
0.103 ($V = 20B$)	2.626	1.183	2.001

These results indicate that one should certainly not ignore the possibility of bias that arises from inadequacy of model approximation when choosing a response surface design. In fact, it would even seem that errors that occur due to bias play an even more important role, as far as $\hat{y}$ is concerned, than those errors which result from sampling variation.

ACTUAL SPACING OF LEVELS FOR FITTING A STRAIGHT LINE

The development of appropriate experimental designs for fitting a straight line is very simple. One very important restriction is that the third moment $\sum_{u=1}^{N} x_u^3/N$ should be made zero. This is accomplished by arranging the points symmetrically about the midpoint of the scaled interval $[-1, +1]$. If the bias in representing the true function as a straight line is known to be negligible, then the second moment $\sum_{u=1}^{N} x_u^2/N$ should be made as large as possible. The appropriate spacing of the design points for N even is to apply $N/2$ points at the extreme of the region in which the straight line is considered to be a good approximation. For N odd, apply $(N-1)/2$ points at each of the extremes and a single point at $x = 0$.

If the experimenter is interested in affording himself a certain amount of protection against the existence of a quadratic term in the model, then the design should have, in addition to a zero value for $[111]$, a second moment which is approximately $1/3$. As an example, if two levels of x are to be used, an appropriate design is to assign an even number of points in the following way:

$$N/2 \text{ at } x = -0.58, \qquad N/2 \text{ at } x = +0.58.$$

For three levels, an appropriate design is a uniform distribution of observations among the levels $-\sqrt{0.5}$, 0, $+\sqrt{0.5}$. One sees that as the chosen number of design levels becomes larger, more flexibility enters the picture. For example, consider the case of four levels illustrated in Fig. 9.1.

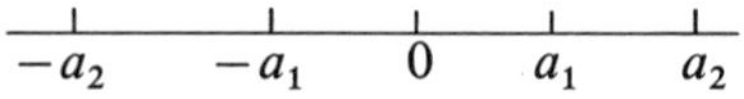

Fig. 9.1. Spacing of $N/4$ observations at a_1, a_2, $-a_1$, and $-a_2$.

The values a_1 and a_2 are such that

$$\frac{(a_1^2 + a_2^2)}{2} = 1/3.$$

There are many choices for a_1 and a_2; for example $a_2 = \sqrt{1/2}$ and $a_1 = \sqrt{1/6}$ or $a_2 = \sqrt{5/12}$ and $a_1 = 1/2$.

more than one independent variable

The selection of appropriate designs, using the bias and variance criteria, can be extended to k independent variables. That is, the same experimental design criteria are used in a case where the true relationship is unknown, but the experimenter assumes that it can be approximated by the usual first order model

$$\hat{y} = b_0 + \sum_{j=1}^{k} b_j x_j \tag{9.12}$$

in some region of interest R of the independent variables. In vector notation, Eq. 9.12 is written as

$$\hat{y} = \mathbf{x}_1' \hat{\boldsymbol{\beta}}_1 \tag{9.13}$$

where

$$\mathbf{x}_1' = [1, x_1, x_2, \ldots, x_k]$$
$$\boldsymbol{\beta}_1' = [b_0, b_1, \ldots, b_k].$$

The last k elements in $\mathbf{x}_1'$ represent a point on which $\hat{y}$ is evaluated. Realistically, however, one might think of the true model as being best explained by

$$E(y) = \mathbf{x}_1' \boldsymbol{\beta}_1 + \mathbf{x}_2' \boldsymbol{\beta}_2 \qquad (9.14)$$

where $\mathbf{x}_2' \boldsymbol{\beta}_2$ represents the contribution of terms beyond the first order model. For the case where the true model is second order,

$$\boldsymbol{\beta}_2 = [\beta_{11}, \beta_{22}, \ldots, \beta_{kk}, \beta_{12}, \beta_{13}, \ldots, \beta_{k-1,k}]$$
$$\mathbf{x}_2' = [x_1^2, x_2^2, \ldots, x_k^2, x_1 x_2, x_1 x_3, \ldots, x_{k-1} x_k].$$

Now, the variance of $\hat{y}$ for the fitted model can be written very simply as

$$\operatorname{var} \hat{y} = \operatorname{var} \mathbf{x}_1' \hat{\boldsymbol{\beta}}_1$$
$$= \mathbf{x}_1'[\operatorname{var} \hat{\boldsymbol{\beta}}_1] \mathbf{x}_1. \qquad (9.15)$$

If the experimental design takes the form

$$D = \begin{bmatrix} x_{11} & x_{21} & \cdots & x_{k1} \\ x_{12} & x_{22} & \cdots & x_{k2} \\ \cdots & \cdots & \cdots & \cdots \\ x_{1N} & x_{2N} & \cdots & x_{kN} \end{bmatrix}, \qquad (9.16)$$

then the first order model, in general linear model form, is written

$$E(\mathbf{y}) = X_1 \boldsymbol{\beta}_1$$

where

$$X_1 = [\mathbf{1} \mid D]$$

and $\mathbf{1}$ represents a column of ones. The reader will recall from the development in Chapter 3 that $\operatorname{var} \hat{\boldsymbol{\beta}}_1 = \sigma^2 (X_1' X_1)^{-1}$ and thus from Eq. 9.15,

$$(\operatorname{var} \hat{y})/\sigma^2 = \mathbf{x}_1' (X_1' X_1)^{-1} \mathbf{x}_1.$$

Returning now to the criteria discussed in the previous section for choosing experimental designs, the variance portion of J in Eq. 9.16 can be written

$$V = NK \int_R \mathbf{x}_1' (X_1' X_1)^{-1} \mathbf{x}_1 \, d\mathbf{x}. \qquad (9.17)$$

The portion $\mathbf{x}_1' (X_1' X_1)^{-1} \mathbf{x}_1$ is, of course, a quadratic form in the variables of the vector $\mathbf{x}_1$. Before the bias portion is written, perhaps it would be well to reiterate the bias of the elements in $\hat{\boldsymbol{\beta}}_1$.

$$E(\hat{\boldsymbol{\beta}}_1) = \boldsymbol{\beta}_1 + A \boldsymbol{\beta}_2$$

where A is the alias matrix which accounts for the existence of the higher order terms. The matrix $A = (X_1'X_1)^{-1}X_1'X_2$, where, in the case in which X_2 describes a second order model,

$$
X_2 = \begin{bmatrix}
x_{11}^2 & x_{21}^2 & \cdots & x_{k1}^2 & x_{11}x_{21} & \cdots & x_{k-1,1}x_{k1} \\
x_{12}^2 & x_{22}^2 & \cdots & x_{k2}^2 & x_{12}x_{22} & \cdots & x_{k-1,2}x_{k2} \\
\cdots & \cdots & \cdots & \cdots & \cdots & \cdots & \cdots \\
x_{1N}^2 & x_{2N}^2 & \cdots & x_{kN}^2 & x_{1N}x_{2N} & \cdots & x_{k-1,N}x_{kN}
\end{bmatrix}.
$$

The bias of $\hat{y}$ at a point $(x_1, x_2, \ldots, x_k)$ is given by

$$
E[\mathbf{x}_1'\hat{\boldsymbol{\beta}}_1 - (\mathbf{x}_1'\boldsymbol{\beta}_1 + \mathbf{x}_2'\boldsymbol{\beta}_2)] = \mathbf{x}_1'[\boldsymbol{\beta}_1 + A\boldsymbol{\beta}_2] - [\mathbf{x}_1'\boldsymbol{\beta}_1 + \mathbf{x}_2'\boldsymbol{\beta}_2]
$$
$$
= \mathbf{x}_1'A\boldsymbol{\beta}_2 - \mathbf{x}_2'\boldsymbol{\beta}_2.
$$

Thus the bias contribution to J is given by

$$
B = \frac{NK}{\sigma^2} \int_R [\mathbf{x}_1'A\boldsymbol{\beta}_2 - \mathbf{x}_2'\boldsymbol{\beta}_2]^2 \, d\mathbf{x}
$$
$$
= \frac{NK}{\sigma^2} \int_R \boldsymbol{\beta}_2'[A'\mathbf{x}_1 - \mathbf{x}_2][\mathbf{x}_1'A - \mathbf{x}_2']\boldsymbol{\beta}_2 \, d\mathbf{x}. \tag{9.18}
$$

Attention should be given at this point regarding the region of interest R. In the case of a single variable, R was an interval, and the variance and bias in $\hat{y}$ were averaged uniformly over that interval. For example, if the variable in question were temperature and the interval of interest is given by $[100°C, 200°C]$, then the variable x is coded as

$$
x = \frac{\text{temp.} - 150}{50}.
$$

In the case of more than one variable, the region chosen for use in much of the theoretical work in this area (Box and Draper; 1959, 1963) is a sphere, the latter being arranged so that its center is in the center of a coordinate system chosen by the experimenter; the region, scaled so that its radius is unity, contains all points $(x_1, x_2, \ldots, x_k)$ which satisfy

$$
\sum_{i=1}^{k} x_i^2 \leq 1. \tag{9.19}
$$

Consider an example in two dimensions (time, temp.) in which an experimenter feels as if the center of R should be the point defined by $T = 150°C$ and $t = 2$ hr, and interest lies basically in an elliptical region around this point, with distances from the center being 50°C and 1 hr. Thus, in defining the coordinate system, a unit in temperature corresponds to 50°C and a unit in time corresponds to 1 hr. Thus we can form the design variables given by

$$x_1 = \frac{T - 150}{50}, \qquad x_2 = \frac{t - 2}{1},$$

and the experimental region R is the sphere, or actually a circle in this situation, given by

$$x_1^2 + x_2^2 \le 1,$$

and is illustrated by Fig. 9.2. It should certainly be pointed out that the choice of R definitely affects the results one obtains in his search for designs which approach "optimality."

Consider once again V and B given in Eqs. 9.17 and 9.18, respectively. We shall present one result without proof which becomes quite helpful in evaluating J. If the region R is that given by Eq. 9.19, then

$$\int_R x_1^{\delta_1} x_2^{\delta_2} \ldots x_k^{\delta_k} \, d\mathbf{x}$$

$$= \frac{\Gamma\left(\frac{\delta_1 + 1}{2}\right) \Gamma\left(\frac{\delta_2 + 1}{2}\right) \ldots \Gamma\left(\frac{\delta_k + 1}{2}\right)}{\Gamma\left(\frac{\sum_{i=1}^{k}(\delta_i + 1)}{2} + 1\right)} \qquad \text{(all } \delta_i \text{ even)}$$

$$= 0 \qquad \text{(any } \delta_i \text{ odd)} \tag{9.20}$$

where $\Gamma(-)$ refers to the usual *gamma function*, that is,

$$\Gamma(p) = \int_0^\infty v^{p-1} e^{-v} \, dv \qquad (p > 0).$$

From Eq. 9.17, $K^{-1}V$ can be written

$$K^{-1}V = \sum_{i=0}^{k} \sum_{j=0}^{k} c^{ij} \int_R x_i x_j \, d\mathbf{x} \tag{9.21}$$

where c^{ij} is the (ij) element of $N(X_1'X_1)^{-1}$, the precision matrix, and x_0 is taken as unity. The rows and columns of $N(X_1'X_1)^{-1}$ are numbered

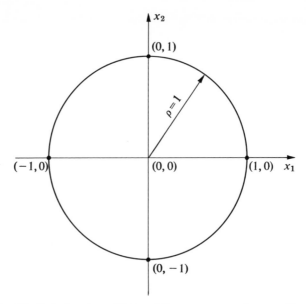

Fig. 9.2. Coded region of interest for response surface problem in two dimensions.

$0, 1, 2, \ldots, k$ for convenience. The integral $\int_R x_i x_j \, d\mathbf{x}$ will take a zero value unless $i = j$. For $i = j = 0$, $\int_R x_i x_j \, d\mathbf{x} = K$, and for $i = j = 1, 2, \ldots, k$,

$$\int_R x_i^2 \, d\mathbf{x} = \frac{\pi^{k/2}}{(k + 2)\Gamma\left(\dfrac{k + 2}{2}\right)} \tag{9.22}$$

since $\Gamma(p + 1) = p\Gamma(p)$ and $\Gamma(1/2) = \sqrt{\pi}$. Evaluating K^{-1}, we have

$$K^{-1} = \int_R d\mathbf{x} = \frac{\pi^{k/2}}{\Gamma\left(\dfrac{k + 2}{2}\right)}. \tag{9.23}$$

It is assumed, as in the case of a single variable, that the design, specified by the matrix D in Eq. 9.16 is such that the levels of each variable are located centrally around zero. Then

$$\sum_{u=1}^{N} x_{iu} = 0.$$

Thus, in $N(X_1'X_1)^{-1}$, $c^{0j} = 0$ for $j = 1, 2, \ldots, k$, and $c^{00} = 1$. From Eqs. 9.21–9.23,

$$V = 1 + \sum_{j=1}^{k} c^{jj}/(k + 2). \tag{9.24}$$

As far as B is concerned, if it is assumed that the *response surface is actually quadratic*, Eq. 9.18 can be written

$$B = \frac{1}{(k+2)} \sum_{g=1}^{k} \left\{ \sum_{i=1}^{k} \sum_{j=i}^{k} \alpha_{ij} \sum_{h=1}^{k} c^{gh}[hij] \right\}^2$$

$$+ \left\{ \sum_{i=1}^{k} \sum_{j=i}^{k} \alpha_{ij}([ij] - \delta_{ij}/(k+2)) \right\}^2$$

$$+ \frac{2(k+2) \sum_{i=1}^{k} \alpha_{ii}^2 + (k+2) \sum_{i=1}^{k} \sum_{j=i+1}^{k} \alpha_{ij}^2 - 2 \left(\sum_{i=1}^{k} \alpha_{ii} \right)^2}{(k+2)^2(k+4)}. \qquad (9.25)$$

The details of the derivation of this result are found in Appendix b, Section b.1. In Eq. 9.25,

$$\alpha_{ij} = \beta_{ij}\sqrt{N}/\sigma, \qquad \delta_{ij} = \begin{cases} 0 & i \neq j \\ 1 & i = j \end{cases}.$$

The term $[hij]$ refers to the third moment of the design. In the case of V, the important parameters are the second moments, which affect the c_{jj}, the diagonal elements of the inverse of the moment matrix. In the case of B, the third moments, the second moments, and the β_{ij}, the second order coefficients, are contained in the expression. It is initially observed that the third order moments enter only in the first term of B in Eq. 9.25, therefore B and thus $V + B$ is minimized with respect to $[hij]$ by making the latter zero. As in the case where $k = 1$, after making the third moments zero, J cannot be minimized with respect to the $[ii]$ without the assumption of knowledge of the β_{ij}. As a result, V and B are again considered separately.

CONSIDERATION OF VARIANCE ALONE

Consider first the situation where the experimenter is not concerned with the bias due to quadratic effects in the first order model approximation. The goal in this case is to disregard B and thus minimize V. From Eq. 9.24, V is minimized when each c^{jj} is as small as possible; this is tantamount to restricting the variances of the b_j to be as small as possible. Using a minor variation of the proof on page 109 it can easily be shown that in order to minimize V,

Choose $[ii]$ as large as possible, without extending beyond the region where the first order model is appropriate.

Make $[ij] = 0$, that is, make the first order design *orthogonal*.

CONSIDERATION OF BIAS ALONE

We now turn our attention to the other extreme, namely, the case in which the experimenter feels as if the bias contribution from fitting a first order model likely dominates sampling variation. For minimizing B, observe the second term of Eq. 9.25, the first term having been removed by setting the third moments to zero. It becomes clear that B is minimized when

$$[ij] = 0$$
$$[ii] = 1/(k + 2). \qquad (9.26)$$

So, for this case, the optimum design is also an orthogonal design. However, the two extremes present diverse choices for the spread in the design points. This is what the reader would expect after observing the results given in the section on the Single Independent Variable (p. 198).

PROPER CHOICE OF A DESIGN

Unless the experimenter has knowledge about the response system that would lead him to either the all-bias design (above) or the all-variance design (p. 207), a "compromise" between the two is perhaps the most fruitful approach. The reader recalls that in the $k = 1$ case, evidence was presented which indicated that the all-bias plan, or a design plan which was close to all-bias, gave values of J which, in cases where the bias *and* variance are both contributors, did not deviate a great deal from the J values for the design which minimizes J. The same seems to hold true for $k > 1$. These results are illustrated and explained in Appendix b for the case where $k > 1$. Box and Draper (1959) define the *size* of the design as the root mean square distance of the design points from the center of the region R. That is the size is given by

$$\dot{r} = \sqrt{N^{-1} \sum_{u=1}^{N} \sum_{i=1}^{k} x_{iu}^2} \, .$$

If all of the second moments are equal, then

$$\dot{r} = \sqrt{k[ii]} \qquad (9.27)$$

which for the all-bias design becomes

$$\dot{r} = \sqrt{k/(k + 2)}. \qquad (9.28)$$

In nearly all of the situations described in Table b.1 in Appendix b, the size of the optimal design is between that of the all-bias design given in Eq. 9.28 and unity, the latter representing a design in which all points are on the border of the region R. In addition, the J value for the all-bias design is not far from the J value for the optimal design.

In light of what has been presented in this and previous sections, unless one is immediately led by previous information about the system to either the all-bias or all-variance design, the appropriate first order experimental design should have the following characteristics:

1. The design should be orthogonal.
2. All third moments should be zero.
3. The pure second moments, $[ii]$, should be equal and such that $\dot{r} = \sqrt{k[ii]}$ is between $\sqrt{k/(k+2)}$ and unity.

It is very simple to construct designs which satisfy the necessary requirements. In fact, the class of 2^k factorial designs for which $[ii]$ meets requirement (3) is a good example. Suppose for $k = 3$, on the basis of requirement (3), it is decided that $\dot{r}$ should be 0.8, slightly more than the value $\dot{r} = 0.77$ for the all-bias design. Then $[ii]$ should be $(0.8)^2/k = 0.213$; using a 2^3 factorial design, $N = 8$ and thus

$$\sum_{u=1}^{8} x_{iu}^2 = 8(0.213) = 1.704.$$

Then, using the scale basis that the region of interest is the unit sphere, the appropriate design matrix is

$$D = \begin{array}{ccc} x_1 & x_2 & x_3 \end{array}
\begin{bmatrix}
-g & -g & -g \\
-g & g & -g \\
-g & -g & g \\
-g & g & g \\
g & -g & -g \\
g & g & -g \\
g & -g & g \\
g & g & g
\end{bmatrix}$$

where
$$g = \sqrt{0.213}.$$

Notice that conditions (1), (2), and (3) hold for this design. The reader should be cautioned to emphasize requirement (2) as well as requirement (3). That is, the search for these designs is *not* merely one of finding an orthogonal design and changing the spread in the design points to fit requirement (3). In fact, all first order orthogonal designs do not *necessarily* satisfy requirement (2).

If the experimenter cannot afford the number of experimental trials required by the full 2^k factorial design, certain fractional factorial designs fit the requirements. These designs are first order orthogonal, and the third moments will vanish *if no two factor interaction is aliased with a main effect.* For example, for $k = 4$, the design given by

$$
D = \begin{array}{c} \begin{array}{cccc} x_1 & x_2 & x_3 & x_4 \end{array} \\ \begin{bmatrix} g & -g & -g & -g \\ -g & g & -g & -g \\ -g & -g & g & -g \\ -g & -g & -g & g \\ g & g & g & -g \\ g & g & -g & g \\ g & -g & g & g \\ -g & g & g & g \end{bmatrix} \end{array}
\tag{9.29}
$$

is a 1/2 fraction of 2^4 with defining contrast $ABCD$. A quick check will reveal that all third moments are zero. If a value of $\dot{r} = 0.9$ is selected, this value being between $\sqrt{2/3}$ (all-bias) and unity, then the appropriate value of g is $0.9/\sqrt{k} = 0.45$.

More generally, for k factors to be investigated with N trials, where N is even and $k \leq N/2$, designs which meet the requirements can be established by initially constructing a $(N/2 \times k)$ matrix D_1 in which the columns are orthogonal and the sum of squares of the elements in each column are given by $(N/2)\,[ii]$, where $[ij]$ is predetermined from restriction (3). The appropriate design matrix is merely

$$
D_{N \times k} = \begin{bmatrix} D_1 \\ \hline -D_1 \end{bmatrix}.
\tag{9.30}
$$

The design D has been constructed so that it is orthogonal. The size $\dot{r}$ will satisfy restriction (3), and the third moments are all zero. To prove this latter result, we merely begin by considering the matrix

$$
Z = \begin{array}{c} \begin{array}{cccccc} x_1^2 & x_2^2 \cdots x_k^2, & x_1 x_2, & x_1 x_3 \cdots x_{k-1} x_k \end{array} \\ \begin{bmatrix} \cdot & \cdot & \cdot & \cdot & \cdot & \cdot \\ \cdot & \cdot & \cdot & \cdot & \cdot & \cdot \\ \cdot & \cdot & \cdot & \cdot & \cdot & \cdot \end{bmatrix} \end{array},
$$

where the entries are determined from the design levels given by the design matrix D. This matrix can be partitioned

$$
Z = \begin{bmatrix} D_2 \\ \hline D_2 \end{bmatrix} \begin{array}{l} N/2 \text{ rows} \\ N/2 \text{ rows} \end{array}.
$$

The matrix $D'Z$ is seen to contain the third moments of the design, each multiplied by N. For example, the (1, 1) element of $D'Z$ is $\sum_{u=1}^{N} x_{iu}^3$ and the (1, 2) element is $\sum_{u=1}^{N} x_{1u}x_{2u}^2$. Now, from Eq. 9.30

$$D'Z = [D_1 \mid -D_1] \begin{bmatrix} D_2 \\ ----- \\ D_2 \end{bmatrix} = D_1D_2 - D_1D_2$$

$$= 0.$$

Thus the design given by D in Eq. 9.30 fulfills requirements (1), (2), and (3).

As an example of the illustration of the above procedure for $k = 4$, consider the design matrix given by Eq. 9.29. The first four points correspond to D_1 and the second four, arranged in a different order, correspond to $-D_1$.

9.3 | the second order model

Much of the essentials regarding design criteria, fundamental philosophy, etc., in this section are equivalent to that given in the development concerning the first order model in Section 9.2. The work presented in Section 9.2 led to the recommendation that certain orthogonal, and thus rotatable first order designs were appropriate in many practical situations.

It is assumed here that the experimenter desires to fit a quadratic response surface in a spherical region R but that the true function is best described by a cubic polynomial. This is merely an extension by one stage of the work presented in Section 9.2. Once again, the actual measured variables have been transformed to $x_1, x_2, \ldots, x_k$ which are scaled so that the region of interest R is a unit sphere. Also the assumption on the design is made that its center of gravity is at the origin $(0, 0, \ldots, 0)$ of the sphere. The equation of the fitted model, that is,

$$\hat{y} = \mathbf{x}_1'\hat{\boldsymbol{\beta}}_1,$$

will have

$$\mathbf{x}_1' = [1, x_1, \ldots, x_k; x_1^2, \ldots, x_k^2; x_1x_2, \ldots, x_{k-1}x_k]$$

$$(9.31)$$

$$\hat{\boldsymbol{\beta}}_1 = [b_0, b_1, \ldots, b_k; b_{11}, \ldots, b_{kk}; b_{12}, \ldots, b_{k-1,k}].$$

The true relationship is written

$$E(y) = \mathbf{x}_1'\boldsymbol{\beta}_1 + \mathbf{x}_2'\boldsymbol{\beta}_2$$

and

$$\mathbf{x}_2' = [x_1^3, x_1x_2^2, \ldots, x_1x_k^2; x_2^3, x_2x_1^2, \ldots, x_2x_k^2, \ldots, x_k^3, x_kx_1^2, \ldots, x_kx_{k-1}^2;$$

$$\ldots, x_1x_2x_3; x_1x_2x_4, \ldots, x_{k-2}x_{k-1}x_k] \quad (9.32)$$

contains the cubic contribution to the actual model. The vector β_2' contains the coefficients corresponding to terms in x_2'; terms such as β_{111}, β_{122}, ... are included. The matrix X_1 is given by

$$X_1 = \begin{bmatrix} 1 & x_{11} & x_{21} & \cdots & x_{k1}; & x_{11}^2 & \cdots & x_{k1}^2; & x_{11}x_{21} & \cdots & x_{k-1,1}x_{k,1} \\ 1 & x_{12} & x_{22} & \cdots & x_{k2}; & x_{12}^2 & \cdots & x_{k2}^2; & x_{12}x_{22} & \cdots & x_{k-1,2}x_{k,2} \\ \cdots & \cdots & \cdots & \cdots & \cdots & \cdots & \cdots & \cdots & \cdots & \cdots & \cdots \\ 1 & x_{1N} & x_{2N} & \cdots & x_{kN}; & x_{1N}^2 & \cdots & x_{kN}^2; & x_{1N}x_{2N} & \cdots & x_{k-1,N}x_{k,N} \end{bmatrix}.$$

In this case the matrix X_2 is

$$X_2 = \begin{bmatrix} x_{11}^3 & x_{11}x_{21}^2 & \cdots & x_{11}x_{k1}^2; & x_{21}^3 & x_{21}x_{11}^2 & \cdots & x_{21}x_{k1}^2 & \cdots & x_{k1}^3 \\ x_{12}^3 & x_{12}x_{22}^2 & \cdots & x_{12}x_{k2}^2; & x_{22}^3 & x_{22}x_{12}^2 & \cdots & x_{22}x_{k2}^2 & \cdots & x_{k2}^3 \\ \cdots & \cdots & \cdots & \cdots & \cdots & \cdots & \cdots & \cdots & \cdots & \cdots \\ x_{1N}^3 & x_{1N}x_{2N}^2 & \cdots & x_{1N}x_{kN}^2; & x_{2N}^3 & x_{2N}x_{1N}^2 & \cdots & x_{2N}x_{kN}^2 & \cdots & x_{kN}^3 \end{bmatrix}$$

$$\begin{bmatrix} x_{k1}x_{11}^2 & \cdots & x_{k1}x_{k-1,1}^2 & \cdots & x_{11}x_{21}x_{31} & \cdots & x_{k-2,1}x_{k-1,1}x_{k,} \\ x_{k2}x_{12}^2 & \cdots & x_{k2}x_{k-1,2}^2 & \cdots & x_{12}x_{22}x_{32} & \cdots & x_{k-2,2}x_{k-1,2}x_{k,} \\ \cdots & \cdots & \cdots & \cdots & \cdots & \cdots & \cdots \\ x_{kN}x_{k2}^2 & \cdots & x_{kN}x_{k-1,N}^2 & \cdots & x_{1N}x_{2N}x_{3N} & \cdots & x_{k-2,N}x_{k-1,N}x_{k,} \end{bmatrix}$$

As further notation we shall call

$$M_{11} = N^{-1}(X_1'X_1)$$
$$M_{12} = N^{-1}(X_1'X_2) \tag{9.33}$$
$$M_{22} = N^{-1}(X_2'X_2).$$

Also define matrices containing the *region moments* by

$$\mu_{11} = K \int_R \mathbf{x}_1\mathbf{x}_1' \, dx \qquad \mu_{12} = K \int_R \mathbf{x}_1\mathbf{x}_2' \, dx ,$$

and

$$\mu_{22} = K \int_R \mathbf{x}_2\mathbf{x}_2' \, dx.$$

The region moment matrices contain elements which actually involve powers and products in the x's, integrated uniformly over the region of interest. For example, for the case of μ_{12}, the (1, 1) and (1, 2) elements are

$$K \int_R x_1^3 \, dx$$

and

$$K \int_R x_1 x_2^2 \, d\mathbf{x},$$

respectively. Recall that such terms can be evaluated by using Eq. 9.20.

Consider for the present case, the general expression for V and B given by Eqs. 9.17 and 9.18, respectively. In light of the importance of the bias contribution, we shall initially consider B. From the preceding definitions of the design moment matrices and region moment matrices, one can write the bias term

$$B = \alpha_2'[(\mu_{22} - \mu_{12}'\mu_{11}^{-1}\mu_{12})$$
$$+ (M_{11}^{-1}M_{12} - \mu_{11}^{-1}\mu_{12})'\mu_{11}(M_{11}^{-1}M_{12} - \mu_{11}^{-1}\mu_{12})]\alpha_2. \qquad (9.34)$$

This result is obtained by expanding Eq. 9.18 and applying the definition of the alias matrix A. The first term in the square brackets in Eq. 9.34 contains only the region moment matrices and thus is independent of the design. It is shown in Appendix b that the bias term can be no smaller than the positive semidefinite quadratic form $\alpha_2'[\mu_{22} - \mu_{12}'\mu_{11}^{-1}\mu_{12}]\alpha_2$. The problem then becomes one of making zero the second term in the square brackets of Eq. 9.34, that is, the design should be such that

$$M_{11}^{-1}M_{12} = \mu_{11}^{-1}\mu_{12}. \qquad (9.35)$$

One way to make Eq. 9.35 hold is to choose a design for which

$$M_{11} = \mu_{11} \quad \text{and} \quad M_{12} = \mu_{12}. \qquad (9.36)$$

Equation 9.36 represents a solution to the problem of minimizing B in the general case, that is, for the case when a model of order d_1 is being fitted in the presence of an existing model of order $d_2 > d_1$. For the case considered in this section, $d_1 = 2$ and $d_2 = 3$. Thus, equating sample moment matrices to region moment matrices as in Eq. 9.36 implies that design moments through order five are equal to corresponding region moments. Applying Eq. 9.20 and making $M_{11} = \mu_{11}$, it is not difficult to find values in the matrix M_{11} which minimize B. Initially, it can be seen that

$$N^{-1} \sum_u x_{1u}^{\delta_1} x_{2u}^{\delta_2} \cdots x_{ku}^{\delta_k} = 0 \qquad \text{(any } \delta_i \text{ odd)}. \qquad (9.37)$$

From Eq. 9.23,

$$K = \frac{\Gamma[(k + 2)/2]}{\pi^{k/2}}$$

and from Eq. 9.22,

$$K \int_R x_i^2 \, d\mathbf{x} = 1/(k + 2).$$

Thus the second pure design moment must take on the value

$$[ii] = 1/(k + 2).$$

For the pure fourth moment, we first observe that

$$K \int_R x_i^4 \, d\mathbf{x} = K \frac{\pi^{k/2}(3/4)}{\Gamma[(k + 6)/2]}$$

$$= \frac{3}{(k + 2)(k + 4)}.$$

Thus for the design which minimizes B

$$[iiii] = 3/[(k + 2)(k + 4)]. \tag{9.38}$$

In addition, we must consider the mixed fourth moment $[iijj]$. The corresponding region moment is given by

$$K \int_R x_i^2 x_j^2 \, d\mathbf{x} = \frac{K\pi^{k/2}(1/4)}{\Gamma[(k + 6)/2]}$$

$$= \frac{1}{(k + 2)(k + 4)}.$$

Therefore, in order to minimize B,

$$[iijj] = 1/[(k + 2)(k + 4)]. \tag{9.39}$$

Also as a further restriction, one must use the second equation of Eq. 9.36. This implies that design moments of order five are to be equated to the corresponding region moments. All region moments of order five are clearly zero from Eq. 9.20. A very interesting fact becomes apparent when one considers Eqs. 9.37–9.39; namely, the second order design which minimizes B is, in fact, a second order *rotatable design* with zero moments of order five. Due to the apparent importance in considering all-bias designs (or designs which are nearly all-bias), in what follows, only second order rotatable designs with zero fifth moments are considered. As in the case of the fitted first order model, designs from this class which minimize J, in many practical situations where V and B are both contributors, have design parameters which are close to those of the design which minimizes B.

second order rotatable designs which minimize $J = V + B$

Consider now the possibility of selecting from the class of rotatable designs having zero fifth moments, that class which has the design characteristics that result in $J = V + B$ being a minimum. As in the case of Section 9.2 for first order designs, minimization of J is impossible without knowledge of the existing cubic parameters β_{111}, β_{122}, etc. In Box and Draper (1963), curves are drawn which give values of $[ii]$ and $\lambda = [iiii]/[ii]^2$ for the design (with the restrictions of rotatability and zero fifth moments) which minimize J for cases where V/B ranges from 0 to ∞. For examples, for $k = 1$, as B approaches infinity, the value of $\sqrt{[ii]}$ approaches 0.606, and λ approaches 1.632. Unless V is *considerably* larger than B, the optimum design is one in which $[ii]$ is reasonably close to the value 0.606 and λ reasonably close to 1.632. The same is true for $k > 1$ except, of course, the numbers are different. That is, the optimal design has characteristics similar to those of the all-bias design. As the variance contribution becomes larger, the optimal $\sqrt{[ii]}$ becomes larger, as one would expect. Likewise, λ becomes larger with a larger V. Using the general rule that the moment should be between 0 and 10% larger than that of the optimal design for $B = \infty$, Table 9.2 was constructed to provide a range of values of $[ii]$ and λ which are suggested as appropriate (for $k = 1, 2, 3, 4,$ and 5) in cases where nothing is known about the relative contributions of V and B.

Table 9.2. Appropriate Values of Second and Fourth Moments for Second Order Rotatable Design[a]

k	$[ii]$	$\sqrt{[ii]}$	$\lambda = [iiii]/[ii]^2$
1	0.3856	0.621	1.669
2	0.3158	0.562	1.993
3	0.2581	0.508	2.170
4	0.2430	0.493	2.384
5	0.2275	0.477	2.540

[a]Fifth moments are zero and $[iijj] = [iiii]/3$.

Example Designs. In this section, several rotatable central composite designs are tabulated which are in the category described by Table 9.2. That is, the designs given are constructed to systematically protect against bias and variance as described in this chapter. Table 9.3 is given for $k = 2$, indicating the number of center points, n_2, and the values of the parameters g and α

corresponding to the design characteristics $[ii]$ and λ. The parameters g and α are the parameters of a ccd with design matrix given by

$$
D =
\begin{array}{c}
\begin{array}{cccc} x_1 & x_2 & \cdots & x_k \end{array} \\
\left[
\begin{array}{cccc}
\pm g & \pm g & \cdots & \pm g \\
-\alpha & 0 & \cdots & 0 \\
\alpha & 0 & \cdots & 0 \\
0 & -\alpha & \cdots & 0 \\
0 & \alpha & \cdots & 0 \\
0 & 0 & \cdots & 0 \\
0 & 0 & \cdots & 0 \\
\cdot & \cdot & & \cdot \\
\cdot & \cdot & & \cdot \\
\cdot & \cdot & & \cdot \\
0 & 0 & & -\alpha \\
0 & 0 & \cdots & \alpha \\
\hline
0 & 0 & \cdots & 0
\end{array}
\right]
\end{array}
$$

The quantity g takes on values <1 for the cases considered, and for rotatability $\alpha = 2^{k/4} \, g$. All of these designs involve eight points plus n_2 center points.

Table 9.3. Parameters for Appropriate Central Composite Designs
for $k = 2$

n_2	$\sqrt{[ii]}$	λ	g	α
0	0.628	1.500	0.628	0.880
1	0.578	1.688	0.613	0.867
2	0.505	1.875	0.565	0.799
3	0.583	2.063	0.684	0.967
4	0.627	2.250	0.768	1.086
5	0.663	2.438	0.846	1.196
6	0.696	2.625	0.921	1.303
7	0.727	2.813	0.996	1.408

SOURCE: G. E. P. Box and N. R. Draper, "The Choice of a Second Order Rotatable Design," *Tech. Rept. 10*, University of Wisconsin, Dept. of Statistics, Madison, Wisconsin, July 1962. See also *Biometrika* **50**, 335–352 (1963).

The experimenter should use a design with large values of $[ii]$ and λ if bias is considered to be of secondary importance; if there is uncertainty regarding adequacy of the second order model, the design used should be selected from those with smaller values for λ and $[ii]$, with the values $\sqrt{[ii]} = 0.562$ and $\lambda = 1.993$ from Table 9.2 being used as a guide in cases where little is known. Tables 9.4–9.6 contain similar parameters for suggested central composite designs for $k = 3, 4,$ and 5. The same general comments apply with regard to selecting a design from one of these sets.

Table 9.4. Parameters for Appropriate Central Composite Designs
for $k = 3$ ($14 + n_2$ Points)

n_2	$\sqrt{[ii]}$	λ	g	α
0	0.536	1.802	0.542	0.912
1	0.507	1.930	0.531	0.894
2	0.453	2.059	0.490	0.825
3	0.514	2.188	0.573	0.964
4	0.548	2.316	0.630	1.059
5	0.577	2.445	0.681	1.145
6	0.603	2.574	0.730	1.228
7	0.628	2.702	0.778	1.309
8	0.651	2.831	0.826	1.389
9	0.673	2.960	0.873	1.468

SOURCE: G. E. P. Box and N. R. Draper, "The Choice of a Second Order Rotatable Design," *Tech. Rept. 10*, University of Wisconsin, Dept. of Statistics, Madison, Wisconsin, July 1962. See also *Biometrika* **50**, 335–352 (1963).

Table 9.5. Parameters for Appropriate Central Composite Designs
for $k = 4$ ($24 + n_2$ Points)

n_0	$\sqrt{[ii]}$	λ	g	α
0	0.475	2.000	0.475	0.950
1	0.459	2.083	0.469	0.937
2	0.421	2.167	0.438	0.876
3	0.450	2.250	0.478	0.955
4	0.479	2.333	0.517	1.034
5	0.502	2.417	0.551	1.103
6	0.522	2.500	0.584	1.167
7	0.541	2.583	0.615	1.229
8	0.558	2.667	0.645	1.290
9	0.575	2.750	0.675	1.349

SOURCE: G. E. P. Box and N. R. Draper, "The Choice of a Second Order Rotatable Design," *Tech. Rept. 10*, University of Wisconsin, Dept. of Statistics, Madison, Wisconsin, July 1962. See also *Biometrika* **50**, 335–352 (1963).

Table 9.6. Parameters for Appropriate Central Composite Designs for $k = 5$ $(42 + n_2$ Points)

n_0	$\sqrt{[ii]}$	λ	g	α
0	0.430	2.149	0.423	1.007
1	0.421	2.200	0.419	0.997
2	0.402	2.252	0.406	0.965
3	0.397	2.303	0.405	0.963
4	0.422	2.354	0.435	1.034
5	0.440	2.405	0.458	1.089
6	0.455	2.456	0.479	1.139
7	0.469	2.507	0.499	1.187
8	0.482	2.559	0.518	1.232
9	0.495	2.610	0.537	1.277

SOURCE: G. E. P. Box and N. R. Draper, "The Choice of a Second Order Rotatable Design," *Tech. Rept. 10*, University of Wisconsin, Dept. of Statistics, Madison, Wisconsin, July 1962. See also *Biometrika* **50**, 335–352 (1963).

references

Box, G. E. P. and N. R. Draper: "A Basis for the Selection of a Response Surface Design," *J. Amer. Statist. Assoc.* **54**, 622–654 (1959).

———: "The Choice of a Second Order Rotatable Design," *Tech. Rept. 10*, University of Wisconsin, Dept. of Statistics, Madison, Wisconsin, July 1962.

———: "The Choice of a Second Order Rotatable Design," *Biometrika* **50**, 335–352 (1963).

David, H. A. and B. Arens: "Optimal Spacing in Regression Analysis," *Ann. Math. Statist.* **30** (4), 1072–1081 (1959).

appendix a

The material in this appendix involves derivations of results which are given and used in Chapter 7. These results pertain to *rotatable* response surface designs for the general case, that is, rotatable designs used to fit models of degree *d*.

The first development is the derivation of the important result which gives the form of the moment matrix for a rotatable design. This result is given by Eqs. 7.20 and 7.21.

a.1 | moment matrix of a rotatable design

In the development that follows, it is convenient in expressing the polynomial model to make use of *derived power vectors* and *Schlaifflian matrices*. If $\mathbf{z}' = [z_1, z_2, \ldots, z_k]$, then $\mathbf{z}'^{[p]}$, the derived power vector of degree p, is defined such that

$$\mathbf{z}'^{[p]}\mathbf{z}^{[p]} = (\mathbf{z}'\mathbf{z})^p.$$

For example if $\mathbf{z}' = [z_1, z_2, z_3]$, then

$$\mathbf{z}'^{[2]} = [z_1^2, z_2^2, z_3^2, \sqrt{2}z_1z_2, \sqrt{2}z_1z_3, \sqrt{2}z_2z_3]$$

and

$$\mathbf{z}'^{[1]} = \mathbf{z}'.$$

If a vector $\mathbf{x}$ is formed from a vector $\mathbf{z}$ containing k elements through the transformation

$$\mathbf{x} = H\mathbf{z}, \tag{a.1}$$

then the Schlaifflian matrix $H^{[p]}$ is defined such that

$$\mathbf{x}^{[p]} = H^{[p]}\mathbf{z}^{[p]}.$$

It is readily seen that if the transformation matrix H is orthogonal, then $H^{[p]}$ is also orthogonal. One can write

$$\mathbf{x}'^{[p]}\mathbf{x}^{[p]} = \mathbf{z}'^{[p]}H'^{[p]}H^{[p]}\mathbf{z}^{[p]}. \tag{a.2}$$

The left-hand side of Eq. a.2 is by definition $(\mathbf{x}'\mathbf{x})^p$. Since H is orthogonal,

$$(\mathbf{x}'\mathbf{x})^p = (\mathbf{z}'\mathbf{z})^p = \mathbf{z}'^{[p]}\mathbf{z}^{[p]},$$

and thus the Schlaifflian matrix $H^{[p]}$ is orthogonal. Another result which is quite useful in what follows is that, given two vectors $\mathbf{x}$ and $\mathbf{z}$, each having k elements, then

$$(\mathbf{x}'\mathbf{z})^p = \mathbf{x}'^{[p]}\mathbf{z}^{[p]}.$$

For a response function of order d, the estimated response $\hat{y}$ can be written in the form

$$\hat{y} = \mathbf{x}'^{[d]}\mathbf{b} \tag{a.3}$$

where for a point $(x_1, x_2, \ldots, x_k)$,

$$\mathbf{x}' = (1, x_1, x_2, \ldots, x_k)$$

and the vector $\mathbf{b}$ contains the least squares estimators b_0, b_1, ... etc., with suitable multipliers. For example for $k = 2$ and $d = 2$, $\mathbf{x}' = [1, x_1, x_2]$, and $\mathbf{b}'$ and $\mathbf{x}'^{[2]}$ are given by

$$\mathbf{b}' = \begin{bmatrix} b_0 & b_1/\sqrt{2} & b_2/\sqrt{2} & b_{11} & b_{22} & b_{12}/\sqrt{2} \end{bmatrix}$$

$$\mathbf{x}'^{[2]} = \begin{bmatrix} 1, & \sqrt{2}x_1, & \sqrt{2}x_2, & x_1^2, & x_2^2, & \sqrt{2}x_1x_2 \end{bmatrix}.$$

Thus, from Eq. a.3,

$$\begin{aligned} \text{var } \hat{y}_x &= \mathbf{x}'^{[d]}[\text{var } \mathbf{b}]\mathbf{x}^{[d]} \\ &= \sigma^2\mathbf{x}'^{[d]}[X'X]\mathbf{x}^{[d]} \end{aligned} \tag{a.4}$$

where $\sigma^2(X'X)^{-1}$ is the variance–covariance matrix of the vector $\mathbf{b}$.

Consider now a *second* point $(z_1, z_2, \ldots, z_k)$ which is the same distance from the origin as the point described by $(x_1, x_2, \ldots, x_k)$. Denote by $\mathbf{z}'$ the vector $(1, z_1, z_2, \ldots, z_k)$. There is, then, an orthogonal matrix R for which

$$\mathbf{z} = R\mathbf{x} \tag{a.5}$$

where R is of the form

$$R = \begin{bmatrix} 1 & 0 & 0 & \cdots & 0 \\ 0 & & & & \\ 0 & & & & \\ \cdots & & H_{k \times k} & & \\ 0 & & & & \end{bmatrix} \tag{a.6}$$

and H is an orthogonal matrix with the dimensions indicated in Eq. a.6. The variance of the estimated response at the second point is then

$$\operatorname{var} \hat{y}_z = \sigma^2 z'^{[d]}(X'X)^{-1}z^{[d]}.$$

Let $R^{[d]}$ be the Schlaifflian matrix of the transformation in Eq. a.5.

$$\operatorname{var} \hat{y}_z = \sigma^2 x^{[d]'} R'^{[d]}(X'X)^{-1} R^{[d]}x^{[d]}$$
$$= \sigma^2 x^{[d]'}[R'^{[d]}(X'X)R^{[d]}]^{-1}x^{[d]} \tag{a.7}$$

since $R^{[d]}$ is orthogonal. For the design to be rotatable, var $\hat{y}$ is constant on spheres, which implies that for any orthogonal matrix H,

$$X'X = R'^{[d]}(X'X)R^{[d]} \tag{a.8}$$

where R is of the form indicated in Eq. a.6. The requirement in Eq. a.8 essentially means that the moment matrix remains the same if the design is *rotated*, that is, if the rows of the *design* matrix, denoted by D in the equation

$$\begin{bmatrix} 1 \\ 1 \\ \cdots \\ 1 \end{bmatrix} D = \begin{bmatrix} 1 & x_{11} & x_{21} & \cdots & x_{k1} \\ 1 & x_{12} & x_{22} & \cdots & x_{k2} \\ \cdots & \cdots & \cdots & \cdots & \cdots \\ 1 & x_{1N} & x_{2N} & \cdots & x_{kN} \end{bmatrix} = \begin{bmatrix} x'_1 \\ x'_2 \\ \cdots \\ x'_N \end{bmatrix} \tag{a.9}$$

are rotated via the transformation

$$z_i = R'x_i.$$

It is easily seen that the rotated design will have moment matrix (apart from the constant N^{-1}) equal to the right-hand side of Eq. a.8.

Consider now a vector $t' = [1, t_1, t_2, \ldots, t_k]$ of dummy variables. The utility of these variables is in the construction of a generating function for the design moments. Consider the quantity

$$M.F. = N^{-1}t^{[d]'}X'Xt^{[d]}. \tag{a.10}$$

The matrix $X'X$ is alternatively given by

$$X'X = \sum_{u=1}^{N} x_u^{[d]}x_u^{[d]'}$$

where the vector $\mathbf{x}'_u = [1, x_{1u}, x_{2u}, \ldots, x_{ku}]$ refers to the uth row of the design matrix, augmented by 1, that is, the uth row of the matrix in Eq. a.9.

$$M.F. = N^{-1} \sum_u \{\mathbf{t}^{[d]'}\mathbf{x}_u^{[d]}\mathbf{x}_u^{[d]'}\mathbf{t}^{[d]}\}$$

$$= N^{-1} \sum_u \{\mathbf{t}'\mathbf{x}_u\}^{2d}. \tag{a.11}$$

From Eq. a.11, it is seen that upon expanding $\mathbf{t}'\mathbf{x}_u$

$$M.F. = N^{-1} \sum_u \{1 + t_1 x_{1u} + t_2 x_{2u} + \cdots + t_k x_{ku}\}^{2d}. \tag{a.12}$$

When Eq. a.12 is expanded, the terms involve moments of the design through order $2d$. In fact, the coefficient of $t_1^{\delta_1} t_2^{\delta_2} \ldots t_k^{\delta_k}$ is

$$\frac{(2d)!}{\prod\limits_{i=1}^{k} (\delta_i)!(2d - \delta)!} [1^{\delta_1} 2^{\delta_2} \ldots k^{\delta_k}] \tag{a.13}$$

where $\sum_{i=1}^{k} \delta_i = \delta \leq 2d$. For a rotatable design,

$$M.F. = N^{-1}\mathbf{t}^{[d]'}(X'X)\mathbf{t}^{[d]} = N^{-1}\mathbf{t}'^{[d]}R'^{[d]}X'XR^{[d]}\mathbf{t}^{[d]}$$

$$= N^{-1}(\mathbf{t}'R')^{[d]}X'X[R\mathbf{t}]^{[d]}$$

where R is a $(k + 1) \times (k + 1)$ orthogonal matrix introduced in Eq. a.6. This implies that for a rotatable design, an orthogonal transformation on $\mathbf{t}$ does not affect the $M.F.$ Since $M.F.$ is a polynomial in the t's (also involving the design moments), for a rotatable design, $M.F.$ must be a function of $\sum_{i=1}^{k} t_i^2$. That is, it is of the form

$$M.F. = \sum_{j=0}^{d} a_{2j} \left[\sum_{i=1}^{k} t_i^2 \right]^j. \tag{a.14}$$

It is easily seen that the coefficient of $t_1^{\delta_1} t_2^{\delta_2} \cdots t_k^{\delta_k}$ in Eq. a.14 is zero *if any of the δ_i are odd*. For the case where all δ_i are even, the coefficient from the multinomial expansion of $[\sum_{i=1}^{k} t_i^2]^j$, is given by

$$\frac{a_\delta(\delta/2)!}{\prod\limits_{i=1}^{k} (\delta_i/2)!}. \tag{a.15}$$

The reader should now consider Eq. a.15 in conjunction with Eq. a.13, the former pertaining to the generating function for the moments *in general*, and the latter pertaining to the case of a rotatable design, with the value being zero for moments with any δ_i odd. Upon equating the two and solving for the moment, the result is as given in Eq. 7.20 and 7.21, and with

$$\lambda_\delta = \frac{a_\delta 2^{\delta/2}(\delta/2)!(2d - \delta)!}{(2d)!}.$$

a.2 | biases of model coefficients for rotatable second order designs

The parameters λ_4 and A in the expressions given here are those defined in Chapter 7. The square bracket notation refers to moments. Here, of course, moments of order five appear in the bias terms. These moments are a result of the alias matrix $A = (X_1'X_1)^{-1}X_1'X_2$. Examples of moments of order five are $[13344] = N^{-1}\sum_{u=1}^{N} X_{1u}X_{3u}X_{4u}^2$ and $[11111] = N^{-1}\sum_{u=1}^{N} X_{1u}^5$. The biases of the coefficients in the second order model in the presence of third order terms are given by

$$E(b_0) = \beta_0 - 2\lambda_4 A \sum_{f=1}^{k} \sum_{g=f}^{k} \sum_{h=g}^{k} \sum_{i=1}^{k} [fghii]\beta_{fgg}$$

$$E(b_i) = \beta_i + 3\lambda_4\beta_{iii} + \lambda_4 \sum_{\substack{h=1 \\ h \neq i}}^{k} \beta_{hhi}$$

$$E(b_{ii}) = \beta_{ii} + \{[k + 2]\lambda_4 - k\} A[iiiii]\beta_{iii}$$

$$+ (1 - \lambda_4)A \sum_{f=1}^{k} \sum_{g=f}^{k} \sum_{h=g}^{k} \sum_{i=1}^{k} [fghii]\beta_{fgh}$$

$$E(b_{ij}) = \beta_{ij} + \lambda_4^{-1} \sum_{f=1}^{k} \sum_{g=f}^{k} \sum_{h=g}^{k} [fghii]\beta_{fgh}.$$

a.3 | moment matrix for equiradial second order designs in two variables

In this section the development of the elements of the moment matrix is given in the case of a design with $n_1 \geq 5$ points equally spaced on a circle. The design matrix is specified by Eq. 7.42, and the moment matrix is specified by Eqs. 7.43–7.50. The design is in fact rotatable, and when augmented by center points, can be a useful experimental plan for fitting second order models.

Consider first the moment of x_1 of order $\delta(\delta = 1, 2, 3, 4)$. After multiplication by n_1,

$$\sum_{u=0}^{n_1-1} x_{1u}^\delta = \sum_{u=0}^{n_1-1} \{\rho \cos (\theta + 2\pi u/n_1)\}^\delta. \tag{a.16}$$

Since $\cos \tau = [e^{i\tau} + e^{-i\tau}]/2$, Eq. a.16 can be written

$$\sum_{u=0}^{n_1-1} x_{1u}^{\delta} = (\rho/2)^{\delta} \sum_{u=0}^{n_1-1} [a\omega^u + a^{-1}\omega^{-u}]^{\delta}$$

where $\omega = e^{2i\pi/n_2}$ and $a = e^{i\theta}$. Using a binomial expansion,

$$\sum_{u=0}^{n_1-1} x_{iu}^{\delta} = (\rho/2)^{\delta} \sum_{t=0}^{\delta} \binom{\delta}{t} a^{\delta-2t} \sum_{u=0}^{n_1-1} \omega^{(\delta-2t)u}. \qquad (a.17)$$

An expression similar to Eq. a.17 for the moments of x_2 can be established with little difficulty. In considering the portion $\sum_{u=0}^{n_1-1} \omega^{(\delta-2t)u}$ of Eq. a.17 for $t = 0, 1, 2, \ldots, \delta$, it is first noted that

$$-\delta \leq (\delta - 2t) \leq \delta.$$

The interest here is in moments of order $n_1 - 1$ and less since $n_1 \geq 5$. If $\delta - 2t = 0$,

$$\sum_{u=0}^{n_1-1} \omega^{(\delta-2t)u} = n_1.$$

On the other hand, it is not difficult to show that for $|\delta - 2t| \leq n_1 - 1$ and nonzero,

$$\sum_{u=0}^{n_1-1} \omega^{(\delta-2t)u} = 0.$$

Using Eq. a.17 for $\delta = 1$, $(\delta - 2t)$ takes on values -1 and $+1$ and thus $\sum_{u=0}^{n_1-1} x_{1u} = 0$. Likewise, for the case of $\delta = 3$, it is found that $\sum_{u=0}^{n_1-1} x_{1u}^3 = 0$. In a similar fashion, it can be shown that the odd moments of x_2 are zero. For $\delta = 2$, $\delta - 2t$ does take on a zero value when $t = 1$. Evaluating Eq. a.17

$$n_1[11] = n_1 \binom{2}{1} \rho^2/4$$

and thus

$$[11] = \rho^2/2.$$

For $\delta = 4$, the nonzero contribution in Eq. a.17 appears when $t = 2$. Thus the pure fourth moment is given by

$$[1111] = \binom{4}{2} \rho^4/16$$

$$= \frac{3\rho^4}{8}.$$

Similar procedures can be used for the case of x_2 to show that

$$n_1[2^2] = \rho^2 n_1/2; \quad n_1[2^4] = 3\rho^4 n_1/8.$$

At this point, consider moments of the type $\sum_{u=0}^{n_1-1} x_{1u}^{\delta_1} x_{2u}^{\delta_2}$ where $\delta_1 + \delta_2 \leq 4$. One can write

$$\sum_{u=0}^{n_1-1} x_{1u}^{\delta_1} x_{2u}^{\delta_2} = \sum_{u=0}^{n_1-1} \{\rho \cos (\theta + 2\pi u/n_1)\}^{\delta_1} \{\rho \sin (\theta + 2\pi u/n_1)\}^{\delta_2}$$

$$= (\rho/2)^{\delta_1 + \delta_2} \left(\frac{1}{i}\right)^{\delta_2} \sum_{u=0}^{n_1-1} \{a\omega^u + a^{-1}\omega^{-u}\}^{\delta_1} \{a\omega^u - a^{-1}\omega^{-u}\}^{\delta_2}$$

$$\text{(a.18)}$$

where a and ω are as before and $i = \sqrt{-1}$. For $\delta_1 = 1$ and $\delta_2 = 1$, Eq. a.18 is easily seen to be zero after making use of the fact that $\sum_{u=0}^{n_1-1} \omega^{2u}$ and $\sum_{u=0}^{n_1-1} \omega^{-2u} = 0$. Likewise, $n_1[112]$ and $n_1[122]$ are found to be zero. For $n_1[1112]$, Eq. a.18 becomes

$$(\rho/2)^4 (1/i) \sum_{u=0}^{n_1-1} \{a^3\omega^{3u} + a^{-3}\omega^{-3u} + 3a\omega^u + 3a^{-1}\omega^{-u}\}\{a\omega^u - a^{-1}\omega^{-u}\}$$

$$= \left(\frac{\rho}{2}\right)^4 \left(\frac{1}{i}\right) \{-3n_1 + 3n_1\}$$

$$= 0.$$

Similarly $n_1[1222]$ can be shown to be zero.

It remains now to develop the expression for $\sum_{u=0}^{n_1-1} x_{1u}^2 x_{2u}^2$. We can once again use Eq. a.18 to develop the following:

$$\sum_{u=0}^{n_1-1} x_{1u}^2 x_{2u}^2$$

$$= (\rho/2)^4 (-1) \sum_{u=0}^{n_1-1} \{a^2\omega^{2u} + 2 + a^{-2}\omega^{-2u}\}\{a^2\omega^{2u} - 2 + a^{-2}\omega^{-2u}\}$$

$$= \frac{\rho^4}{16}(-1)\{n_1 - 4n_1 + n_1\}$$

$$= \frac{\rho^4 n_1}{8}.$$

appendix b

This appendix presents developments of certain results which are given in Chapter 9, which deals with certain integrated or average bias and variance criteria on which the choice of a first or second order design can be based.

b.1 | average bias for first order model

The first development is a derivation of the average bias given by the expression in Eq. 9.25. We shall begin by considering the more general expression for the bias, given by Eq. 9.18.

$$B = \frac{NK}{\sigma^2} \int_R \boldsymbol{\beta}_2'[A'\mathbf{x}_1 - \mathbf{x}_2][\mathbf{x}_1'A - \mathbf{x}_2']\boldsymbol{\beta}_2 d\mathbf{x} \qquad \text{(b.1)}$$

where the terms in Eq. b.1 are explained on page 203. Upon expanding Eq. b.1, we obtain

$$K^{-1}B = \boldsymbol{\alpha}_2'A'\left[\int_R \mathbf{x}_1\mathbf{x}_1'd\mathbf{x}\right]A\boldsymbol{\alpha}_2$$

$$- 2\boldsymbol{\alpha}_2'\left[\int_R \mathbf{x}_2\mathbf{x}_1'd\mathbf{x}\right]A\boldsymbol{\alpha}_2 + \boldsymbol{\alpha}_2'\left[\int_R \mathbf{x}_2\mathbf{x}_2'd\mathbf{x}\right]\boldsymbol{\alpha}_2, \qquad \text{(b.2)}$$

where the vector $\boldsymbol{\alpha}_2$ is merely $\boldsymbol{\beta}_2\sqrt{N}/\sigma$. We can use the general Eq. 9.20 for the case of the spherical region to evaluate the quadratic forms in Eq. 6.2.

For example, consider

$$K \int_R \mathbf{x}_1 \mathbf{x}_1' d\mathbf{x} = \begin{bmatrix} f_{00} & f_{01} & \cdots & f_{0k} \\ & f_{11} & \cdots & f_{1k} \\ & & \cdots & \cdots \\ & & f_{k-1,k-1} & f_{k-1,k} \\ & & & f_{kk} \end{bmatrix} \tag{b.3}$$

where from Eq. 9.23,

$$K = \frac{\Gamma\left(\dfrac{k+2}{2}\right)}{\pi^{k/2}}.$$

The initial diagonal element is unity and $f_{ii}(i = 1, 2, \ldots, k)$ is given by

$$f_{ii} = K \int_R x_i^2 d\mathbf{x}.$$

From Eq. 9.22, we have

$$f_{ii} = 1/(k+2).$$

All off-diagonal elements will be of the form

$$K \int_R x_i x_j d\mathbf{x}$$

which are of course zero from Eq. 9.20. Thus Eq. b.3 can be written

$$K \int_R \mathbf{x}_1 \mathbf{x}_1' d\mathbf{x} = \begin{bmatrix} 1 & 0 & 0 & \cdots & 0 \\ 0 & & & & \\ 0 & & (k+2)^{-1} I_k & & \\ \cdots & & & & \\ 0 & & & & \end{bmatrix}. \tag{b.4}$$

A similar procedure can be used to obtain the elements of $K \int_R \mathbf{x}_2 \mathbf{x}_1' d\mathbf{x}$ and $K \int_R \mathbf{x}_2 \mathbf{x}_2' d\mathbf{x}$. In the former case, the only nonzero contribution appears in the first k elements of the first column. The result is given by

$$K \int_R \mathbf{x}_2 \mathbf{x}_1' d\mathbf{x} = \left.\begin{bmatrix} (k+2)^{-1} & 0 & 0 & \cdots & 0 \\ (k+2)^{-1} & 0 & 0 & \cdots & 0 \\ \cdots & \cdots & \cdots & \cdots & \cdots \\ (k+2)^{-1} & 0 & 0 & \cdots & 0 \\ \hline 0 & 0 & 0 & \cdots & 0 \end{bmatrix}\right\} k \text{ rows.} \tag{b.5}$$

Finally, it can be shown that

$$K \int_R \mathbf{x}_2 \mathbf{x}_2' d\mathbf{x} = (k+2)^{-1}(k+4)^{-1} \begin{bmatrix} 2I_k + \mathbf{j}_k\mathbf{j}_k' & \vdots & 0 \\ \text{-----} & \vdots & \text{--} \\ 0 & \vdots & I \end{bmatrix}. \qquad \text{(b.6)}$$

In Eq. b.6, $\mathbf{j}_k'$ is a row vector of k unity elements. Thus the matrix in the upper left-hand partition is $k \times k$ containing 3's on the diagonal and 1's on the off-diagonals. The matrix in the lower right partition is an identity matrix of order $\binom{k}{2}$.

Using Eqs. b.4, b.5, and b.6 in conjunction with Eq. b.1 gives the result of Eq. 9.25.

b.2 | minimum value of average bias

Equation 9.34 gives an expression for the integrated bias in terms of the region moment matrices and matrices involving the sample moments. It was indicated in Chapter 9 that the average bias B can be no smaller than the positive semidefinite quadratic form $\alpha_2'[\mu_{22} - \mu_{12}'\mu_{11}^{-1}\mu_{12}]\alpha_2$.

The matrices μ_{11}, μ_{22}, and μ_{12} are defined in Section 9.3. The proof of this result will presently be given. From Eq. 9.34.

$$B = \alpha_2'\Delta_1\alpha_2 + \gamma_2'\mu_{11}\gamma_2 \qquad \text{(b.7)}$$

where $\Delta_1 = \mu_{22} - \mu_{12}'\mu_{11}^{-1}\mu_{12}$ and

$$\gamma_2' = \alpha_2'[M_{11}^{-1}M_{12} - \mu_{11}^{-1}\mu_{12}]. \qquad \text{(b.8)}$$

Both quadratic forms in Eq. b.7 are positive semidefinite. This is shown by initially writing

$$\int_R \left[(\mathbf{x}_1' \mathbin{\vdots} \mathbf{x}_2') \begin{pmatrix} \alpha_1 \\ \text{--} \\ \alpha_2 \end{pmatrix} \right]^2 d\mathbf{x} \geq 0 = \alpha' \left\{ \int_R \begin{pmatrix} \mathbf{x}_1 \\ \text{--} \\ \mathbf{x}_2 \end{pmatrix} (\mathbf{x}_1' \mathbin{\vdots} \mathbf{x}_2') d\mathbf{x} \right\} \alpha$$

$$= K^{-1}\alpha' \begin{bmatrix} \mu_{11} & \mu_{12} \\ \mu_{12}' & \mu_{22} \end{bmatrix} \alpha$$

where $\alpha' = [\alpha_1' \mathbin{\vdots} \alpha_2']$, $\alpha_1 = \sqrt{N}\beta_{11}/\sigma$ and $\alpha_2 = \sqrt{N}\beta_{22}/\sigma$. Therefore, μ_{11} and the matrix

$$\begin{bmatrix} \mu_{11} & \mu_{12} \\ \mu_{12}' & \mu_{22} \end{bmatrix}$$

are both positive semidefinite. It is easily verified that

$$\begin{bmatrix} \mu_{11} & \vdots & 0 \\ \text{---} & \vdots & \text{---} \\ 0 & \vdots & \Delta_1 \end{bmatrix} = F' \begin{bmatrix} \mu_{11} & \mu_{12} \\ \mu_{12}' & \mu_{22} \end{bmatrix} F \qquad \text{(b.9)}$$

where

$$F = \begin{bmatrix} I_a & | & -\mu_{11}^{-1}\mu_{12} \\ \text{--} & |\text{--------} \\ 0 & | & I_b \end{bmatrix}.$$

I_a and I_b are identity matrices with the order of I_a equal to the number of terms in the vector x_1, while the order of I_b is equal to the number of elements in x_2. From the expression in Eq. b.9 and, in addition, due to the positive semidefinite nature of the middle matrix on the right-hand side in Eq. b.9, Δ_1 is also positive semidefinite.

Since both quadratic forms in Eq. b.7 are positive semidefinite, the contribution $\alpha_2'\Delta_1\alpha_2$ and $\gamma_2'\mu_{11}\gamma_2$ are both ≥ 0; the bias is minimized by making zero the form $\gamma_2'\mu_{11}\gamma_2$. This can be accomplished as indicated by Eq. 9.35. The value of the bias at its minimum is thus given by $\alpha_2'\Delta_1\alpha_2$.

b.3 | J value for optimum and all-bias first order designs in the presence of second order effects

The table presented here shows evidence which indicates that in many practical situations, one does not sacrifice much (in terms of average mean squared error as defined in Eq. 9.1 by choosing either the all-bias design or an experimental plan which is close to the all-bias design. If we assume a design which is first order orthogonal with second moments equal, and third moments zero, the expression for $J = V + B$ can be written

$$J = \left\{1 + \frac{k}{(k+2)[ii]}\right\} + \theta\left\{\varphi\left([ii] - \frac{1}{k+2}\right)^2 + \frac{2(k+2-\varphi)}{(k+2)^2(k+4)}\right\}$$

where

$$\theta = \frac{N}{\sigma^2}\left\{\sum_{i=1}^{k}\beta_{ii}^2 + 1/2\sum_{i<j}\sum\beta_{ij}^2\right\}$$

$$\varphi = \left(\sum_{i=1}^{k}\beta_{ii}\right)^2/(\theta\sigma^2/N).$$

It is assumed here that a first order model is being fitted in the presence of a second order surface with the β_{ij} representing the second order coefficients. Table b.1 gives values for $\dot{r} = \sqrt{k[ii]}$, indicating the optimal root mean square distance of the experimental points from the design center, J_0, the minimum value for J, and J_B, and J value when the all-bias design is used for chosen values of φ and θ. Also included is the ratio of V to B to indicate the relative importance of each for the choices made.

Table b.1. J Values for Optimum and All Bias First Order Designs

$k = 2$

	$\varphi = 0.6$				$\varphi = 1.0$				$\varphi = 2.0$		
	$\dot{r}$	J_o	J_B	$\sqrt{\bar{\theta}}$	$\dot{r}$	J_o	J_B	$\sqrt{\bar{\theta}}$	$\dot{r}$	J_o	J_B	$\sqrt{\bar{\theta}}$
$V = 10B$	1.87	1.41	3.01	0.3	1.84	1.42	3.00	0.25	1.81	1.43	3.00	0.18
$V = 4B$	1.11	2.26	3.21	1.73	1.00	2.50	3.25	2.00	0.84	3.01	3.39	3.07
$V = 2B$	0.93	3.22	3.83	3.42	0.86	3.53	3.96	3.91	0.77	4.01	4.20	5.37
$V = B$	0.84	4.81	5.20	5.57	0.79	5.17	5.42	6.23	0.74	5.63	5.73	8.10
$V = \frac{1}{4}B$	0.79	7.83	8.06	8.46	0.76	8.25	8.39	9.29	0.73	8.70	8.75	11.75

$k = 3$

	$\varphi = 0.9$				$\varphi = 1.5$				$\varphi = 3.0$		
	$\dot{r}$	J_o	J_B	$\sqrt{\bar{\theta}}$	$\dot{r}$	J_o	J_B	$\sqrt{\bar{\theta}}$	$\dot{r}$	J_o	J_B	$\sqrt{\bar{\theta}}$
$V = 10B$	2.55	1.41	4.00	0.19	2.53	1.41	4.00	0.15	2.52	1.41	4.00	0.11
$V = 4B$	1.25	2.70	4.18	1.98	1.10	3.13	4.25	2.50	0.88	4.13	4.56	4.95
$V = 2B$	1.00	4.91	5.04	4.70	0.92	4.71	5.26	5.62	0.82	5.47	5.67	8.54
$V = B$	0.90	6.41	6.91	7.88	0.85	6.96	7.27	9.04	0.80	7.62	7.72	12.76
$V = \frac{1}{4}B$	0.85	10.50	10.79	12.04	0.82	11.10	11.26	13.48	0.79	11.70	11.75	18.42

$k = 4$

	$\varphi = 1.2$				$\varphi = 2.4$				$\varphi = 3.2$		
	$\dot{r}$	J_o	J_B	$\sqrt{\bar{\theta}}$	$\dot{r}$	J_o	J_B	$\sqrt{\bar{\theta}}$	$\dot{r}$	J_o	J_B	$\sqrt{\bar{\theta}}$
$V = 10B$	3.14	1.40	5.00	0.14	3.13	1.40	5.00	0.10	3.12	1.40	5.00	0.09
$V = 4B$	1.35	3.07	5.15	2.13	1.08	4.13	5.34	3.67	0.97	4.87	5.55	5.34
$V = 2B$	1.04	5.23	6.27	6.18	0.92	6.23	6.74	8.35	0.88	6.66	6.98	10.09
$V = B$	0.94	8.09	8.68	10.51	0.87	9.05	9.32	13.14	0.85	9.39	9.56	15.31
$V = \frac{1}{4}B$	0.88	13.26	13.59	16.05	0.84	14.22	14.35	19.34	0.83	14.52	14.60	22.22

The conclusions that can be drawn are certainly clear enough. Notice that for example for $k = 3$ and even when the variance contribution is twice the bias, there is only a slight increase in average mean square error over the minimum J when one uses the all-bias design.

appendix c

Table c.1. The Normal Probability Function. The Integral $P(X)$
in Terms of the Standardized Deviate X

X	$P(X)$	X	$P(X)$	X	$P(X)$	X	$P(X)$
0.00	0.5000000						
0.01	0.5039894	0.16	0.5635595	0.31	0.6217195	0.46	0.6772419
0.02	0.5079783	0.17	0.5674949	0.32	0.6255158	0.47	0.6808225
0.03	0.5119665	0.18	0.5714237	0.33	0.6293000	0.48	0.6843863
0.04	0.5159534	0.19	0.5753454	0.34	0.6330717	0.49	0.6879331
0.05	0.5199388	0.20	0.5792597	0.35	0.6368307	0.50	0.6914625
0.06	0.5239222	0.21	0.5831662	0.36	0.6405764	0.51	0.6949743
0.07	0.5279032	0.22	0.5870644	0.37	0.6443088	0.52	0.6984682
0.08	0.5318814	0.23	0.5909541	0.38	0.6480273	0.53	0.7019440
0.09	0.5358564	0.24	0.5948349	0.39	0.6517317	0.54	0.7054015
0.10	0.5398278	0.25	0.5987063	0.40	0.6554217	0.55	0.7088403
0.11	0.5437953	0.26	0.6025681	0.41	0.6590970	0.56	0.7122603
0.12	0.5477584	0.27	0.6064199	0.42	0.6627573	0.57	0.7156612
0.13	0.5517168	0.28	0.6102612	0.43	0.6664022	0.58	0.7190427
0.14	0.5556700	0.29	0.6140919	0.44	0.6700314	0.59	0.7224047
0.15	0.5596177	0.30	0.6179114	0.45	0.6736448	0.60	0.7257469

$$P(X) = \int_{-\infty}^{X} e^{-\frac{1}{2}u^2} / \sqrt{(2\pi)} \, du$$

SOURCE: This table is abridged from Table 1, pp.110–114, of E. S. Pearson and
H. O. Hartley, *Biometrika Tables For Statisticians,* Vol. 1, 3rd. ed., Cambridge
University Press, 1966, with permission of Biometrika Trustees.

Table c.1. (continued)

X	P(X)	X	P(X)	X	P(X)	X	P(X)
0.61	0.7290691	1.06	0.8554277	1.51	0.9344783	1.96	0.9750021
0.62	0.7323711	1.07	0.8576903	1.52	0.9357445	1.97	0.9755808
0.63	0.7356527	1.08	0.8599289	1.53	0.9369916	1.98	0.9761482
0.64	0.7389137	1.09	0.8621434	1.54	0.9382198	1.99	0.9767045
0.65	0.7421539	1.10	0.8643339	1.55	0.9394292	2.00	0.9772499
0.66	0.7453731	1.11	0.8665005	1.56	0.9406201	2.01	0.9777844
0.67	0.7485711	1.12	0.8686431	1.57	0.9417924	2.02	0.9783083
0.68	0.7517478	1.13	0.8707619	1.58	0.9429466	2.03	0.9788217
0.69	0.7549029	1.14	0.8728568	1.59	0.9440826	2.04	0.9793248
0.70	0.7580363	1.15	0.8749281	1.60	0.9452007	2.05	0.9798178
0.71	0.7611479	1.16	0.8769756	1.61	0.9463011	2.06	0.9803007
0.72	0.7642375	1.17	0.8789995	1.62	0.9473839	2.07	0.9807738
0.73	0.7673049	1.18	0.8809999	1.63	0.9484493	2.08	0.9812372
0.74	0.7703500	1.19	0.8829768	1.64	0.9494974	2.09	0.9816911
0.75	0.7733726	1.20	0.8849303	1.65	0.9505285	2.10	0.9821356
0.76	0.7763727	1.21	0.8868606	1.66	0.9515428	2.11	0.9825708
0.77	0.7793501	1.22	0.8887676	1.67	0.9525403	2.12	0.9829970
0.78	0.7823046	1.23	0.8906514	1.68	0.9535213	2.13	0.9834142
0.79	0.7852361	1.24	0.8925123	1.69	0.9544860	2.14	0.9838226
0.80	0.7881446	1.25	0.8943502	1.70	0.9554345	2.15	0.9842224
0.81	0.7910299	1.26	0.8961653	1.71	0.9563671	2.16	0.9846137
0.82	0.7938919	1.27	0.8979577	1.72	0.9572838	2.17	0.9849966
0.83	0.7967306	1.28	0.8997274	1.73	0.9581849	2.18	0.9853713
0.84	0.7995458	1.29	0.9014747	1.74	0.9590705	2.19	0.9857379
0.85	0.8023375	1.30	0.9031995	1.75	0.9599408	2.20	0.9860966
0.86	0.8051055	1.31	0.9049021	1.76	0.9607961	2.21	0.9864474
0.87	0.8078498	1.32	0.9065825	1.77	0.9616364	2.22	0.9867906
0.88	0.8105703	1.33	0.9082409	1.78	0.9624620	2.23	0.9871263
0.89	0.8132671	1.34	0.9098773	1.79	0.9632730	2.24	0.9874545
0.90	0.8159399	1.35	0.9114920	1.80	0.9640697	2.25	0.9877755
0.91	0.8185887	1.36	0.9130850	1.81	0.9648521	2.26	0.9880894
0.92	0.8212136	1.37	0.9146565	1.82	0.9656205	2.27	0.9883962
0.93	0.8238145	1.38	0.9162067	1.83	0.9663750	2.28	0.9886962
0.94	0.8263912	1.39	0.9177356	1.84	0.9671159	2.29	0.9889893
0.95	0.8289439	1.40	0.9192433	1.85	0.9678432	2.30	0.9892759
0.96	0.8314724	1.41	0.9207302	1.86	0.9685572	2.31	0.9895559
0.97	0.8339768	1.42	0.9221962	1.87	0.9692581	2.32	0.9898296
0.98	0.8364569	1.43	0.9236415	1.88	0.9699460	2.33	0.9900969
0.99	0.8389129	1.44	0.9250663	1.89	0.9706210	2.34	0.9903581
1.00	0.8413447	1.45	0.9264707	1.90	0.9712834	2.35	0.9906133
1.01	0.8437524	1.46	0.9278550	1.91	0.9719334	2.36	0.9908625
1.02	0.8461358	1.47	0.9292191	1.92	0.9725711	2.37	0.9911060
1.03	0.8484950	1.48	0.9305634	1.93	0.9731966	2.38	0.9913437
1.04	0.8508300	1.49	0.9318879	1.94	0.9738102	2.39	0.9915758
1.05	0.8531409	1.50	0.9331928	1.95	0.9744119	2.40	0.9918025

Table c.1. (continued)

X	P(X)	X	P(X)	X	P(X)	X	P(X)
2.41	0.9920237	2.81	0.9975229	3.21	0.9993363	3.61	0.9998469
2.42	0.9922397	2.82	0.9975988	3.22	0.9993590	3.62	0.9998527
2.43	0.9924506	2.83	0.9976726	3.23	0.9993810	3.63	0.9998583
2.44	0.9926564	2.84	0.9977443	3.24	0.9994024	3.64	0.9998637
2.45	0.9928572	2.85	0.9978140	3.25	0.9994230	3.65	0.9998689
2.46	0.9930531	2.86	0.9978818	3.26	0.9994429	3.66	0.9998739
2.47	0.9932443	2.87	0.9979476	3.27	0.9994623	3.67	0.9998787
2.48	0.9934309	2.88	0.9980116	3.28	0.9994810	3.68	0.9998834
2.49	0.9936128	2.89	0.9980738	3.29	0.9994991	3.69	0.9998879
2.50	0.9937903	2.90	0.9981342	3.30	0.9995166	3.70	0.9998922
2.51	0.9939634	2.91	0.9981929	3.31	0.9995335	3.71	0.9998964
2.52	0.9941323	2.92	0.9982498	3.32	0.9995499	3.72	0.9999004
2.53	0.9942969	2.93	0.9983052	3.33	0.9995658	3.73	0.9999043
2.54	0.9944574	2.94	0.9983589	3.34	0.9995811	3.74	0.9999080
2.55	0.9946139	2.95	0.9984111	3.35	0.9995959	3.75	0.9999116
2.56	0.9947664	2.96	0.9984618	3.36	0.9996103	3.76	0.9999150
2.57	0.9949151	2.97	0.9985110	3.37	0.9996242	3.77	0.9999184
2.58	0.9950600	2.98	0.9985588	3.38	0.9996376	3.78	0.9999216
2.59	0.9952012	2.99	0.9986051	3.39	0.9996505	3.79	0.9999247
2.60	0.9953388	3.00	0.9986501	3.40	0.9996631	3.80	0.9999277
2.61	0.9954729	3.01	0.9986938	3.41	0.9996752	3.81	0.9999305
2.62	0.9956035	3.02	0.9987361	3.42	0.9996869	3.82	0.9999333
2.63	0.9957308	3.03	0.9987772	3.43	0.9996982	3.83	0.9999359
2.64	0.9958547	3.04	0.9988171	3.44	0.9997091	3.84	0.9999385
2.65	0.9959754	3.05	0.9988558	3.45	0.9997197	3.85	0.9999409
2.66	0.9960930	3.06	0.9988933	3.46	0.9997299	3.86	0.9999433
2.67	0.9962074	3.07	0.9989297	3.47	0.9997398	3.87	0.9999456
2.68	0.9963189	3.08	0.9989650	3.48	0.9997493	3.88	0.9999478
2.69	0.9964274	3.09	0.9989992	3.49	0.9997585	3.89	0.9999499
2.70	0.9965330	3.10	0.9990324	3.50	0.9997674	3.90	0.9999519
2.71	0.9966358	3.11	0.9990646	3.51	0.9997759	3.91	0.9999539
2.72	0.9967359	3.12	0.9990957	3.52	0.9997842	3.92	0.9999557
2.73	0.9968333	3.13	0.9991260	3.53	0.9997922	3.93	0.9999575
2.74	0.9969280	3.14	0.9991553	3.54	0.9997999	3.94	0.9999593
2.75	0.9970202	3.15	0.9991836	3.55	0.9998074	3.95	0.9999609
2.76	0.9971099	3.16	0.9992112	3.56	0.9998146	3.96	0.9999625
2.77	0.9971972	3.17	0.9992378	3.57	0.9998215	3.97	0.9999641
2.78	0.9972821	3.18	0.9992636	3.58	0.9998282	3.98	0.9999655
2.79	0.9973646	3.19	0.9992886	3.59	0.9998347	3.99	0.9999670
2.80	0.9974449	3.20	0.9993129	3.60	0.9998409	4.00	0.9999683

Table c.2. Percentage Points of the Student's t-Distribution

ν	$\alpha^a = 0.4$	0.25	0.1	0.05	0.025	0.01	0.005	0.0025	0.001	0.0005
1	0.325	1.000	3.078	6.314	12.706	31.821	63.657	127.32	318.31	636.62
2	0.289	0.816	1.886	2.920	4.303	6.965	9.925	14.089	22.327	31.598
3	0.277	0.765	1.638	2.353	3.182	4.541	5.841	7.453	10.214	12.924
4	0.271	0.741	1.533	2.132	2.776	3.747	4.604	5.598	7.173	8.610
5	0.267	0.727	1.476	2.015	2.571	3.365	4.032	4.773	5.893	6.869
6	0.265	0.718	1.440	1.943	2.447	3.143	3.707	4.317	5.208	5.959
7	0.263	0.711	1.415	1.895	2.365	2.998	3.499	4.029	4.785	5.408
8	0.262	0.706	1.397	1.860	2.306	2.896	3.355	3.833	4.501	5.041
9	0.261	0.703	1.383	1.833	2.262	2.821	3.250	3.690	4.297	4.781
10	0.260	0.700	1.372	1.812	2.228	2.764	3.169	3.581	4.144	4.587
11	0.260	0.697	1.363	1,796	2.201	2.718	3.106	3.497	4.025	4.437
12	0.259	0.695	1.356	1.782	2.179	2.681	3.055	3.428	3.930	4.318
13	0.259	0.694	1.350	1.771	2.160	2.650	3.012	3.372	3.852	4.221
14	0.258	0.692	1.345	1.761	2.145	2.624	2.977	3.326	3.787	4.140
15	0.258	0.691	1.341	1.753	2.131	2.602	2.947	3.286	3.733	4.073
16	0.258	0.690	1.337	1.746	2.120	2.583	2.921	3.252	3.686	4.015
17	0.257	0.689	1.333	1.740	2.110	2.567	2.898	3.222	3.646	3.965
18	0.257	0.688	1.330	1.734	2.101	2.552	2.878	3.197	3.610	3.922
19	0.257	0.688	1.328	1.729	2.093	2.539	2.861	3.174	3.579	3.883
20	0.257	0.687	1.325	1.725	2.086	2.528	2.845	3.153	3.552	3.850
21	0.257	0.686	1.323	1.721	2.080	2.518	2.831	3.135	3.527	3.819
22	0.256	0.686	1.321	1.717	2.074	2.508	2.819	3.119	3.505	3.792
23	0.256	0.685	1.319	1.714	2.069	2.500	2.807	3.104	3.485	3.767
24	0.256	0.685	1.318	1.711	2.064	2.492	2.797	3.091	3.467	3.745
25	0.256	0.684	1.316	1.708	2.060	2.485	2.787	3.078	3.450	3.725
26	0.256	0.684	1.315	1.706	2.056	2.479	2.779	3.067	3.435	3.707
27	0.256	0.684	1.314	1.703	2.052	2.473	2.771	3.057	3.421	3.690
28	0.256	0.683	1.313	1.701	2.048	2.467	2.763	3.047	3.408	3.674
29	0.256	0.683	1.311	1.699	2.045	2.462	2.756	3.038	3.396	3.659
30	0.256	0.683	1.310	1.697	2.042	2.457	2.750	3.030	3.385	3.646
40	0.255	0.681	1.303	1.684	2.021	2.423	2.704	2.971	3.307	3.551
60	0.254	0.679	1.296	1.671	2.000	2.390	2.660	2.915	3.232	3.460
120	0.254	0.677	1.289	1.658	1.980	2.358	2.617	2.860	3.160	3.373
∞	0.253	0.674	1.282	1.645	1.960	2.326	2.576	2.807	3.090	3.291

^{a}The quantity α is the upper-tail area of the distribution for ν degrees of freedom.

Table c.3. Percentage Points of the F-Distribution With Degrees Of Freedom v_1
and v_2, Upper 10% Points

v_2 \ v_1	1	2	3	4	5	6	7	8	9
1	39.86	49.50	53.59	55.83	57.24	58.20	58.91	59.44	59.86
2	8.53	9.00	9.16	9.24	9.29	9.33	9.35	9.37	9.38
3	5.54	5.46	5.39	5.34	5.31	5.28	5.27	5.25	5.24
4	4.54	4.32	4.19	4.11	4.05	4.01	3.98	3.95	3.94
5	4.06	3.78	3.62	3.52	3.45	3.40	3.37	3.34	3.32
6	3.78	3.46	3.29	3.18	3.11	3.05	3.01	2.98	2.96
7	3.59	3.26	3.07	2.96	2.88	2.83	2.78	2.75	2.72
8	3.46	3.11	2.92	2.81	2.73	2.67	2.62	2.59	2.56
9	3.36	3.01	2.81	2.69	2.61	2.55	2.51	2.47	2.44
10	3.29	2.92	2.73	2.61	2.52	2.46	2.41	2.38	2.35
11	3.23	2.86	2.66	2.54	2.45	2.39	2.34	2.30	2.27
12	3.18	2.81	2.61	2.48	2.39	2.33	2.28	2.24	2.21
13	3.14	2.76	2.56	2.43	2.35	2.28	2.23	2.20	2.16
14	3.10	2.73	2.52	2.39	2.31	2.24	2.19	2.15	2.12
15	3.07	2.70	2.49	2.36	2.27	2.21	2.16	2.12	2.09
16	3.05	2.67	2.46	2.33	2.24	2.18	2.13	2.09	2.06
17	3.03	2.64	2.44	2.31	2.22	2.15	2.10	2.06	2.03
18	3.01	2.62	2.42	2.29	2.20	2.13	2.08	2.04	2.00
19	2.99	2.61	2.40	2.27	2.18	2.11	2.06	2.02	1.98
20	2.97	2.59	2.38	2.25	2.16	2.09	2.04	2.00	1.96
21	2.96	2.57	2.36	2.23	2.14	2.08	2.02	1.98	1.95
22	2.95	2.56	2.35	2.22	2.13	2.06	2.01	1.97	1.93
23	2.94	2.55	2.34	2.21	2.11	2.05	1.99	1.95	1.92
24	2.93	2.54	2.33	2.19	2.10	2.04	1.98	1.94	1.91
25	2.92	2.53	2.32	2.18	2.09	2.02	1.97	1.93	1.89
26	2.91	2.52	2.31	2.17	2.08	2.01	1.96	1.92	1.88
27	2.90	2.51	2.30	2.17	2.07	2.00	1.95	1.91	1.87
28	2.89	2.50	2.29	2.16	2.06	2.00	1.94	1.90	1.87
29	2.89	2.50	2.28	2.15	2.06	1.99	1.93	1.89	1.86
30	2.88	2.49	2.28	2.14	2.05	1.98	1.93	1.88	1.85
40	2.84	2.44	2.23	2.09	2.00	1.93	1.87	1.83	1.79
60	2.79	2.39	2.18	2.04	1.95	1.87	1.82	1.77	1.74
120	2.75	2.35	2.13	1.99	1.90	1.82	1.77	1.72	1.68
∞	2.71	2.30	2.08	1.94	1.85	1.77	1.72	1.67	1.63

SOURCE: This table is abridged from Table 18, pp. 170–173, of E. S. Pearson and H. O. Hartley, *Biometrika Tables For Statisticians,* Vol. 1, 3rd ed., Cambridge University Press, 1966, with permission of Biometrika Trustees.

Table c.3. (continued)

10	12	15	20	24	30	40	60	120	∞
60.19	60.71	61.22	61.74	62.00	62.26	62.53	62.79	63.06	63.33
9.39	9.41	9.42	9.44	9.45	9.46	9.47	9.47	9.48	9.49
5.23	5.22	5.20	5.18	5.18	5.17	5.16	5.15	5.14	5.13
3.92	3.90	3.87	3.84	3.83	3.82	3.80	3.79	3.78	3.76
3.30	3.27	3.24	3.21	3.19	3.17	3.16	3.14	3.12	3.10
2.94	2.90	2.87	2.84	2.82	2.80	2.78	2.76	2.74	2.72
2.70	2.67	2.63	2.59	2.58	2.56	2.54	2.51	2.49	2.47
2.54	2.50	2.46	2.42	2.40	2.38	2.36	2.34	2.32	2.29
2.42	2.38	2.34	2.30	2.28	2.25	2.23	2.21	2.18	2.16
3.32	2.28	2.24	2.20	2.18	2.16	2.13	2.11	2.08	2.06
2.25	2.21	2.17	2.12	2.10	2.08	2.05	2.03	2.00	1.97
2.19	2.15	2.10	2.06	2.04	2.01	1.99	1.96	1.93	1.90
2.14	2.10	2.05	2.01	1.98	1.96	1.93	1.90	1.88	1.85
2.10	2.05	2.01	1.96	1.94	1.91	1.89	1.86	1.83	1.80
2.06	2.02	1.97	1.92	1.90	1.87	1.85	1.82	1.79	1.76
2.03	1.99	1.94	1.89	1.87	1.84	1.81	1.78	1.75	1.72
2.00	1.96	1.91	1.86	1.84	1.81	1.78	1.75	1.72	1.69
1.98	1.93	1.89	1.84	1.81	1.78	1.75	1.72	1.69	1.66
1.96	1.91	1.86	1.81	1.79	1.76	1.73	1.70	1.67	1.63
1.94	1.89	1.84	1.79	1.77	1.74	1.71	1.68	1.64	1.61
1.92	1.87	1.83	1.78	1.75	1.72	1.69	1.66	1.62	1.59
1.90	1.86	1.81	1.76	1.73	1.70	1.67	1.64	1.60	1.57
1.89	1.84	1.80	1.74	1.72	1.69	1.66	1.62	1.59	1.55
1.88	1.83	1.78	1.73	1.70	1.67	1.64	1.61	1.57	1.53
1.87	1.82	1.77	1.72	1.69	1.66	1.63	1.59	1.56	1.52
1.86	1.81	1.76	1.71	1.68	1.65	1.61	1.58	1.54	1.50
1.85	1.80	1.75	1.70	1.67	1.64	1.60	1.57	1.53	1.49
1.84	1.7	1.749	1.69	1.66	1.63	1.59	1.56	1.52	1.48
1.83	1.78	1.73	1.68	1.65	1.62	1.58	1.55	1.51	1.47
1.82	1.77	1.72	1.67	1.64	1.61	1.57	1.54	1.50	1.46
1.76	1.71	1.66	1.61	1.57	1.54	1.51	1.47	1.42	1.38
1.71	1.66	1.60	1.54	1.51	1.48	1.44	1.40	1.35	1.29
1.65	1.60	1.55	1.48	1.45	1.41	1.37	1.32	1.26	1.19
1.60	1.55	1.49	1.42	1.38	1.34	1.30	1.24	1.17	1.00

Table c.3. Upper 5% Points (continued)

v_2 \ v_1	1	2	3	4	5	6	7	8	9
1	161.4	199.5	215.7	224.6	230.2	234.0	236.8	238.9	240.5
2	18.51	19.00	19.16	19.25	19.30	19.33	19.35	19.37	19.38
3	10.13	9.55	9.28	9.12	9.01	8.94	8.89	8.85	8.81
4	7.71	6.94	6.59	6.39	6.26	6.16	6.09	6.04	6.00
5	6.61	5.79	5.41	5.19	5.05	4.95	4.88	4.82	4.77
6	5.99	5.14	4.76	4.53	4.39	4.28	4.21	4.15	4.10
7	5.59	4.74	4.35	4.12	3.97	3.87	3.79	3.73	3.68
8	5.32	4.46	4.07	3.84	3.69	3.58	3.50	3.44	3.39
9	5.12	4.26	3.86	3.63	3.48	3.37	3.29	3.23	3.18
10	4.96	4.10	3.71	3.48	3.33	3.22	3.14	3.07	3.02
11	4.84	3.98	3.59	3.36	3.20	3.09	3.01	2.95	2.90
12	4.75	3.89	3.49	3.26	3.11	3.00	2.91	2.85	2.80
13	4.67	3.81	3.41	3.18	3.03	2.92	2.83	2.77	2.71
14	4.60	3.74	3.34	3.11	2.96	2.85	2.76	2.70	2.65
15	4.54	3.68	3.29	3.06	2.90	2.79	2.71	2.64	2.59
16	4.49	3.63	3.24	3.01	2.85	2.74	2.66	2.59	2.54
17	4.45	3.59	3.20	2.96	2.81	2.70	2.61	2.55	2.49
18	4.41	3.55	3.16	2.93	2.77	2.66	2.58	2.51	2.46
19	4.38	3.52	3.13	2.90	2.74	2.63	2.54	2.48	2.42
20	4.35	3.49	3.10	2.87	2.71	2.60	2.51	2.45	2.39
21	4.32	3.47	3.07	2.84	2.68	2.57	2.49	2.42	2.37
22	4.30	3.44	3.05	2.82	2.66	2.55	2.46	2.40	2.34
23	4.28	3.42	3.03	2.80	2.64	2.53	2.44	2.37	2.32
24	4.26	3.40	3.01	2.78	2.62	2.51	2.42	2.36	2.30
25	4.24	3.39	2.99	2.76	2.60	2.49	2.40	2.34	2.28
26	4.23	3.37	2.98	2.74	2.59	2.47	2.39	2.32	2.27
27	4.21	3.35	2.96	2.73	2.57	2.46	2.37	2.31	2.25
28	4.20	3.34	2.95	2.71	2.56	2.45	2.36	2.29	2.24
29	4.18	3.33	2.93	2.70	2.55	2.43	2.35	2.28	2.22
30	4.17	3.32	2.92	2.69	2.53	2.42	2.33	2.27	2.21
40	4.08	3.23	2.84	2.61	2.45	2.34	2.25	2.18	2.12
60	4.00	3.15	2.76	2.53	2.37	2.25	2.17	2.10	2.04
120	3.92	3.07	2.68	2.45	2.29	2.17	2.09	2.02	1.96
∞	3.84	3.00	2.60	2.37	2.21	2.10	2.01	1.94	1.88

Table c.3. Upper 5% Points (continued)

10	12	15	20	24	30	40	60	120	∞
241.9	243.9	245.9	248.0	249.1	250.1	251.1	252.2	253.3	254.3
19.40	19.41	19.43	19.45	19.45	19.46	19.47	19.48	19.49	19.50
8.79	8.74	8.70	8.66	8.64	8.62	8.59	8.57	8.55	8.53
5.96	5.91	5.86	5.80	5.77	5.75	5.72	5.69	5.66	5.63
4.74	4.68	4.62	4.56	4.53	4.50	4.46	4.43	4.40	4.36
4.06	4.00	3.94	3.87	3.84	3.81	3.77	3.74	3.70	3.67
3.64	3.57	3.51	3.44	3.41	3.38	3.34	3.30	3.27	3.23
3.35	3.28	3.22	3.15	3.12	3.08	3.04	3.01	2.97	2.93
3.14	3.07	3.01	2.94	2.90	2.86	2.83	2.79	2.75	2.71
2.98	2.91	2.85	2.77	2.74	2.70	2.66	2.62	2.58	2.54
2.85	2.79	2.72	2.65	2.61	2.57	2.53	2.49	2.45	2.40
2.75	2.69	2.62	2.54	2.51	2.47	2.43	2.38	2.34	2.30
2.67	2.60	2.53	2.46	2.42	2.38	2.34	2.30	2.25	2.21
2.60	2.53	2.46	2.39	2.35	2.31	2.27	2.22	2.18	2.13
2.54	2.48	2.40	2.33	2.29	2.25	2.20	2.16	2.11	2.07
2.49	2.42	2.35	2.28	2.24	2.19	2.15	2.11	2.06	2.01
2.45	2.38	2.31	2.23	2.19	2.15	2.10	2.06	2.01	1.96
2.41	2.34	2.27	2.19	2.15	2.11	2.06	2.02	1.97	1.92
2.38	2.31	2.23	2.16	2.11	2.07	2.03	1.98	1.93	1.88
2.35	2.28	2.20	2.12	2.08	2.04	1.99	1.95	1.90	1.84
2.32	2.25	2.18	2.10	2.05	2.01	1.96	1.92	1.87	1.81
2.30	2.23	2.15	2.07	2.03	1.98	1.94	1.89	1.84	1.78
2.27	2.20	2.13	2.05	2.01	1.96	1.91	1.86	1.81	1.76
2.25	2.18	2.11	2.03	1.98	1.94	1.89	1.84	1.79	1.73
2.24	2.16	2.09	2.01	1.96	1.92	1.87	1.82	1.77	1.71
2.22	2.15	2.07	1.99	1.95	1.90	1.85	1.80	1.75	1.69
2.20	2.13	2.06	1.97	1.93	1.88	1.84	1.79	1.73	1.67
2.19	2.12	2.04	1.96	1.91	1.87	1.82	1.77	1.71	1.65
2.18	2.10	2.03	1.94	1.90	1.85	1.81	1.75	1.70	1.64
2.16	2.09	2.01	1.93	1.89	1.84	1.79	1.74	1.68	1.62
2.08	2.00	1.92	1.84	1.79	1.74	1.69	1.64	1.58	1.51
1.99	1.92	1.84	1.75	1.70	1.65	1.59	1.53	1.47	1.39
1.91	1.83	1.75	1.66	1.61	1.55	1.50	1.43	1.35	1.25
1.83	1.75	1.67	1.57	1.52	1.46	1.39	1.32	1.22	1.00

Table c.3. Upper 2.5% Points (continued)

v_2 \ v_1	1	2	3	4	5	6	7	8	9
1	647.8	799.5	864.2	899.6	921.8	937.1	948.2	956.7	963.3
2	38.51	39.00	39.17	39.25	39.30	39.33	39.36	39.37	39.39
3	17.44	16.04	15.44	15.10	14.88	14.73	14.62	14.54	14.47
4	12.22	10.65	9.98	9.60	9.36	9.20	9.07	8.98	8.90
5	10.01	8.43	7.76	7.39	7.15	6.98	6.85	6.76	6.68
6	8.81	7.26	6.60	6.23	5.99	5.82	5.70	5.60	5.52
7	8.07	6.54	5.89	5.52	5.29	5.12	4.99	4.90	4.82
8	7.57	6.06	5.42	5.05	4.82	4.65	4.53	4.43	4.36
9	7.21	5.71	5.08	4.72	4.48	4.32	4.20	4.10	4.03
10	6.94	5.46	4.83	4.47	4.24	4.07	3.95	3.85	3.78
11	6.72	5.26	4.63	4.28	4.04	3.88	3.76	3.66	3.59
12	6.55	5.10	4.47	4.12	3.89	3.73	3.61	3.51	3.44
13	6.41	4.97	4.35	4.00	3.77	3.60	3.48	3.39	3.31
14	6.30	4.86	4.24	3.89	3.66	3.50	3.38	3.29	3.21
15	6.20	4.77	4.15	3.80	3.58	3.41	3.29	3.20	3.12
16	6.12	4.69	4.08	3.73	3.50	3.34	3.22	3.12	3.05
17	6.04	4.62	4.01	3.66	3.44	3.28	3.16	3.06	2.98
18	5.98	4.56	3.95	3.61	3.38	3.22	3.10	3.01	2.93
19	5.92	4.51	3.90	3.56	3.33	3.17	3.05	2.96	2.88
20	5.87	4.46	3.86	3.51	3.29	3.13	3.01	2.91	2.84
21	5.83	4.42	3.82	3.48	3.25	3.09	2.97	2.87	2.80
22	5.79	4.38	3.78	3.44	3.22	3.05	2.93	2.84	2.76
23	5.75	4.35	3.75	3.41	3.18	3.02	2.90	2.81	2.73
24	5.72	4.32	3.72	3.38	3.15	2.99	2.87	2.78	2.70
25	5.69	4.29	3.69	3.35	3.13	2.97	2.85	2.75	2.68
26	5.66	4.27	3.67	3.33	3.10	2.94	2.82	2.73	2.65
27	5.63	4.24	3.65	3.31	3.08	2.92	2.80	2.71	2.63
28	5.61	4.22	3.63	3.29	3.06	2.90	2.78	2.69	2.61
29	5.59	4.20	3.61	3.27	3.04	2.88	2.76	2.67	2.59
30	5.57	4.18	3.59	3.25	3.03	2.87	2.75	2.65	2.57
40	5.42	4.05	3.46	3.13	2.90	2.74	2.62	2.53	2.45
60	5.29	3.93	3.34	3.01	2.79	2.63	2.51	2.41	2.33
120	5.15	3.80	3.23	2.89	2.67	2.52	2.39	2.30	2.22
∞	5.02	3.69	3.12	2.79	2.57	2.41	2.29	2.19	2.11

Table c.3. Upper 2.5% Points (continued)

10	12	15	20	24	30	40	60	120	∞
968.6	976.7	984.9	993.1	997.2	1001	1006	1010	1014	1018
39.40	39.41	39.43	39.45	39.46	39.46	39.47	39.48	39.49	39.50
14.42	14.34	14.25	14.17	14.12	14.08	14.04	13.99	13.95	13.90
8.84	8.75	8.66	8.56	8.51	8.46	8.41	8.36	8.31	8.26
6.62	6.52	6.43	6.33	6.28	6.23	6.18	6.12	6.07	6.02
5.46	5.37	5.27	5.17	5.12	5.07	5.01	4.96	4.90	4.85
4.76	4.67	4.57	4.47	4.42	4.36	4.31	4.25	4.20	4.14
4.30	4.20	4.10	4.00	3.95	3.89	3.84	3.78	3.73	3.67
3.96	3.87	3.77	3.67	3.61	3.56	3.51	3.45	3.39	3.33
3.72	3.62	3.52	3.42	3.37	3.31	3.26	3.20	3.14	3.08
3.53	3.43	3.33	3.23	3.17	3.12	3.06	3.00	2.94	2.88
3.37	3.28	3.18	3.07	3.02	2.96	2.91	2.85	2.79	2.72
3.25	3.15	3.05	2.95	2.89	2.84	2.78	2.72	2.66	2.60
3.15	3.05	2.95	2.84	2.79	2.73	2.67	2.61	2.55	2.49
3.06	2.96	2.86	2.76	2.70	2.64	2.59	2.52	2.46	2.40
2.99	2.89	2.79	2.68	2.63	2.57	2.51	2.45	2.38	2.32
2.92	2.82	2.72	2.62	2.56	2.50	2.44	2.38	2.32	2.25
2.87	2.77	2.67	2.56	2.50	2.44	2.38	2.32	2.26	2.19
2.82	2.72	2.62	2.51	2.45	2.39	2.33	2.27	2.20	2.13
2.77	2.68	2.57	2.46	2.41	2.35	2.29	2.22	2.16	2.09
2.73	2.64	2.53	2.42	2.37	2.31	2.25	2.18	2.11	2.04
2.70	2.60	2.50	2.39	2.33	2.27	2.21	2.14	2.08	2.00
2.67	2.57	2.47	2.36	2.30	2.24	2.18	2.11	2.04	1.97
2.64	2.54	2.44	2.33	2.27	2.21	2.15	2.08	2.01	1.94
2.61	2.51	2.41	2.30	2.24	2.18	2.12	2.05	1.98	1.91
2.59	2.49	2.39	2.28	2.22	2.16	2.09	2.03	1.95	1.88
2.57	2.47	2.36	2.25	2.19	2.13	2.07	2.00	1.93	1.85
2.55	2.45	2.34	2.23	2.17	2.11	2.05	1.98	1.91	1.83
2.53	2.43	2.32	2.21	2.15	2.09	2.03	1.96	1.89	1.81
2.51	2.41	2.31	2.20	2.14	2.07	2.01	1.94	1.87	1.79
2.39	2.29	2.18	2.07	2.01	1.94	1.88	1.80	1.72	1.64
2.27	2.17	2.06	1.94	1.88	1.82	1.74	1.67	1.58	1.48
2.16	2.05	1.94	1.82	1.76	1.69	1.61	1.53	1.43	1.31
2.05	1.94	1.83	1.71	1.64	1.57	1.48	1.39	1.27	1.00

Table c.3. Upper 1% Points (continued)

ν_2 \ ν_1	1	2	3	4	5	6	7	8	9
1	4052	4999.5	5403	5625	5764	5859	5928	5981	6022
2	98.50	99.00	99.17	99.25	99.30	99.33	99.36	99.37	99.39
3	34.12	30.82	29.46	28.71	28.24	27.91	27.67	27.49	27.35
4	21.20	18.00	16.69	15.98	15.52	15.21	14.98	14.80	14.66
5	16.26	13.27	12.06	11.39	10.97	10.67	10.46	10.29	10.16
6	13.75	10.92	9.78	9.15	8.75	8.47	8.26	8.10	7.98
7	12.25	9.55	8.45	7.85	7.46	7.19	6.99	6.84	6.72
8	11.26	8.65	7.59	7.01	6.63	6.37	6.18	6.03	5.91
9	10.56	8.02	6.99	6.42	6.06	5.80	5.61	5.47	5.35
10	10.04	7.56	6.55	5.99	5.64	5.39	5.20	5.06	4.94
11	9.65	7.21	6.22	5.67	5.32	5.07	4.89	4.74	4.63
12	9.33	6.93	5.95	5.41	5.06	4.82	4.64	4.50	4.39
13	9.07	6.70	5.74	5.21	4.86	4.62	4.44	4.30	4.19
14	8.86	6.51	5.56	5.04	4.69	4.46	4.28	4.14	4.03
15	8.68	6.36	5.42	4.89	4.56	4.32	4.14	4.00	3.89
16	8.53	6.23	5.29	4.77	4.44	4.20	4.03	3.89	3.78
17	8.40	6.11	5.18	4.67	4.34	4.10	3.93	3.79	3.68
18	8.29	6.01	5.09	4.58	4.25	4.01	3.84	3.71	3.60
19	8.18	5.93	5.01	4.50	4.17	3.94	3.77	3.63	3.52
20	8.10	5.85	4.94	4.43	4.10	3.87	3.70	3.56	3.46
21	8.02	5.78	4.87	4.37	4.04	3.81	3.64	3.51	3.40
22	7.95	5.72	4.82	4.31	3.99	3.76	3.59	3.45	3.35
23	7.88	5.66	4.76	4.26	3.94	3.71	3.54	3.41	3.30
24	7.82	5.61	4.72	4.22	3.90	3.67	3.50	3.36	3.26
25	7.77	5.57	4.68	4.18	3.85	3.63	3.46	3.32	3.22
26	7.72	5.53	4.64	4.14	3.82	3.59	3.42	3.29	3.18
27	7.68	5.49	4.60	4.11	3.78	3.56	3.39	3.26	3.15
28	7.64	5.45	4.57	4.07	3.75	3.53	3.36	3.23	3.12
29	7.60	5.42	4.54	4.04	3.73	3.50	3.33	3.20	3.09
30	7.56	5.39	4.51	4.02	3.70	3.47	3.30	3.17	3.07
40	7.31	5.18	4.31	3.83	3.51	3.29	3.12	2.99	2.89
60	7.08	4.98	4.13	3.65	3.34	3.12	2.95	2.82	2.72
120	6.85	4.79	3.95	3.48	3.17	2.96	2.79	2.66	2.56
∞	6.63	4.61	3.78	3.32	3.02	2.80	2.64	2.51	2.41

Table c.3. Upper 1% Points (continued)

10	12	15	20	24	30	40	60	120	∞
6056	6106	6157	6209	6235	6261	6287	6313	6339	6366
99.40	99.42	99.43	99.45	99.46	99.47	99.47	99.48	99.49	99.50
27.23	27.05	26.87	26.69	26.60	26.50	26.41	26.32	26.22	26.13
14.55	14.37	14.20	14.02	13.93	13.84	13.75	13.65	13.56	13.46
10.05	9.89	9.72	9.55	9.47	9.38	9.29	9.20	9.11	9.02
7.87	7.72	7.56	7.40	7.31	7.23	7.14	7.06	6.97	6.88
6.62	6.47	6.31	6.16	6.07	5.99	5.91	5.82	5.74	5.65
5.81	5.67	5.52	5.36	5.28	5.20	5.12	5.03	4.95	4.86
5.26	5.11	4.96	4.81	4.73	4.65	4.57	4.48	4.40	4.31
4.85	4.71	4.56	4.41	4.33	4.25	4.17	4.08	4.00	3.91
4.54	4.40	4.25	4.10	4.02	3.94	3.86	3.78	3.69	3.60
4.30	4.16	4.01	3.86	3.78	3.70	3.62	3.54	3.45	3.36
4.10	3.96	3.82	3.66	3.59	3.51	3.43	3.34	3.25	3.17
3.94	3.80	3.66	3.51	3.43	3.35	3.27	3.18	3.09	3.00
3.80	3.67	3.52	3.37	3.29	3.21	3.13	3.05	2.96	2.87
3.69	3.55	3.41	3.26	3.18	3.10	3.02	2.93	2.84	2.75
3.59	3.46	3.31	3.16	3.08	3.00	2.92	2.83	2.75	2.65
3.51	3.37	3.23	3.08	3.00	2.92	2.84	2.75	2.66	2.57
3.43	3.30	3.15	3.00	2.92	2.84	2.76	2.67	2.58	2.49
3.37	3.23	3.09	2.94	2.86	2.78	2.69	2.61	2.52	2.42
3.31	3.17	3.03	2.88	2.80	2.72	2.64	2.55	2.46	2.36
3.26	3.12	2.98	2.83	2.75	2.67	2.58	2.50	2.40	2.31
3.21	3.07	2.93	2.78	2.70	2.62	2.54	2.45	2.35	2.26
3.17	3.03	2.89	2.74	2.66	2.58	2.49	2.40	2.31	2.21
3.13	2.99	2.85	2.70	2.62	2.54	2.45	2.36	2.27	2.17
3.09	2.96	2.81	2.66	2.58	2.50	2.42	2.33	2.23	2.13
3.06	2.93	2.78	2.63	2.55	2.47	2.38	2.29	2.20	2.10
3.03	2.90	2.75	2.60	2.52	2.44	2.35	2.26	2.17	2.06
3.00	2.87	2.73	2.57	2.49	2.41	2.33	2.23	2.14	2.03
2.98	2.84	2.70	2.55	2.47	2.39	2.30	2.21	2.11	2.01
2.80	2.66	2.52	2.37	2.29	2.20	2.11	2.02	1.92	1.80
2.63	2.50	2.35	2.20	2.12	2.03	1.94	1.84	1.73	1.60
2.47	2.34	2.19	2.03	1.95	1.86	1.76	1.66	1.53	1.38
2.32	2.18	2.04	1.88	1.79	1.70	1.59	1.47	1.32	1.00

index

a

alias, 54, 110
$\frac{1}{2}$ fraction of the 2^k, 55
$\frac{1}{4}$ fraction of the 2^k, 58
alias matrix, 112, 114, 199, 223
axial points, 129
analysis of variance, 31
  for 2^k factorial experiment, 48, 50

b

bias:
  all bias design, 200, 201, 208, 210, 215, 229, 231
  average bias, 197, 198, 225–29
  of model coefficients, 110–14, 223–25
  for simplex design, 121
blocking, 178–95
  for first order model, 176–83
  for second order model, 183–95
  orthogonal, 178, 183, 189

c

canonical analysis, 72, 82, 95
canonical form, 15, 73, 83, 87
central composite design, 132, 153
  orthogonal, 133, 153
  rotatable, 150, 153, 187, 214–18
characteristic roots, 14, 74, 87, 96
coding, 43, 167
cofactor, 10, 109
confounding, 54, 177
contrast, 45

d

defining contrast, 55, 58
derived power vector, 219
design (see experimental design)
design matrix, 40
design moments (see moments)
design variable, 61
determinant:
  minor, 9
  principal minor, 17
dodecahedron, 162

e

efficiency, 135
eigenvalue (see characteristic root)
eigenvector, 14, 74, 88
equiradial designs, 154–61
  orthogonal, 155
  uniform precision, 155
experimental design:
  basic concept of, 2, 27
  first order models, 107–25
  orthogonal, 45, 107, 121
  rotatable, 139, 162
  second order models, 126–75

f

factorial experiments, 40–60
  fractional replicates of, 53–60, 110
  three level experiments, 50, 135
  two level experiments, 43
fitted surface, 64, 68

g

generalized interaction, 55, 56

h

hexagonal (see equiradial)

i

icosahedron, 161
index of a quadratic form, 16

l

lack-of-fit, 48, 115, 123
latent root (*see* characteristic root)
least squares, 27–40
    hypothesis testing, 30
    mean and variance of estimators,
    29

m

matrix, 4
    diagonal, 5
    idempotent, 13
    identity, 6
    inverse of, 9
    minor, 9
    moment, 140, 219, 223
    multiplication of, 6
    nonsingular, 10
    orthogonal, 13
    precision, 140
    principal minor, 17
    rank of, 9
    singular, 10
    square, 4
    symmetric, 5, 7, 12
    trace of, 18
    transpose of, 5, 8, 11
maximization, 91, 96

minimization, 96, 197, 215, 220
moment, 135, 137, 141, 199, 200, 207,
    209, 214, 215
region, 212
multiple response, 167

o

octagonal (*see* equiradial)
orthogonal polynomials, 35–40
orthogonal transformation, 15, 74

p

pentagonal (*see* equiradial)

q

quadratic form, 15

r

regression sum of squares, 31, 81
response, 1
    function, 87, 159, 169
    surface analysis, 68–88
ridge analysis, 95
rising ridge, 71, 72, 77, 95
rotatable designs (*see also* central
    composite), 150, 153, 187
    definition of, 165
    general, 219
    second order, 139, 153

s

saddle point, 70, 75
simplex design, 118–21
stationary point, 69, 75, 83, 87, 91, 95,
    96
stationary ridge, 72, 76
steepest ascent, 88–90